Electronic Measurement
Techniques

Electronic Measurement Techniques

D. F. A. EDWARDS, A.Inst.P., F.B.I.S.

LONDON
BUTTERWORTHS

THE BUTTERWORTH GROUP

ENGLAND
Butterworth & Co (Publishers) Ltd
London: 88 Kingsway WC2B 6AB

AUSTRALIA
Butterworth & Co (Australia) Ltd
Sydney: 20 Loftus Street
Melbourne: 343 Little Collins Street
Brisbane: 240 Queen Street

CANADA
Butterworth & Co (Canada) Ltd
Toronto: 14 Curity Avenue, 374

NEW ZEALAND
Butterworth & Co (New Zealand) Ltd
Wellington: 49/51 Ballance Street
Auckland: 35 High Street

SOUTH AFRICA
Butterworth & Co (South Africa) (Pty.) Ltd
Durban: 33/35 Beach Grove

First published 1971
© D. F. A. Edwards, 1971

ISBN 0 408 70090 4 Standard
     0 408 70091 2 Limp

Printed by photo-lithography and made in Great Britain at
The Pitman Press, Bath

Preface

Electronic measurement is becoming an increasingly important branch of technology, since electronic instrumentation is now used not only by electronic engineers, but in nearly all other branches of engineering.

The main object of this book is to provide in one volume practical information concerning the latest techniques in electronic measurements. Another justification for the present work is the fact that many people take up electronics or communications engineering as a career with a good working knowledge of the theory involved but with little idea of how to adopt and use the appropriate measuring instruments. A mechanical engineer who was unsure of how to use micrometer and vernier scales would be little thought of, yet it is just as essential that the intending electronic engineer knows how to use the corresponding tools of this trade.

The book is written entirely in SI units, and from the purely educational point of view it should be of great value to H.N.C. students, while it contains sufficiently advanced material to serve those studying for B.Sc. (Eng) Part III or the appropriate C.E.I. examinations. Each chapter includes one or more worked examples and some exercises, with answers, given at the end of the chapters. The questions have been mainly taken from B.Sc. and I.E.E. examination papers together with some City and Guilds questions to give a more practical bias. The subject matter will therefore be additionally of interest to City and Guilds students, and it is hoped that those taking Electronics as the special subject in the Grad. Inst. P. examination will also find the book useful. In several cases the original questions have been modified so as to use SI units and modern terms and symbols. The author is grateful to the City and Guilds of London Institute; The Institution of Electrical Engineers and The University of London for permission to use their examination questions.

D. F. A. EDWARDS.

Acknowledgements

Several industrial organisations have been of great help in supplying details of their products and giving permission to use this information in the present work, and the author wishes to acknowledge the co-operation of the following:

AVO Ltd.

The Cambridge Instrument Co. Ltd.

Crompton Parkinson Ltd.

Fielden Electronics Ltd.

Hewlett Packard Ltd.

Johnson Matthey Metals Ltd.

Philips Electrical Ltd.

Racal Instruments Ltd.

H. W. Sullivan Ltd.

H. Tinsley & Co. Ltd.

Contents

tuning coils – Distributed or self-capacitance – Measurement of small capacitances – High-frequency resistance – Q measurements.

Introduction – The I_c/V_{ce} characteristic – Current gain a' – The I_b/V_{be} characteristic – Leakage current I'_{co} – Cut-off frequency f'_c – Resistance tests – Use of the cathode-ray tube – Hybrid or h parameters – Bridge measurements – High-frequency parameters – Integrated circuits – Measurements in integrated circuits.

A.C. power – Dynamometer wattmeters – Induction meters – Three-ammeter method – Three-phase power – A.F. and h.f. power – Valve wattmeters – Three-ammeter method for h.f. – Power output and power level – Peak power – Bolometric and calorimetric methods – Use of cathode-ray tube.

Introduction – Test oscillators – Standard signal generators – V.H.F. signal generators – Use of signal generators – Measurement of conversion conductance – Measurement of oscillator harmonic response – Measurements on detectors – Factory testing of radio receivers – Routine tests – Attenuators.

Introduction – Use of deflection magnetometer – Vibration magnetometer – Determination of H_0 – Relation between magnetising force and intensity of magnetisation – Flux measurement – Magnetic susceptibility measurements – Forces on materials in an electric field – Testing of permanent magnet materials – Measurement of permittivity at high frequencies – Appendix – Theory of the Grassot fluxmeter.

Audio-frequency amplifiers – Measurements of overall characteristics – Forms of distortion – Frequency

response – Transient distortion – Phase distortion –
Non-linear distortion – Methods of measuring distortion –
Square-wave generator – Distortion measurements using
sine waves.

CHAPTER 1

Units and Principles of Electronic Measurements

1.1. INTRODUCTION

Until 1948 most textbooks on electrical engineering were written in
c.g.s. units. In that year the rationalised M.K.S. system was recognised as
the international standard and this was succeeded about 20 years later
by the SI system, which is used in this book. The c.g.s. system will not
be described here but a description of the evolution of units up to and
including the M.K.S. system will be found in a book by Fewkes and
Yarwood.[1]

1.2. THE M.K.S. SYSTEM OF UNITS

The M.K.S. system was suggested by Giorgi in 1901, who stated that if
the units of mass, length and time were taken as the kilogramme, metre
and second respectively and one electrical unit (the ampere) added, then
a completely self-consistent system of units could be devised such that
the fundamental electrical units were the same as the practical ones.
Further improvement is obtained by rationalising, so that the factors
2π and 4π are logically placed in essentially circular and spherical
expressions respectively. The Institution of Electrical Engineers
recommended the adoption of the rationalised M.K.S. system (also
known as the m.k.s.a. system, due to the addition of the ampere) in the
U.K. in 1952.

The fundamental units in the M.K.S. system are as follows:

Unit of length — one *metre* (very nearly one ten-millionth part of a
quadrant of the earth measured from the equator to the pole).

Unit of mass — one *kilogramme* (very nearly the mass of one
thousand cubic centimetres of water at the temperature of its maximum density).

Unit of time — one *second* (one eighty-six thousand four hundredth
part of a mean solar day).

The units in any system may be much smaller or larger than the
quantities which have to be expressed by means of them. To avoid the

consequent necessity of using very large numerical multipliers or divisors, the multiplication by one million (= 10^6) is expressed by the prefix *mega-*, and division by one million by the prefix *micro-*.

Special names are given to some of the most important derived units of the M.K.S. system. Thus the unit of force, namely the force which, when acting on a kilogramme, causes its velocity to change at the rate of one metre per second in a second, is called a *newton*. The weight of a kilogramme is equal to about 9·81 such units, since 9·81 m/s² is the acceleration due to gravity in the M.K.S. system.

The M.K.S. unit of work or energy is the work done or energy expended when a force of one newton acts through a distance of one metre, and is called a *joule*.

The main electrical units in the M.K.S. system are defined as follows.

The *ampere* is that steady current which, when flowing in each of two infinitely long parallel straight conductors placed 1 metre apart *in vacuo*, produces a force of 2×10^{-7} newtons per 1 metre length of each conductor.

The *coulomb* is the quantity of electricity passing a given point in a circuit when one ampere of current flows for one second.

Now since W joules = Q coulombs $\times$ V volts, the *volt* is the potential difference between two points if when one coulomb of charge passes between them, one joule of work is done.

By Ohm's Law, V volts = I amps $\times$ R ohms. Therefore the *ohm* is the resistance of a passive conductor which carries one ampere when the potential difference across it is one volt.

The ampere, coulomb, volt and ohm are the familiar practical units.

The unit of capacitance is called the *farad*. It is the capacitance of an electric field which has a charge of one coulomb when the difference of potentials between its boundaries is one volt.

The unit of inductance is called the *henry*. The self-inductance of a circuit is one henry if an opposing electromotive force of one volt results from a variation of the strength of current in the circuit at the rate of one ampere per second. Finally, magnetic flux is measured in *webers* and flux density therefore in *webers per square metre*.

1.3. THE SI SYSTEM

The Système International d'Unités is a rationalised set of metric units now coming into international use. It consists basically of the m.k.s.a. system with the addition of the degree Kelvin for temperature measurement and the candela for use in the measurement of luminous intensity, however, some of the units have been renamed, i.e. flux density is measured in Teslas (T) instead of webers per square metre

(1 T = 1 Wb/m^2) and conductivity is measured in Siemens (S) instead of mhos (1 S = 1 mho). Frequency is measured in Hertz (Hz) instead of cycles/second (c/s).

The degree Kelvin (°K) is the unit of measurement on the absolute temperature scale, and is equal to one degree Celsius, (°C). However, the absolute temperature scale is the Celsius scale extrapolated to absolute zero temperature, −273°C, so that, for example, a temperature of 50°C is equivalent to a temperature of 323°K. Molten platinum is used as a practical standard in defining the candela. One square centimetre of freezing (i.e. solidifying) platinum has a luminous intensity of 60 candelas. The solidifying temperature is 1737°C.

Further information on the degree Kelvin and the candela will be found in textbooks of physics. An account of the history and application of SI units and conversion from other systems is given in BS. PD5686[2].

1.4. ABSOLUTE MEASUREMENTS

An absolute measurement is one made in terms of the fundamental units of length, mass and time in the system being used. From the definition of the ampere given earlier it is clear that the measurement of current involves the measurement of a force. It can be shown also, from the theory of dimensions[1], that the absolute determination of resistance involves the measurement of a velocity and the determination of e.m.f. involves a force multiplied by the square of a velocity. As the latter obviously involves more difficult procedure than the other two, it is desirable to regard the determination of current and resistance as fundamental and to derive the unit of e.m.f. by Ohm's Law.

At least eight methods of measuring resistance in absolute units have been devised. Perhaps the most interesting is that due to Lorenz: it is briefly as follows. A metal disc is rotated within a solenoid and the e.m.f. produced between its centre and its periphery is balanced against the potential drop due to the solenoid current flowing through the unknown resistance. The only measurement required is the speed of rotation. A full description of this method and improved versions of it is given in Fewkes and Yarwood[1] (pp. 490–495).

The force of which measurement is necessary to determine current may be exerted in several ways, at least one of which will be familiar to the reader. Fig. 1.1 shows the couple acting on a rectangular coil carrying I ampere in a plane magnetic field of B tesla. The deflecting torque is given by

$$\tau\theta = BAIN \cos\theta \text{ so that } I = \frac{\tau\theta}{BAN \cos\theta} \tag{1.1}$$

where A is the area of the coil and N the number of turns. Notice how many possible sources of error there are in this method: B has to be determined by special experiments themselves liable to error, θ is uncertain because of errors in the scale (assuming that Fig. 1.1. represents

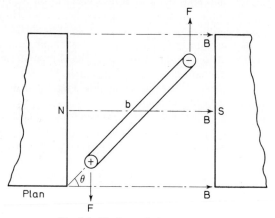

Fig. 1.1. Moving-coil meter movement

a moving-coil meter movement), and the formula itself assumes that the coil is exactly vertical.

The most accurate method for the absolute measurement of current is to weigh the pull between two circuits connected in series. Two coils are fixed horizontally and a third is suspended from a balance, so as to hang centrally between the fixed pair. The force is given by $i^2 k$, where i is the current in absolute units and k is a constant depending upon the ratio of the diameters of the coils. This ratio can be determined, to a high degree of accuracy, by electrical means, and the weighing can be carried out to within one part in ten million. If precautions are taken to guard against such disturbing factors as convection currents due to the heating of the coil, electric current can be measured to within two parts in a million by this means.

The methods of measurement just discussed are too delicate and troublesome for ordinary purposes. In fact, these methods are carried out only at such places as the National Physical Laboratory, the U.S. National Bureau of Standards and the German Reichsanstalt. To enable electrical quantities to be estimated with comparative ease these delicate methods have been used to prepare 'standards', with which unknown currents and resistances can be compared. All ordinary electrical measurements are really comparisons with a standard: it is much easier to compare two quantities than to measure one by absolute methods. Details of absolute measurements in general are given in Ref. 3.

1.5. ERRORS OF MEASUREMENT

Usually, when a measurement has to be made, several methods are available. The reader should learn how to decide for himself which one will best suit the particular occasion and finding the right compromise between accuracy, speed of carrying out the experiment, and cost of apparatus. An attitude of 'good enough' leads to slack mental habits and slipshod laboratory methods. The only measurement that is good enough is the one that is as accurate as circumstances permit.

This chapter only discusses errors in general: methods of evaluating the errors in particular cases are shown in the worked examples at the end of this chapter and Chapters 2, 3, and 4. In later chapters a considerable variety of practical techniques are described. For most measurements there are several possible methods which can be used. The choice of method in each individual case rests largely upon the purpose or application for which the measurement is being made. These possibilities can be divided under the following three broad headings.

1.5.1. Laboratory Measurements

Irrespective of the purpose of the laboratory, the general requirement will be for precision measurements. This is obvious, in the case of research, for instance, since lack of precision will destroy the validity of the results obtained and the conclusions reached. In production laboratories, where the object is to produce adequate designs for production methods, then allowable tolerances on various components for satisfactory performance must be found. This will involve precision measurement of errors from nominal values, and combinations of such errors, in order to decide what errors shall be allowable in production tests.

1.5.2. Production Test Measurements

Here, as with all other aspects of production, the accent is on economy of time. Testing of all components in which there is any likelihood of error beyond tolerable values will take time, but may save in later assembly operations. For both individual component tests and later assembly tests, the ideal is to aim at some pass/no-pass technique that will merely indicate whether the component or assembly is to be passed or rejected. It may not be considered economic to reject as scrap some expensive assembly items, as rejection would involve further expenditure of time by skilled personnel in locating the faulty component. This requires serious consideration to find the most economic way of treating the problem.

1.5.3. Maintenance Test Measurements

Two factors require special attention:

(a) The maintenance or service engineer will want to carry the minimum of equipment consistent with enabling him to make all necessary tests;

(b) the measurements he has to make should be simplified as much as possible in order to facilitate his work and save time and maintenance costs.

Multi-range multi-purpose equipment is of greatest value to the maintenance engineer, and personnel engaged on similar work. The equipment should be consistent with simplicity of operation and a reasonable degree of accuracy and reliability.

No measurement can be made with absolute accuracy, but the limits between which the accurate results lie can usually be determined. Thus, if a voltage is measured correct to the nearest tenth of a volt and it is given as 90·7 V approximately (i.e. three significant figures), this means that the true voltage is greater than 90·65 V and less than 90·75 V and consequently the maximum error in the voltage reading is 0·05 V.

When numbers which are approximately correct are used as multiplying factors, the errors which they involve will clearly affect the final results. Thus is the approximate number 3·14, instead of π, is multiplied by 9, then 3·14 × 9 = 28·26. But since the number lies between 3·135 and 3·145, then the product lies between 3·135 × 9 = 28·215 and 3·145 × 9 = 28·305.

Clearly, it cannot be determined whether the first decimal place is 2 or 3. Consequently the number of significant figures which can be obtained accurately is only two, or the product will be 28 to two significant figures. It will be seen that a set of operations cannot be ended with a greater number of significant figures than are contained in the approximated numbers which have been employed. The rule may be stated as follows: *If several approximated numbers are used, the number of significant figures which can be depended upon in the final result will in general be less than the least number of significant figures given among the numbers employed.*

The full mathematical treatment of the possible error in an experiment is usually exceedingly difficult and involved. However, the general principles which enable one to choose between one method and another are straightforward.

There are two kinds of error that may arise in any measurement; one due to the method used and the other arising from the fact that it is impossible to be sure that any given observation is correctly made. The first is a fixed error which makes all similar measurements appear too high or too high or too low, but the second means that different observations of the quantity will not exactly agree.

1.5.4. Error of Method

There may be a factor which causes a constant error, e.g. the heating of a coil may cause an expansion which makes the real dimensions greater than those measured at normal temperature. Every experiment performed with this apparatus would have the same error; hence it would be desirable to check the result by a different method.

In the case of a coil suspended in a *radial* magnetic field the coil deflection is directly proportional to the current in the coil, and equation (1.1) becomes:

$$\tau\theta = BAIN \text{ or } I = \frac{\tau\theta}{BAN}. \tag{1.2}$$

If θ is increased by a small amount $d\theta$ the true value of the current is

$$I_t = \frac{\tau}{BAN}(\theta + d\theta)$$

The difference between I_t and I is the error

$$dI = \frac{\tau}{BAN} d\theta.$$

If $d\theta$ can be determined it can be easily corrected for in any experiment. In general, if y is the quantity to be measured and x is a variable in the experiment then $y = f(x)$ and the error in y is given by $dy = \dfrac{\partial y}{\partial x} dx$.

Clearly, if $y = kx^n$ then $dy = nkx^{n-1}dx$. The larger n is, the greater the error in y due to an error in x. A method which involves a linear law is naturally preferable to one involving, say, a quadratic.

In the moving-coil meter it can be assumed that the number of turns N is known exactly. Hence the error in I is due to the errors in three quantities, namely B, A and θ, assuming that τ also remains constant. This resultant error can be found by means of partial differentiation.

$$dI = \frac{\partial I}{\partial B} dB + \frac{\partial I}{\partial A} dA + \frac{\partial I}{\partial \theta} d\theta,$$

where $\partial I/\partial B$ means the differential of I with respect to B, treating A and θ as constants. The other terms have corresponding meanings, dB, dA and $d\theta$ representing the errors in B, A and θ respectively.

Application of the above formula gives

$$dI = \frac{\tau}{N}\left(\frac{-\theta}{B^2 A} - dB + \frac{-\theta}{BA^2} dA + \frac{1}{BA} d\theta\right) = \frac{\tau}{N}\left(\frac{1}{BA} d\theta - \frac{\theta}{B^2 A} dB - \frac{\theta}{BA^2} dA\right)$$

and dividing by I from equation (1.2) gives the proportional error, i.e. one hundredth of the percentage error:

$$\frac{\mathrm{d}I}{I} = \frac{\mathrm{d}\theta}{\theta} - \frac{\mathrm{d}B}{B} - \frac{\mathrm{d}A}{A}.$$

Now the accuracy with which an angle can be measured is independent of the size of the angle, therefore the first term will be a minimum when θ has its maximum value.

As an example suppose that θ can be measured to within $0.1°$ (i.e. $\mathrm{d}\theta = 0.00175$ radian) and B and A each to within 0.1% then for a reading about $57.3°$ (1 radian), $\dfrac{\mathrm{d}I}{I} = 0.00175 - 0.001 - 0.001 = -0.00025$ or -0.025%. Note that the error in θ tends to cancel those of B and A. To obtain a given accuracy in any estimation, the various quantities in the experiment must be measured to a much higher degree of precision.

The scale of an electrical instrument is an important component; a poor or defective scale can result in errors greater than that claimed by the manufacturer. An evenly divided scale is desirable, but if the same percentage accuracy of reading of the measured quantity is desired at all points, the divisions should be wider at the beginning than at the end of the scale.

One of the prerequisites of a good instrument is that its scale be calibrated accurately, i.e. the cardinal scale marks must be located correctly and the intermediate division marks must not be out of position by more than the desired accuracy. These marks may be out of place because of

(1) errors in the reference instrument used originally for calibrating the scale,

(2) random errors in locating the cardinal points,

(3) failure to sub-divide between cardinal marks in accordance with the scale law,

(4) erratic spacing of the sub-division marks between two adjacent cardinal marks,

(5) changes that have occurred in components since the original calibration.

In order that the pointer indications may be read accurately, a high-grade instrument should have an anti-parallax mirror and a knife-edge pointer with the knife-edge thickness about equal to that of the division lines, and preferably not more than 1/10 that of the distance between two successive scale division marks. These scale division marks should be at least 1 mm apart.

1.5.5. Variable Errors or Errors of Observation

There is another kind of error which arises in the most delicate measurements. It will be found that various readings of the same quantity do not exactly agree, due to such causes as friction at the pivot of a galvanometer needle, contact resistances changing and actual human errors of observation. The method of overcoming this trouble is well-known; a large number of observations are made and the mean is taken. If, however, the readings differ by a large amount, a large number of readings would have to be taken before one could be sure that the mean of them was really the most accurate value obtainable. For example, out of four readings 44·2, 43·8, 44·0 and 45·6 the mean is 44·4. But the mean of the first three is only 44·0. Thus it would be necessary to take more readings before one would be justified in taking this mean as correct. If the readings were too erratic the method or the apparatus or even the experiment would have to be supplanted.

However, if the various readings differ by no more than the limits of accuracy normally expected from the particular method of measurement concerned, it is no use considering the variable error further, since no amount of care in observation or in working out a true mean value can yield a more accurate result than the error of method permits.

As far as meters are concerned, observational errors usually result from

(1) reading the scale incorrectly,
(2) failure to eliminate parallax on reading,
(3) failure to estimate correctly fractional divisions.

The first may be minimised by careful attention on the part of the observer in taking readings. The parallax error is effectively eliminated by the correct use of anti-parallax mirrors and other optical devices. The third error mentioned can be obviated by careful scale design and care on the part of the observer.

Taking as an example the earlier International and Legal definitions of current, it should be noted that while the Rayleigh current balance can give an accuracy of two parts in a million, the International definition was given to one part in a hundred thousand and the Legal definition to only one part in a thousand. Thus, the further one departs from the original standard the poorer becomes the accuracy. This fact should always be borne in mind when measurement work is being planned. All the quantities involved in the test must be known to a much higher degree of precision, depending on the purpose for which the measurement is intended.,

1.6. COMPARISON OF ELECTRICAL MAGNITUDES

The term 'comparison' is used since, strictly speaking, electrical 'measurements' are the absolute measurements in terms of non-electrical units. However, since methods of comparison are generally, if incorrectly, known as measurements, the latter term will be used in this book.

The methods can be divided into two main types, namely, Null methods and Deflectional methods.

1.6.1. Null Methods

A circuit can be arranged in such a way that the two quantities being compared neutralise each other. The state of balance is determined by the absence of current in a certain part of the circuit. Methods using this principle are called 'null methods' and are generally more accurate than any others since, if the apparatus is properly designed, the accuracy is determined principally by that of the standard with which the comparison is being made. The requirements are a suitable circuit and an indicator that will show the presence or absence of a current with sufficient accuracy.

A familiar example of a null method is the beam balance used for highly accurate weighing in physics and chemical laboratories. The indicator in this case is a long pointer used in conjunction with a simple scale. As is well known, the unknown weight is balanced against known weights until the pointer reads at the centre of the scale, thus the latter is only used as a 'null indicator' and the unknown weight is found directly in terms of the known weights in the other scale pan.

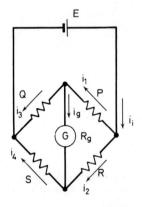

Fig. 1.2. Wheatstone Bridge

The Wheatstone bridge (Fig. 1.2) is used to measure resistance by comparison with standards. It consists of a source of d.c. voltage E (2–4 V), an indicator G (normally a galvanometer), fixed standard resistances P and Q, and a variable standard resistance S. The unknown resistance is R.

To measure R, resistance S is varied until the balance point is reached, i.e. there is zero reading on G. At balance there is no p.d. across the galvanometer,

$$i_g = 0, i_1 = i_3 \text{ and } i_2 = i_4,$$

therefore p.d. drop across P = p.d. drop across R,

and   p.d. drop across Q = p.d. drop across S.

By Ohm's Law,
$$i_1 P = i_2 R$$
$$\text{and} \quad i_1 Q = i_2 S$$

On division,
$$\frac{P}{Q} = \frac{R}{S} \text{ or } PS = RQ$$

Thus the condition of balance for the Wheatstone bridge is $R = SP/Q$. It is evident that the accuracy with which R can be obtained depends upon the possible errors in the three resistances P, Q and S. It has been assumed that there is no error in the process of detecting the balance; in practice, as will be seen in a later chapter, the degree of uncertainty with which the balance can be obtained is governed by the sensitivity of the galvanometer and its suitability for the particular bridge.

The potentiometer (Fig. 1.3) effects a comparison in a more indirect way. The unknown p.d. x is balanced against the fall of potential along

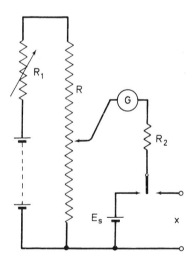

Fig. 1.3. The potentiometer

a uniform wire, and this potential in turn is balanced against a standard e.m.f. E_s. The fall of potential along the wire serves as the comparing medium. The relationship is $x = E_s l_1 / l_2$ where l_1 and l_2 are the lengths of wire required to produce a balance with the unknown and standard e.m.f. respectively. The accuracy depends upon the possible error in E_s and the errors in the measurement of l_1 and l_2. For the best results the wire should not be assumed uniform but should be calibrated and the measured values of l_1 and l_2 corrected accordingly. The galvanometer should be chosen to suit the instrument, as in the case of the bridge, to obtain the most accurate indication of balance. The potentiometer method is a null method, since the galvanometer is used only to detect a balance, but it may also be used as a substitution method since if the unknown e.m.f. is substituted for the known one, and there is no resulting galvanometer deflection, $x = E_s$.

In a later chapter, substitution methods for more than one purpose will be considered. In these the unknown quantity is made to take the place of a known one and an adjustment made so that the two are equally effective. This method can be used with considerable accuracy at radio frequencies when all others fail or give but poor accuracy.

Notice how, in these methods, the change from standard to unknown causes the minimum possible change in the circuit conditions; extraneous unknown quantities are not introduced by the change, hence the accuracy of measurement is governed solely by the accuracy of the standard employed.

1.6.2. Deflectional Methods

In deflectional methods the comparison is more indirect. In principle the method is to note the movement produced by the unknown quantity on an indicator, then to find the true value of that quantity required to produce the same deflection. For example, suppose a current is passed through an unknown resistance and galvanometer in series and the deflection is ϕ. Now, using the same current the unknown resistance could be replaced by a standard one which could be adjusted to give the same deflection.

This method is clearly impractical in the case of currents, since standard currents are difficult to obtain. Hence the 'law' of the instrument must be known so that if a standard current gives a deflection of θ the value of a current giving a deflection of ϕ can be *inferred*. The ordinary ammeter or voltmeter is calibrated by the manufacturers, i.e. the deflection is noted for a number of different currents, the values marked and the intermediate values inserted from a knowledge of the law of deflection.

Such an instrument has many possible sources of error. It is impossible to measure the deflection with anything like the same certainty that the mere presence or absence of current can be detected. Moreover, the inter-mediate divisions on the scale may not be exactly placed and the constant of the instrument may have changed since the calibration was performed. It is normally assumed that the instrument gives the same reading for the same current on successive occasions; this will only be so if it is substantially free from friction and other causes of variability such as weakening of magnets and the effects of temperature. It should need no further argument to demonstrate that null methods are much more accurate, if more laborious to carry out.

1.7. UNITS OF POWER

The ordinary units of electrical power, i.e. watts and milliwatts, call for no comment, but the use of the decibel does require some careful understanding. The human ear has logarithmic characteristics, i.e. the loudness of a sound is proportional to the logarithm of the power which causes it. This fact can easily be roughly tested with the aid of a broadcast receiver or radiogram having a linear volume control. If the volume control is increased from one-tenth of maximum up to maximum the sound will seem to be about as twice as loud.

Suppose a certain sound power P produces a 'loudness' L. Now let this 'loudness' be increased to mL by increasing the power to kP, where k is a constant. If the loudness is again increased by the same amount it becomes $2mL$ but it is found that the power required is $k \times kP$, i.e. k^2P. If the process is repeated n times, then

$$P_n : k^nP \quad \therefore \quad \log \frac{P_n}{P} = n \log k$$

$$\therefore \quad n = \frac{\log \dfrac{P_n}{P}}{\log k} \tag{1.3}$$

Now consider the case of telephone transmission lines.

A transmission line connected at both ends to impedances equal to its characteristic impedance gives rise to a loss of power such that

$$\frac{P_2}{P_1} = e^{-\beta l} \tag{1.4}$$

where P_1 and P_2 are the sent and received powers respectively, l is the length of the line and β is a constant depending on the type of line considered.

Equation (1.4) can be rewritten as $\log_e \dfrac{P_1}{P_2} = \beta l$

$$\therefore \quad l = \frac{1}{\beta} \log_e \frac{P_1}{P_2} \tag{1.5}$$

This gives a convenient relation between the length of line and the power loss. It is therefore convenient to take $\log_e (P_1/P_2)$ as a unit of power loss. This unit is called the 'Neper' or 'Hyp' and is in common use in Europe.

If equations (1.3) and (1.5) are compared it is seen that they are of the same form, for k and β are both arbitrary constants depending upon the units employed. Taking natural logarithms, equation (1.3) can be written

$$N = k \log \frac{P_n}{P} \tag{1.6}$$

The Neper is a convenient unit and the only objection to it is that use is made of Naperian logarithms which are more trouble to work out in numerical cases. Consequently the Bell Telephone Laboratories in the U.S.A. substituted logarithms to base 10 by writing:

$$N = k \log_e 10 \log_{10} \frac{P_n}{P} = k' \log_{10} \frac{P_n}{P}.$$

This gave a new unit which was not surprisingly called the 'bel'. It was found in practice that a much more convenient unit was obtained, both for transmission line and for acoustic work, by making the constant k' equal to 10, so that

$$N = 10 \log_{10} \frac{P_n}{P}$$

where N is the number of decibels (abbreviated db or dB). Some space has been given to this subject because the real meaning of the unit is so often misunderstood: if its derivation is clearly followed such misunderstanding is not likely to arise.

It is seen that it is a unit of power loss, which is also a measure of loudness loss or of length of transmission line. Its use for measuring other quantities, such as amplification, can be justified only under certain clearly defined conditions.

The relative gain of two amplifiers may be compared by measuring their output powers for a given input. The result can be expressed in decibels because two powers P_1 and P_2 are being compared. If

$$N = 10 \log_{10} \frac{P_2}{P_1},$$

then the second amplifier is N dB more powerful than the first. If P_1 is arbitrarily fixed at 50 mW, then the output of any amplifier can be expressed as so many dB above or below this level. The decibel is then a convenient unit for *comparing* the performance of amplifiers.

The same unit however is often used to express the *gain* of an amplifier. Its use for this purpose is at least questionable. If it is stated that an amplifier has a gain of N dB, it is meant that the *power* in the output circuit is related to the *power* in the input circuit by the equation:

$$N = 10 \log_{10} \frac{\text{power delivered}}{\text{power absorbed}}.$$

The fallacy is that amplifiers usually absorb only minute powers, being in fact 'voltage operated'. Hence, that such a power amplifier has a gain of N dB is a statement of very little value in practice. The gain of voltage amplifiers can be justifiably stated in decibels *provided that the resistances of the output and input circuits are equal,* say R. Then

$$P_1 = \frac{E_1^2}{R} \text{ and } P_2 = \frac{E_2^2}{R}$$

$$\therefore \text{ Gain} = 10 \log_{10} \frac{P_2}{P_1} = 10 \log_{10} \frac{E_2^2}{E_1} = 20 \log_{10} \frac{E_2}{E_1}.$$

WORKED EXAMPLES

Question 1. A simple slide-wire potentiometer is used to compare two e.m.f's. If it is possible to read the position of the sliding contact to within 0·5 mm what is the highest accuracy obtainable for the ratio of the e.m.f's? How does the accuracy depend upon the length of potentiometer wire being actually used? Assume the e.m.f's are nearly equal and that the potentiometer has a wire 1 m long.

Answer 1. By the principle of the potentiometer, the ratio of the e.m.f's being compared is equal to the ratio of the length of wire between the common connection and the sliding contact required to obtain a balance, i.e.

$$\frac{E_1}{E_2} = \frac{l_1}{l_2}.$$

Now if l_1 has a positive error and l_2 a negative error, then the error in the ratio is given by

$$\frac{l_1 + 0\cdot5}{l_2 - 0\cdot5} - \frac{l_1}{l_2} = \frac{l_1 l_2 + 0\cdot5\,l_2 - l_1\,(l_2 - 0\cdot5)}{l_2(l_2 - 0\cdot5)} = \frac{0\cdot5\,l_2 + 0\cdot5\,l_1}{l_2(l_2 - 0\cdot5)} = \frac{0\cdot5\,(l_2 + l_1)}{l_2\,(l_2 - 0\cdot5)}$$

where l_1 and l_2 are measured in millimetres.

If l_2 is large compared with 0·5 mm the above may be written

$$\frac{0\cdot5\,(l_2 + l_1)}{l_2^2}$$

Putting $l_2 + l_1 = 2l_2$, this becomes

$$\frac{0.5 \times 2l_2}{l_2{}^2} \text{ and the error is } \frac{l}{l_2}.$$

Thus it is seen that the larger l_2, that is the longer the potentiometer wire, the less the error, i.e. the error is inversely proportional to the length of wire and the error in this case is $1/l_2$ and for $l_2 = 1000$ mm,

Error = 1 in 1000.

Question 2. The resistances of a Wheatstone bridge are correct to within $\pm 0.1\%$. To what accuracy can an unknown resistance be measured?

Answer 2. The condition of balance in a Wheatstone bridge is $X = RP/Q$ where X is the unknown resistance, R the standard and P and Q the values of the ratio arms (or lengths between the ends and the moving contact, in the case of a metre bridge). It is given that R, P and Q are known to within $\pm 0.1\%$. The greatest error in X arises when P and R are high by 0.1% and Q is low by the amount. Then is δX is the error in X,

$$X + \delta X = \frac{P(1.001)}{Q(0.999)} R(1.001)$$

Hence

$$\delta X = \frac{P}{Q} R \frac{1.001^2}{0.999} - 1$$

Therefore the percentage error in X is

$$\frac{\delta X}{X} \times 100 = \frac{1.001^2 - 0.999}{0.999} \times 100$$

$$= 0.3\% \text{ approx.}$$

Question 3. A milliammeter has to be calibrated. The following four readings, for the actual current when the meter read 2 mA, are taken by potentiometer.

1	2	3	4
1.96	2.04	1.98	1.99

What is the percentage correction to be applied to the milliammeter and within what percentage limits would you guarantee your correction factor?

Answer 3. To find the actual current as nearly as possible take the mean of the four readings.

$$\text{Mean value of current} = \frac{1.96 + 2.04 + 1.98 + 1.99}{4}$$

$$= \frac{7.97}{4} = 1.993 \text{ mA.}$$

The meter, then, reads 0·007 too high. Now the actual values of current range between 1·96 and 2·04. There is therefore a maximum variation of ± 0·04 mA. As this variation is greater than the correction factor the meter can be declared as reading correctly within the limits of ± 0·04 mA. The meter is correct to within an uncertainty of ± 2·0%.

EXERCISES

Define (*a*) 'decibel', (*b*) 'neper'.

A transmission line has an overall loss of 5 db; what is the equivalent loss in nepers?

A low-frequency amplifier has a gain of 40 db. The impedance of the input circuit is 600 Ω (resistance) and the output is arranged for a load of 20 Ω. What will be the current in the load when an alternating potential of 1 volt r.m.s. is applied to the input?   (Grad. I.E.E.)

Answer. 1·15 N, 0·913 A.

REFERENCES

1. FEWKES AND YARWOOD. *Electricity, Magnetism, and Atomic Physics* (Vol. I). University Tutorial Press Ltd. (1956).
2. *The Use of SI Units,* British Standard PD 5686, (1965).
3. GRAY, ANDREW. *Absolute Measurements in Electricity and Magnetism,* Dover Publications Inc., 1967 (Originally published in 1921).

CHAPTER 2

Direct Current Instruments

2.1. INTRODUCTION

In Chapter 1 it was shown how the accuracy to be expected from a given measurement can be estimated and how the accuracy of the final result depends upon the possible errors in the several parts of the experiment.

The two chief types of measurement (or comparison) i.e. deflectional methods and null methods, were discussed and it was seen that deflectional methods are easier and quicker to perform, while null methods are more accurate. Both these methods require instruments to make apparent the presence of the voltage or current, and this chapter covers the construction of these instruments for d.c. measurements.

2.2. GALVANOMETERS

The principles used in the construction of indicators for null methods and in meters for deflectional readings are exactly the same but the actual construction differs considerably. For null measurements, sensitivity is a primary factor and reliability of calibration and robustness are not so important as in direct-reading instruments.

Greater sensitivity leads to special problems. The controlling force has to be made small in comparison with the weight of the moving parts so that the natural period of swing becomes considerable, in fact, several seconds. In general, the more sensitive the instrument the longer the natural period, i.e. the longer it takes the moving parts to swing from rest to their new position, and consequently the longer it takes to make a measurement. These problems can be overcome in a variety of ways, some of which will now be considered.

Note that the term 'sensitivity' as applied to galvanometers usually refers to the current (or voltage) required to produce a deflection of one millimetre, but in direct-reading meters it usually denotes the current required to produce full scale deflection (f.s.d.). These are the meanings given in specifications. The term 'sensitiveness' is sometimes used to mean the least change of current that can be detected.

2.2.1. Moving-magnet Galvanometers

The earliest type of galvanometer consisted of a compass needle situated at the centre of a coil. A current in the coil produced a magnetic field at right angles to the earth's field, thus deflecting the needle.

To increase the sensitivity, the effect of the earth's field, i.e. the 'restoring force', had to be reduced. This was accomplished by using the astatic principle as shown in Fig. 2.1, where two needles are fixed together so that their North poles point in opposite directions. The coil or coils are so placed that the current tends to turn both needles in the same direction, whereas the earth's field tends to turn them in opposite directions.

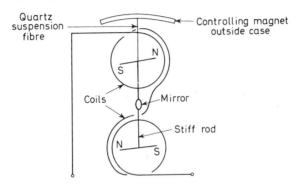

Fig. 2.1. Moving-magnet galvanometer

These types of instrument were so sensitive that the restoring moment due to the suspension fibre had to be taken into account. A pivot was out of the question because the friction was far too great to allow of such a light 'movement' coming to rest at a *definite position.* Quartz fibre was found to be the best material for the purpose. Note that the term 'movement' is used as a noun to describe the mechanism, as it is in clocks and watches.

Another problem was how to make the deflection readable. A pointer could not be used because of the added weight and the impossibility of making it long enough to show a reasonable movement for a small angular deflection. This problem was overcome to a large extent by fixing a small mirror to the moving magnet system and causing it to reflect a spot of light on to a scale, as shown in Fig. 2.2.

With the mirror undeflected, the normal to the mirror at C lies along the line AC, and the incident ray of light is undeviated. When the mirror turns through an angle θ, the normal at C also turns through an angle θ with respect to the incident ray from the fixed source at A.

Now since, by a well-known law in optics, the angle of reflection must be equal to the angle of incidence (each with respect to the normal), the reflected beam makes an angle 2θ with the incident beam. Thus a two-fold magnification is obtained. The actual distance the spot of light moves on the scale depends upon the distance the scale is from the mirror; the distance AB equals d times the tangent of the angle through which the light beam moves.

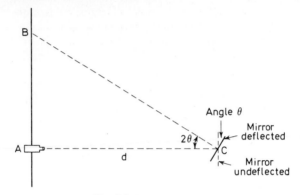

Fig. 2.2. Optical pointer

For small angles, with a scale distance of one metre the distance AB is equal to the angle measured in radians which is twice the angle through which the mirror is deflected. An instrument deflection of one degree then gives a reading of approximately 35 mm.

The optical system has been considered in some detail since it is the method employed in all sensitive galvanometers whatever their deflecting mechanism. Such instruments are generally called reflecting or mirror galvanometers and the optical system is called the lamp-and-scale method. The sensitivity of these instruments is given as the number of millimetres deflection of the spot of light for a scale distance of one metre and a current of one micro-ampere, or a p.d. of one microvolt applied to the instrument terminals.

Electronic galvanometers are becoming widely used. A typical example is the Airmec Galvamp Type 391, which has a sensitivity better than 5 μV or 5 mμA per scale division with nominal battery volts. It consists essentially of a transistorised chopper-type d.c. amplifier feeding a large centre-zero meter. Excellent stability is obtained by means of powerful negative feedback (Chapter 5), and a special circuit ensures that the zero is independent of the source impedance of the input signal. Operation is from an internal 9 V battery or from an external 7-9 V d.c. supply.

2.2.2. Moving-coil Galvanometers

While the moving-magnet principle is still occasionally used for
sensitive electrical instruments, the moving-coil principle is preferred
for all ordinary purposes. It is not possible to construct a suspended
coil with the same lightness and freedom of movement as a suspended
needle system, but the moving-coil galvanometer can be made with a
sensitivity adequate for most purposes and having the advantages of
greater robustness, freedom from disturbances due to stray magnetic
fields and greater speed in use. The last-mentioned advantage is due to
the ease with which damping can be applied and controlled. This will
be discussed later on in this chapter.

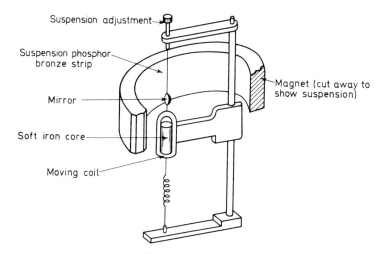

Fig. 2.3. Sullivan-type galvanometer

The construction of a typical moving-coil galvanometer is shown in
Fig. 2.3. The permanent magnet provides a strong field, which is made
radial by a soft iron core, as shown in Fig. 2.4. The advantage of a radial
field is that the turning moment exerted on the coil by the current is
independent of the angle of deflection; if the field is not radial the
magnetic flux threading the coil will vary according to coil position,
and hence the acting couple will vary.

Thus, with a radial field, the restoring couple alone governs the 'law'
of the instrument, and since this normally takes the form of a spring,
the deflection is directly proportional to the current. This follows from
the physical principle known as Hooke's Law, which states that the
extension of a spring is directly proportional to the force applied to
the spring.

When the instrument is to be used solely as a null balance indicator, there is no advantage in having the deflection proportional to the current; all that is necessary is that it shall move away from zero quickly with a very small current and shall just as quickly return to the zero position when the current is off (i.e. when the bridge key is up). The latter condition is obtained by making the moment of inertia small, that is by making the coil long and narrow and dispensing with the iron core as in the Tinsley galvanometer Type 3038, which uses a wooden core. Damping is obtained by connecting a 'link' across two terminals on the base of the instrument, a damping coil being fitted internally.

Special difficulties occur in this method when an attempt is made to obtain high sensitivity by using a very strong magnet, since even slight iron impurities in either the wire, or the frame (if used) on which the coil is wound, or the cementing varnish, will render the coil 'polarised'. This means that the small quantity of iron will tend to make the coil set *along* the magnetic field (the property of a 'paramagnetic' material) whereas the current tends to make it set at right angles to the field. In other words the iron impurities lessen the sensitivity by aiding the restoring couple. In the Moll galvanometer the pole pieces are made adjustable so that the main field can be deliberately distorted in such a manner as to turn any polarisation of the coil to good effect; the coil will tend to set along the distorted field, which tendency can be made to oppose the restoring couple due to the spring of the suspension. An increase in sensitivity of ten times is claimed.

When an instrument is required to be portable, a galvanometer complete with its lamp and scale can be fitted inside a box so that the whole is self-contained.

A different kind of electronic galvanometer to that described in the previous section is the optical type: the current passes through a moving-coil and mirror system in which for zero current input the mirror reflects a beam of light from a lamp into the space between two photo-cells. When a current is applied, the beam is deflected on to one of the photocells depending on the polarity of the current, the degree of illumination depending on the strength of the current. The resulting photocell output voltage is amplified and used to operate a normal moving-coil type centre-zero meter.

2.2.3. Suspension

As mentioned earlier, quartz fibre is used for suspension in moving-magnet instruments but in the moving-coil type provision must be made for conducting the current to the coil. Phosphor-bronze strip is normally used; one strip about 100 mm long supporting the coil from above and the other in the form of a loose spiral (so as to have very little turning moment) serving only as an electrical connection. The construction can be seen in Fig. 2.3.

Unfortunately, phosphor-bronze corrodes easily and gold strip has been tried in its place; it has been found, however, that this is liable to give trouble due to thermo-electric effects. For special work, quartz suspension is used and connection is made by very flexible copper braid, in order to avoid thermo-electric effects. When used on board ships the whole suspension is made taut and in these instances it is then essential that the coil should be perfectly balanced.

2.2.4. Magnets

The most important feature in galvanometer magnets is permanency, and to ensure this, they are given a special ageing treatment. They are first magnetised by being threaded on a bar, which forms a single-turn coil, provided with keepers and then vibrated while a heavy current is passed through the bar. The magnets are then subjected to a moderately high temperature followed by a period of rest. Some manufacturers subject their magnets to a vibration treatment or even to a weak alternating field. The ageing treatment causes about a 20% reduction in strength but the remaining magnetism is very permanent. Cobalt steel is now used extensively to produce a lighter magnet for the same strength as other materials.

Temperature affects the strength of a magnet, so that a galvanometer calibrated at one temperature will not have the same sensitivity at another. The effect is to some extent compensated for by the fact that phosphor-bronze suspension exerts less turning moment at higher temperatures.

2.2.5. Mathematical Treatment

The usual galvanometer suspension is in effect a spring control which exerts a restoring couple directly proportional to the angle through which it is twisted. The restoring couple is therefore given by $\tau\theta$ where τ is the couple for unit angular deflection (in newton metres/rad.) and θ the angle of deflection. The couple exerted by the magnetic effect of the current is given by $BblIN$ for the case of a radial field and $BblIN$ $\cos\theta$ for a uniform parallel field, where B is the flux density in Wb/m^2, b metres the breadth and l metres the length of the coil (considered rectangular), I the current in amperes and N the total number of turns on the coil.

Equating these results for a condition of equilibrium,

$$\tau\theta = BblIN \tag{2.1}$$
$$\text{or } \tau\theta = BblIN \cos\theta \tag{2.2}$$

It is evident from Fig. 2.4 that in a radial field the breadth of the coil must always be along the lines of force, hence as shown in equation (2.1),

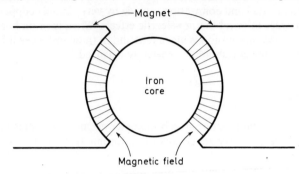

Fig. 2.4. Production of radial field

the deflection is directly proportional to the current, this is obviously a great advantage.

Equation (2.1) can be transposed as

$$\frac{\theta}{I} = \frac{BblN}{\tau} \tag{2.3}$$

Now if L is the distance of the scale from the instrument and D is the linear deflection, then for a small angle, $\theta = D/2L$ (since the light beam turns through 2θ). Therefore the current sensitivity is given by

$$S_i = \frac{D}{I} = \frac{2\theta L}{I} = \frac{2BblNL}{\tau} = \frac{2BblN}{\tau} \text{ if } L = 1 \text{ metre} \tag{2.4}$$

The units are mm/μA at 1 m when I is in microamperes and D is deflection in mm at a scale distance L of 1 m.

This quantity is also the galvanometer constant, i.e. the constant by which the current must be multiplied to obtain the deflection. To obtain a high sensitivity, the restoring couple must obviously be made small, while the field strength and coil dimensions should be large. Unfortunately a large coil necessarily involves a large moment of inertia and hence a long natural period. This is undesirable, for much time will be wasted waiting for the coil to reach its new position every time the current changes. The dimensions of the instrument must therefore be a compromise and one that every manufacturer solves in his own way. Modern permanent magnet technique has made it possible to increase B considerably without any sacrifice of permanence, but as will be shown later a large value of B is not always desirable.

When the dimensions of the instrument and the magnet have been decided upon it is still possible to alter the turns. Many manufacturers supply several coils for use with the same instrument; the coils used in the Tinsley Type 3038 galvanometer described earlier can easily be changed, since they are made up in special tubes for that purpose. Since the coils for use with one galvanometer are of equal size the electrical resistance will depend solely on the number of turns; if the turns are doubled the length of wire is obviously doubled and also its cross-section must be halved to get it in the same space — in fact the resistance varies as the square of the turns. (This is neglecting the thickness of the insulation on the wire; for thin wires the insulation is a large proportion of the total thickness.)

Therefore $$S_i = K \sqrt{R_g} \qquad (2.5)$$

where R_g is the galvanometer resistance and K is a constant equal to $\dfrac{2Bbl}{\tau}$, or $\dfrac{2Bbl}{\tau \times 10^{-3}}$ if S_i is in mm/microamp.

The voltage sensitivity S_e is sometimes required; for a voltage E applied to the instrument terminals the equation is

$$S_e = \frac{D}{E} = \frac{D}{IR_g} = \frac{S_i}{R_g} \qquad (2.6)$$

Thus from equation (2.5),

$$S_e = \frac{K\sqrt{R_g}}{R_g} = \frac{K}{\sqrt{R_g}} \text{ mm/}\mu\text{V at 1 m scale distance.} \qquad (2.7)$$

For maximum current sensitivity the resistance should be as large as possible but for high voltage sensitivity the lower the resistance the better; this is the case in potentiometer work where the galvanometer is used to show out-of-balance potentials.

2.2.6. 'Best Resistance'

When a galvanometer is to be used in connection with a circuit whose resistance is specified or approximately specified, e.g. a Wheatstone bridge, there will be a certain value of R_g that will give maximum current sensitivity. Let the e.m.f. of the circuit be E and its resistance R, then the deflection is given by

$$D = S_i I_g = K I_g \sqrt{R_g} = K \frac{E}{R + R_g} \sqrt{R_g} \qquad (2.8)$$

On differentiation it is seen that D is a maximum when $R = R_g$. Hence the general rule that for maximum sensitivity the galvanometer resistance should be equal to the resistance of the external circuit.

For strict accuracy R_g should be divided by a constant to take into account the thickness of the insulation on the coil wire, in all the above results.

2.2.7. Damping

It has already been mentioned that since the galvanometer movement has mass and elasticity (the spring of the suspension), it will take an appreciable time to reach a new position after a current is applied or changed. The greater the mass of the coil the longer the natural period of oscillation, but the stronger the restoring torque the shorter the period. This behaviour is the mechanical equivalent of the electrical circuit containing inductance and capacitance; the inductance corresponding to the mass and the capacitance to the reciprocal of the elasticity.

The reader will be familiar with the effect of resistance in a circuit. The corresponding damping effect in the case of the galvanometer is of great practical importance, for if the instrument has little damping the pointer will swing backwards and forwards a great many times before coming to rest at its deflected position corresponding to the particular value of current. This would obviously not only waste a lot of time but also be extremely exasperating to the user. For example an instrument having a period of three seconds — by no means long — might oscillate twenty times before coming to rest; an impossible situation!

A method must be found that will make the movement just non-oscillating — corresponding to the electrical case where $R^2/4L^2 = 1/LC$. If the damping exceeds this amount the action will be sluggish, so that when obtaining a balance in a Wheatstone bridge there will be a feeling of 'is it going to move or not'. Most users prefer to have the galvanometer slightly under-damped, so that it makes one swing before coming to rest.

In the moving-coil type, damping is easily obtained by utilising the back e.m.f. generated when the coil is moving in the magnetic field. In some cases a few special turns are provided which can be shorted by a link on the coil itself or the coil is wound on an aluminium frame but usually damping is obtained by adjusting the external circuit resistance, which forms a closed circuit with the coil. The back e.m.f. is given by

$$E_b = BAN \frac{d\theta}{dt} = k \frac{d\theta}{dt} \text{ volts}$$

where A is the area of the coil, k a constant for the particular instrument and the other symbols are as defined previously.

Hence the instantaneous value for current produced in a closed circuit of resistance R is

$$i = \frac{E - L \frac{di}{dt} - k \frac{d\theta}{dt}}{R}$$

where E is the applied e.m.f., R the total resistance in the circuit, and L the total inductance in the circuit including coil inductance which may form the largest part.

The turning moment on the coil is then given by

$$ik - \tau\theta$$

Hence the equation of motion of the system is

$$P\frac{d^2\theta}{dt^2} = ik - \tau\theta \text{ where } P \text{ is the moment of inertia.}$$

(The angular acceleration times the moment of inertia equals the couple acting.) Substituting for i gives

$$P\frac{d^2\theta}{dt^2} = \left(\frac{E - L\dfrac{di}{dt} - k\dfrac{d\theta}{dt}}{R}\right)k - \tau\theta$$

i.e.

$$P\frac{d^2\theta}{dt^2} + \frac{k^2}{R}\frac{d\theta}{dt} + \tau\theta = \left(\frac{E - L\dfrac{di}{dt}}{R}\right)k$$

Compare this with the equation for the charging of a capacitor

$$L\frac{d^2q}{dt^2} + R\frac{dq}{dt} + \frac{q}{C} = 0$$

Obviously the equations are of the same form and hence the conditions that the motion shall be oscillatory, non-oscillatory or critical will be similar in form. For critical damping:

$$\frac{\tau}{P} = \left(\frac{k^2}{R}\right)^2 \frac{1}{4P^2} \tag{2.9}$$

which corresponds to

$$\frac{1}{LC} = \frac{R^2}{4L^2}$$

for the electrical case.

In the above discussion the damping due to air resistance was assumed to be negligible: for a large coil this could be allowed for by writing $(k^2/R + c)$ in place of k^2/R, where c is a constant due to air damping.

It remains to be seen how the condition of equation (2.9) can be obtained. Taking the square root of (2.9) gives $k^2/R = 2\sqrt{\tau P}$ (the negative root has no meaning).

Substituting for k gives

$$\frac{(BAN)^2}{R} = 2\sqrt{\tau P}$$

or

$$R = \frac{(BAN)^2}{2\sqrt{P\tau}}$$

It has already been seen that galvanometer resistance is proportional to the square of the turns so that

$$R = R_g + R_x = \frac{(BA)^2}{2\sqrt{P_T}} k_1 R_g \text{ where } k_1 \text{ is another constant.}$$

Thus

$$R_x = R_g \left\{ \frac{(BA)^2 k_1}{2\sqrt{P_T}} - 1 \right\} \text{ ohms} \qquad (2.10)$$

The ideal case would clearly be such that $\frac{(BA)^2 k_1}{2\sqrt{P_T}} = 2$ for then the critical resistance, i.e. the external resistance required to produce critical damping, would be equal to the galvanometer resistance and this, as shown in the previous section, is also the condition for maximum sensitivity. It would be quite possible to have a galvanometer made satisfying these conditions, for use with a bridge which was to be used for measuring resistances of one nominal value. In practice, however, a galvanometer is generally required to be of use over a fairly wide range of circuit resistances. When switching in a galvanometer, it is not always known what current will be passed through it, consequently a shunt or series resistance has to be used as a safeguard; this, of course, upsets the critical damping just at the time when the instrument is most likely to swing violently. Critical damping is thus required in the early stages of balancing but maximum sensitivity is required when balance has been nearly obtained and therefore damping is not then of great importance. This raises the question of shunts.

In bridge work the galvanometer is often provided with a shunt and tapping key. The key is pressed to damp the instrument and bring it quickly to rest but when actually testing for balance no shunt is used, thus full sensitivity is obtained.

2.2.8. Shunts

The principles of shunts for the purpose of reducing sensitivity by by-passing some of the current that would otherwise pass through the meter are well known, but their use to obtain critical damping resistance in galvanometer work is even more important. From equation (2.10) above it will be clear that only one value of shunt will do this for a particular instrument, and moreover this will only be suitable for one value of external resistance, unless the latter is so high that it has negligible effect.

The universal shunt (Fig. 2.5) is a convenient method of securing critical damping and at the same time providing a means of varying the sensitivity. A constant resistance is connected across the galvanometer but the proportion of the resistance that is shunted across the external circuit can be altered, the remainder becoming a series resistance.

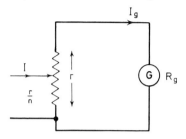

Fig. 2.5. Universal shunt

If I is the current to be measured, I_g the galvanometer current, R_g the galvanometer resistance, r the shunt resistance (i.e. critical damping resistance), and $1/n$ the fraction of the shunt tapped off, then from Fig. 2.6 and the principle of branch currents,

$$I_g = I \frac{\dfrac{r}{n}}{r + Rg} \quad \therefore \quad I = Ig \frac{(Rg + r)n}{r} \tag{2.11}$$

It should be noted that the universal shunt *cannot* be used with different instruments if critical damping is to be obtained.

If the galvanometer has to be used in a circuit of low resistance (compared with its damping resistance), a series resistance R_1 is inserted and then if further reduction of sensitivity is required a shunt R_2 is added directly across the galvanometer, as shown in Fig. 2.6.

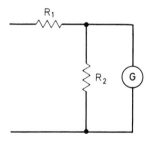

Fig. 2.6. Reduction of galvanometer sensitivity

It might be mentioned that an attenuator works very well for controlling galvanometer sensitivity. An attenuator, it will be remembered, is a resistance network so arranged that the input and output resistances are constant but the proportion of the applied volts delivered at the output can be varied, (see Chapter 13).

Another type of shunt consists of a piece of iron fixed across the magnet so that it forms an alternative path for the magnetic flux. By adjusting this 'magnetic shunt' the proportion of the total flux shorted away from the moving coil can be varied. This is an easy method of adjusting B which not only reduces the sensitivity but also lowers the resistance required for critical damping. Sensitivity varies as B but the damping resistance varies as B^2, therefore it is sometimes convenient to alter both B and the value of the external shunt.

2.2.9. Choice of a Galvanometer

The choice of a suitable instrument is a matter of individual preference, since each particular type and make has its own characteristics and the user becomes accustomed to one particular kind. There are, however, certain principles involved in the choice of a galvanometer for a certain specified measurement.

The sensitivity should be adequate for the purpose in hand but not too sensitive, for then it would have an unnecessarily long period of oscillation as well as being liable to swing violently if an excess current should pass momentarily. A too sensitive instrument is also needlessly expensive and may be easily damaged. A stable zero is of course of the utmost importance since sensitivity is of very little use if the instrument cannot be relied upon to return exactly to zero after each deflection. For null measurements this is the main feature to be taken into account.

Coil resistance has already been considered; it should always be remembered that a high resistance, and therefore a high current sensitivity, does not necessarily mean that the instrument will actually give the greatest possible sensitivity in a particular circuit.

Care must be taken to guard against thermo-electric effects, either at junctions in the galvanometer or in the shunts. This difficulty can be minimised by arranging for the shunts and galvanometer to be maintained at as steady a temperature as possible, and to be kept out of draughts that might cause a sudden cooling of the shunts. These effects can usually be allowed for by quickly reversing the connections and noting if the deflection is the same, if not the mean should be taken, or better still the source of thermo-electric e.m.f. found and corrected.

Where a galvanometer is required to measure currents rather than merely give a null balance, temperature errors are important. A large series resistance, made of a metal with low temperature coefficient, ensures that any change of galvanometer coil resistance with temperature has negligible effect.

2.3. DIRECT-READING INSTRUMENTS

The characteristics required in an instrument for direct deflectional reading are somewhat different from those required in galvanometers. The chief requirement is consistency of reading, so that once the instrument has been calibrated against a standard the same deflection shall always correspond to the same current. To achieve this as well as for other obvious reasons, robustness of construction is necessary; therefore a pivoted system is used instead of a suspended system.

The same two principles are used – moving-coil and moving-magnet (moving-iron types will be considered in Chapter 4). Whereas the moving-magnet principle has to be used for the most sensitive galvanometers it is only used for deflectional instruments of the cheapest type, such as those fitted on car instrument panels. The moving-coil type is almost universally used for d.c. purposes for the following reasons. Large deflectional forces can be obtained with low power consumption and consequent great accuracy. Magnetic damping can very easily be applied. Other minor advantages are an evenly divided scale and relative freedom from the effects of external magnetic fields.

2.3.1. Friction Errors

The chief cause of inaccuracy with a pivoted instrument is friction. Static friction is of such a nature that a definite force must be exerted before motion occurs. If current is passed through a meter having excessive friction, one reading will be obtained if the current is gradually increased from zero, another if it is decreased from a higher value and yet another if in either case the instrument is vibrated. The difficulty is overcome in two ways, first by reducing the friction to a minimum and second by making the operating force as large as possible in comparison with the frictional forces. The first is accomplished by using hard steel pivots turning in jewel seatings. Less friction is obtained with a vertical spindle than with a horizontal one, for in the former case the weight is supported on one ground point but in the latter it is shared between the conical sides of both bearings. A typical moving-coil meter construction using the double pivot system is shown in Fig. 2.7.

Fig. 2.8 shows a meter movement made by Crompton Parkinson to withstand shock and vibration as required for military applications. It has no pivots, jewel bearings or control springs; these being replaced by a taut ribbon at each end of the coil spindle to provide suspension and, by its twisting, the control torque. This is popularly known as 'taut band' suspension. For further information the reader is referred to the articles in the 'Electrical Review'[2,3]

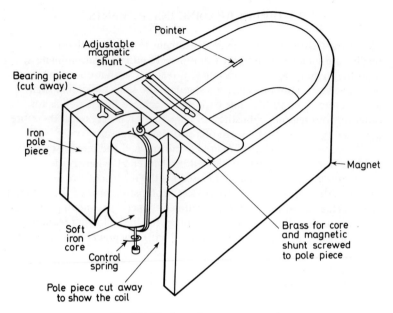

Fig. 2.7. Moving-coil meter construction

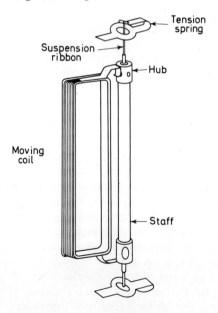

Fig. 2.8. Pivotless movement

In the instrument called the 'Unipivot' made by the Cambridge Instrument Company, the friction is reduced to a very low level in an ingenious way. The iron core used to ensure a radial magnetic field is spherical instead of cylindrical as in most types, and a jewel seating is placed at its centre, so that the circular coil is supported on one steel point at its centre of gravity (Fig. 2.9). The Unipivot can obviously only be used horizontally (i.e. with the spindle vertical) and it will not stand quite the same amount of rough usage as double pivot types, but a very high degree of accuracy can be obtained, together with a sensitivity approaching that of suspended-coil instruments. For this reason Unipivot meters are widely used for Precision Grade instruments.

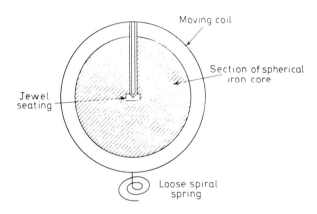

Fig. 2.9. Unipivot system

It is obvious that the effect of friction is relative, i.e. that a much greater actual force of friction can be tolerated in an instrument where the operating forces are large. As in the case of the radial field galvanometer the couple due to the current in the coil is equal to $BAIN$, where A is the area of the coil, and the restoring couple is $\tau\theta$, hence when the deflection is increasing the total couple is given by $BAIN - \tau\theta - F$ where F is the couple due to the friction and is independent of θ. For equilibrium this total couple is equal to zero. Now if $\delta\theta$ is the error in deflection due to friction, then

$$BAIN - \tau(\theta - \delta\theta) - F = 0$$

hence $\qquad \tau\delta\theta = F$

It is evident that the greater τ is, the less is the error $\delta\theta$ for a given value of F. Now F depends only on the design of the bearings and on the weight upon them, therefore it is desirable to make the coil as light as possible. Weights are in the order of 1 to 5 gms, while the operating couples are of the order of 10^{-4} newton-metres. The ratio of couple to weight is then somewhere between 196:1 and 50:1.

Since the operating couple is proportional to the ampere-turns it would appear at first sight that the same design could be used for any range by simply increasing the number of turns on the moving coil. There is however a practical limit (about 47 s.w.g.) to the fineness of wire that can be used. If an instrument is required for still smaller currents and the same degree of accuracy, B can be increased, τ decreased and the size and weight of the moving parts also decreased. Frictional errors can then be further reduced by special bearings such as the Unipivot or by the use of a suspended system.

In recent years there has been a great improvement in permanent magnet techniques; the use of cobalt steel has made it possible to produce magnets of much greater strength and also of much smaller size. Not only has this been of benefit to the better class of instrument but it has also made it possible to put on the market meters with a full scale deflection of 50 μA quite cheaply. These are of considerable value in electronic equipment servicing work.

A variation of the moving-coil meter construction shown in Fig. 2.7 that is coming into wide use is the centre-magnet configuration. In this design the permanent magnet is replaced by a cylinder of low-reluctance magnetic material surrounding the movement, and the soft iron core is replaced by a cylindrical permanent magnet whose poles are at opposite ends of its diameter. Apart from the advantage of a higher magnetic flux in the air gap, there is no stray field inside the instrument due to leakage from the permanent magnet and the meter is little affected by being mounted on a metal panel or by the presence of weak external magnetic fields. Inexpensive commercial meters based on this design are available, including ammeters with full scale deflections of as little as 5 μA.

2.3.2. Other Sources of Error

There are other sources of error besides friction that limit the accuracy of meters. The strength of the magnet decreases with rise of temperature but fortunately the strength of the phosphor bronze restoring springs also decreases; thus the two effects are compensatory except for the highest accuracy, in which case a correction factor can be applied when the meter is used at a temperature widely different from that at which it was calibrated.

The sensitivity of a voltmeter is clearly dependent upon its resistance. If this varies, as it must do with a change of temperature, the current through the meter will vary for the same applied volts. This source of error is easily overcome by ensuring that the series resistance, necessarily used with a voltmeter, has negligible temperature coefficient and is large enough to swamp the coil resistance.

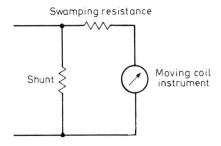

Fig. 2.10. Swamping resistance used with ammeter

In the case of ammeters, the shunt is a possible source of trouble, since if the instrument resistance varies, the multiplying power will also vary. For this reason shunts are made so as to have negligible temperature coefficients and a series resistance is connected directly to the meter to act as a swamp as in a voltmeter, as shown in Fig. 2.10.

2.3.3. Accuracy of Reading

Not only is it necessary that the mechanism of a meter should be as free from errors as possible but also the user must be able to read the position of the pointer accurately. If a knife-edge pointer is used and a mirror fixed beneath it, adjacent to the scale, the user has only to ensure that the image in the mirror is hidden from view by the pointer itself in order to read the deflection to a high degree of accuracy and avoid errors due to parallax.

The accuracy of the reading will clearly depend on how close together the scale divisions are; a long pointer means a longer scale and more divisions of the scale for the same angular deflection of the coil. A pointer about 150 mm long is usual for precision meters but cheap types may have only a 40 mm pointer with perhaps only 25 divisions round the scale. It is undesirable to have a larger number of divisions marked than the accuracy of the mechanism warrants, as it gives a false sense of accuracy as well as wasting time in reading.

The British Standards Institution has drawn up specifications of accuracy for two classes of electrical measuring instruments, namely, 'Precision Grade' and 'Industrial Grade'. Full details are given in British Standard 89:1954.

2.3.4. Choice of a Meter

Sensitivity is of considerable importance in a voltmeter. In current practice the standard p.d. across a meter shunt is 75 mV or on rare occasions 50 mV. In fact the indicator for a universal meter is usually standardised at 75 mV 15 mA giving 5 Ω for the meter coil and swamp resistor. If such a meter has a maximum scale reading of 450 V then its resistance will be 30 000 Ω and it will require a current of 15 mA for full deflection. A meter of this kind is fairly robust and presents no particular problems, either in use or in design, and its current of 15 mA is negligible compared with power circuit currents of say 5 A, therefore the effect of the meter on the circuit is to introduce an error of about three parts in a thousand, which is of no consequence if a good meter is used.

The position is rather different if the voltage across the anode load resistor of a radio valve when the receiver is in operation has to be measured. An audio amplifying stage may take an anode current of 5 mA and have an anode load resistor of 30 000 Ω. When the voltmeter is connected across this resistor the correct reading would be 150 V, but this would not be the case in practice, for the meter puts 30 000 Ω in parallel with the anode resistor. Now assume that in the original condition the valve was taking 5 mA for an anode voltage of 200 V. Then its resistance must be $200/5 \times 10^{-3} = 40\ 000$ Ω. With the voltmeter across the anode resistor and the same supply voltage of 350 the current would be 7·78 mA and this divides between the anode resistor and the meter in inverse ratio to their resistance. Thus in this particular case the current through the meter would be $7·78/2 = 3·89$ mA. Now 15 mA corresponds to 450 V on the meter scale so that 3·89 mA will correspond to 116·7 V, which will be the reading instead of the 150 that ought to be obtained. Not only does this represent an error of 22·2% but it is also a measurement not made under the normal operating conditions of the valve. Obviously if a meter of the same ohms per volt but of 200 V full scale reading were used the situation would be even worse, and again the situation would be worse if a stage with a valve having say 100 000 Ω anode resistance were investigated, while in the case of screen grid circuits the results would be quite meaningless.

There are on the market several meters at a reasonable price having 20 000 Ω/V. Such an instrument should be chosen for the type of measurement described in the previous paragraph, but it is likely that a smaller type such as 1000 Ω/V will be preferred where the extra sensitivity is of no advantage.

Where the measurement to be performed does not demand a high degree of accuracy or the conditions do not permit of its attainment, the meter should be of Industrial Grade, if only on the ground of expense.

Where the calibration of other instruments is required a Precision Grade meter should be used.

2.3.5. Multirange Instruments

On the grounds of both economy and convenience it is often desirable to have a single meter that can be used for many different purposes. The method of using series and shunt resistors to extend the range of volt-meters and ammeters respectively is well known, but will be briefly reviewed here. Assume that a meter is available with a f.s.d. of 1 mA and of resistance 1 Ω. Then by Ohm's Law the f.s.d. voltage is $1 \times 1 \times 10^{-3}$ = 1 mV. Now if the meter is required to read up to 10 mA, then the extra current of 9 mA must be by-passed from the meter by using a shunt (i.e. parallel) resistor of $10^{-3}/9 \times 10^{-3} = 1/9$ or $0 \cdot 11 \ldots \Omega$. If the instrument is required to read up to 1 V, then the extra 999·9 mV must be dropped across a series resistor of $999 \cdot 9 \times 10^{-3}/1 \times 10^{-3}$ = 999·9 Ω.

In commercial multirange instruments a number of current ranges are obtained by fitting a universal shunt and either bringing out the various tappings to terminals or by arranging a switch to make the connections to one terminal, the other terminal being common to all ranges. Such an instrument can of course be provided with additional ranges by the use of external shunts.

Voltage ranges are obtained in a similar way by a tapped resistance in series. When both current and voltage ranges are required in one instrument either the universal shunt can be left permanently in circuit or the

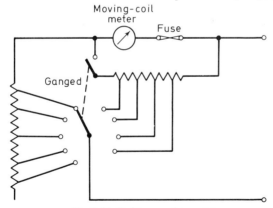

Fig. 2.11. Multi-range d.c. meter

range switch can be made to disconnect it on the voltage ranges. With the latter method a higher ohms per volt is obtained. Fig. 2.11 shows a typical circuit diagram of a multirange meter.

It is a difficult matter to obtain the same accuracy on all ranges, for the shunts and series resistances have to be adjusted to fit one scale (it would hardly be practical to provide separately calibrated scales for say 46 ranges!). The highest accuracy is therefore usually only obtained on single range instruments, where the whole can be directly calibrated and a scale specially made. However, the multirange instruments now on the market are quite good enough for all ordinary electronics work.

2.3.6. The Ballistic Galvanometer

The ballistic galvanometer is used for measuring charge $q = \int i\, dt$, i.e. large currents flowing for a short time, and there is thus very light damping of the moving parts (moving coil and moving magnet types have been made) and a large periodic time of the motion. The whole of the charge or transient current to be measured passes through the coil before the pointer moves appreciably from its zero position, and it can be shown that the charge is then directly proportional to the angle of deflection.

The theory of operation is not difficult but is beyond the scope of this book, and the reader requiring the mathematical analysis is recommended to study the book by Starling[1].

WORKED EXAMPLE

Question. How are the temperature errors of a switchboard type direct current ammeter compensated for?

In a particular case the potential difference between the potential terminals of the shunt of a 1000 A instrument is 0·03 V. The connecting leads to the instrument are of copper and have a resistance of 0·12 Ω, the moving coil has a resistance of 1·20 Ω and requires a current of 15 mA to deflect it to the 1000 A point on the scale. The temperature coefficient of the alloy used for the shunt is 0·00001, and that of copper 0·004 per °C − in terms of the resistance at 15°C. To what extent could this instrument be compensated and, if it is accurately adjusted at 15°C, what error would be expected when all the parts were at 35°C?

Note: Potential terminals are those actually connected to the instrument.

Answer. Temperature errors are due to the fact that the resistance of the moving coil, of the phosphor bronze spring and the connecting leads increase with a rise in temperature. The shunt, however, does not increase in value to any great extent, being made, not of copper as is the moving coil, but of a special alloy such as Manganin. The result is that the magnification of the shunt varies. The difficulty is overcome by connecting a resistance in series with the instrument, large enough to make the changes in the latter's resistance negligible in comparison. This swamping resistance, as it is called, is made of the same alloy as the shunt, (see Fig. 2.10).

Let R ohms be the value of swamping resistance in series with the instrument. Then the current through the moving coil is given by

$$I = \frac{E}{r_1 + r_2 + R}$$

where r_1 and r_2 are the resistances of the coil and leads.

Substituting given values,

$$I = \frac{0 \cdot 03}{0 \cdot 12 + 1 \cdot 2 + R} = 15 \times 10^{-3} \text{ A,}$$

since it is given that 15 mA are required for full-scale deflection. Solving for R,

$$1 \cdot 32 + R = \frac{0 \cdot 03}{15 \times 10^{-3}} \text{ whence } R = 2 - 1 \cdot 32 = 0 \cdot 68 \ \Omega.$$

For $20°$ rise in temperature the shunt resistance increases by

$$0 \cdot 00001 \times 20 = 0 \cdot 0002 \text{ of its value at } 15°.$$

For the same rise the coil circuit resistance changes by

$$\frac{(1 \cdot 32 \times 0 \cdot 004 \times 20) + (0 \cdot 68 \times 20 \times 0 \cdot 00001)}{2} = 0 \cdot 0529 \text{ of its original}$$

value, assuming the swamp to be made of the same material as the shunt.

Now the magnification of a shunt is given by

$1 + R_c/R_s$ where R_c is the coil circuit resistance, R_s the swamp resistance. Hence the change in magnification is

$$1 + \frac{R_c(1 \cdot 0529)}{R_s(1 \cdot 0002)} - 1 - \frac{R_c}{R_s} = \frac{R_c}{R_s}\left(\frac{1 \cdot 0529}{1 \cdot 0002} - 1\right))$$

Hence the proportion of the change in magnification is

$$\frac{0 \cdot 0527}{1 \cdot 0002} = 0 \cdot 0526 \text{ (approx.), i.e. the error is } \underline{5 \cdot 26\%}. \textit{ Answer.}$$

EXERCISES

1. Give an account of the general theory of the moving-coil galvanometer investigating in detail the effect of damping on the manner in which the pointer or 'spot' approaches its final steady deflected position.

2. Sketch and describe the construction of a moving-coil galvano-meter. If the moving coil consists of 100 turns wound on a square frame of sides 30 mm, and the flux density in the air gap is 0·06 tesla, calculate the turning moment acting on the coil when it is passing a current of 12 12 mA.

Answer. $M = 6 \cdot 48 \times 10^{-5}$ newton-metres or $6 \cdot 61 \times 10^{-6}$ kilogramme-metres.

3. Show how the current and voltage sensitivity of a galvanometer of given dimensions depend on the resistance to which it is wound, mentioning the effects of any assumptions made.   (B.Sc.) London.

4. What is meant by critical damping and to what extent should this condition be approached in the case of an ordinary moving coil instrument?   (B.Sc.)

5. Discuss the factors upon which the sensitivity of a moving coil galvanometer depends. Find the value of the resistance of such a galvano-meter which has the greatest sensitivity in a Wheatstone bridge in which all resistances are of the order R ohms and the battery of negligible resistance.

Answer. Galvanometer resistance = R.

REFERENCES

1. STARLING, S. G. *Electricity and Magnetism for Degree Students.* Longmans, Green & Co., 7th ed. (1941).
2. HOCKLEY, H. N. *Pivotless Indicating Instruments.* Electrical Review, (30 March, 1962).
3. TEMPLETON, F. J. *Control of Resonance in Instrument Mechanisms.* Electrical Review, (6 October, 1967).

CHAPTER 3

Measurement of D.C. Resistance

3.1. INTRODUCTION

When high accuracy is not required, d.c. resistance is measured by applying a known voltage to the unknown resistance and measuring the
resulting current. By Ohm's law, the ratio of voltage to current then
gives the resistance value. The voltage may be applied by a hand-driven
generator, as in the Megger tester, or by a cell, as in the ohmmeter and
bonding tester. For high accuracy measurements, bridges or potentiometers are used.

3.2. THE MEGGER TESTER

This is a device for measuring insulation resistance and high resistance
in general. It consists of a moving-coil instrument in which the control
is provided by one coil connected directly across the supply, and the
deflecting torque by another coil connected in series with the resistance
being measured, as shown in Fig. 3.1. The source of supply is a hand-
driven generator contained in the same case.

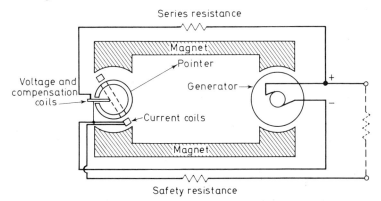

Fig. 3.1. Megger tester

The usefulness of the Megger can be extended by arranging for the moving-coil instrument to serve as the galvanometer in a Wheatstone bridge. Ratio arms are included in the instrument case and the same generator is used as the source of current but an external resistance box is used as the standard. This type is known as the 'Bridge Megger' and can measure resistance to a good degree of accuracy.

3.3. OHMMETERS

The method employed is to pass a current through the unknown resistance and a meter (suitably shunted) in series so that the meter reads the current. The meter switch is then changed over, so that the meter now reads the voltage across the unknown resistance. This method is suitable for low resistances, for, in this case, the meter shunt is of a low value compared with the instrument resistance and the latter has little effect when across the unknown resistance. This method is a rough equivalent of the potentiometer method which was introduced in Chapter 1 and is dealt with more fully later in this chapter. In effect, the meter compares the voltage drop across the unknown resistance and across the shunt which for this purpose is a standard resistance.

For higher resistances the voltmeter is connected in series with the unknown; let its reading be E_1. The meter is then connected directly across the source of e.m.f.; let the reading be E_2. If X is the unknown resistance and R that of the voltmeter, then

$$X = R\left(1 + \frac{E_1}{E_2}\right).$$

This method is, in effect, using the resistance of the meter as a standard. Some manufacturers include a voltmeter and a milliammeter in one instrument case; it is then a simple matter to read the voltage across a resistance and the current through it at the same time and thus determine its value.

The ohmmeter normally included in a multimeter is a development of the method of providing an e.m.f. from a cell and reading the current. Assuming that the cell voltage does not vary, it is obviously possible to calibrate the meter directly in ohms. Zero on the current scale would, of course, correspond to infinite resistance and have to be marked accordingly, while full scale deflection would correspond to $R = V/I_m$, where V is the voltage of the cell and I_m the full scale deflection current of the instrument.

An improvement on this method is to provide an adjustable resistance in the meter case so as to allow for the running-down of the cell; the resistance is adjusted to obtain full scale deflection with the terminals shorted. With this arrangement an accidental short circuit cannot damage the instrument, but the results are still dependent on the constancy of the battery voltage. A change of say 20% (0·3 V per cell) in battery volts means a 20% error in the measurement at half scale. A great improvement in accuracy is obtained if the setting is made by means of an adjustable shunt as shown in Fig. 3.2.

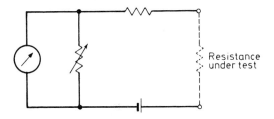

Fig. 3.2. A simple ohmmeter

A multi-range instrument is shown in Fig. 3.3. Although this is a simple circuit the determination of the change in total resistance resulting from an adjustment for a change of voltage is a tedious process. However, the reader who is familiar with electrical circuits will readily appreciate that the greater r_1 is compared with r_s the less effect the changes in the latter have on the total resistance. A numerical example will simplify the matter.

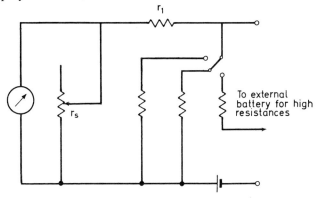

Fig. 3.3. Multi-range ohmmeter with adjustable shunt

Assume that the f.s.d. current of the meter is 1 mA. Then if the total internal resistance is 1000 Ω and the battery voltage is allowed to vary between 1·5 and 1·1 V, the total current will vary between 1·5 and 1·1 mA. Now this total current is given by

$$I = (1 + r_m/r_s)I_m$$

where r_m is the instrument resistance and I_m its full scale current. In the case under consideration I_m = 1 mA and 100 Ω is a probable value for r_m. Substituting these values in the above equation,

$$1 \cdot 5 = (1 + 100/r_s)\,1$$
$$1 \cdot 1 = (1 + 100/r_s)\,1$$

whence r_s varies between 200 and 1000 Ω.

The resistance of r_s and r_m in parallel thus varies between 67 and 91 Ω, and thus changes by 24 Ω in a total circuit resistance of 1000, i.e. by 2·4%.

In order to measure higher resistances it is necessary to increase r_1 to the required value and increase the e.m.f. of the battery; to measure lower resistances a fixed shunt is connected directly across the instrument terminals so that the total resistance of the circuit again equals requisite value for half-scale deflection. One of the most popular ohmmeters of this type is that included in the 'AVO' (Amps-Volts-Ohms) range of multimeters made by Avo Ltd. of Dover, Kent. The author is indebted to this company for permission to publish the following particulars of the d.c. and resistance ranges of the Model 40 Universal AvoMeter.

The 5-in (0·127 m) hand-calibrated scale has three sets of markings;-

(1) the top one is for resistance measurement and is marked 0-1000,

(2) the middle is for current and voltage and is marked 0-120, with divisions of about 1 mm each,

(3) the lowest scale is marked 0-480 and is used for voltage measurements.

By means of a press button marked '÷2' the normal full-scale deflection on the voltage and current ranges may be halved. Thus if the deflection is found to be too small when taking a measurement, it can be doubled by pressing the button.

The meter takes 6 mA for full-scale deflection on the normal ranges, and 3 mA with the press button actuated. The available ranges are:

Amps	*Volts*	*Ohms*
0–12	0–1200	0–1000
0–6	0–600	0–10 000
0–1·2	0–480	0–100 000
0–600 mA	0–240	0–1 megohm
0–120 mA	0–120	
0–60 mA	0–60	
0–12 mA	0–12	
0–6 mA	0–6	
0–3 mA	0–1·2	
	0–600 mV	
	0–120 mV	
	0–60 mV	

The first two resistance ranges are obtained using an internal 1·5-V cell, the next using an internal 9-V battery, and the 0–1 megohm range using a.c. or d.c. mains.

The instrument meets the requirements laid down in Section 6 of B.S. 89:1954 for 5-in (0·127 m) scale length Industrial Portable Instruments. In addition to the Avometer there are, of course, many other excellent makes of meter on the market.

3.4. PRECISION RESISTANCE MEASUREMENTS

The ohmmeters discussed in the preceding paragraphs of this chapter have an accuracy that is quite sufficient for most ordinary electronic applications, but for precision measurements a bridge type of circuit is necessary.

3.4.1. Medium Value Resistances (5 to 10 000 Ω).

The Wheatstone bridge is the best method for measuring resistances in this range. The accuracy obviously depends on the precision with which the particular bridge is made, for the unknown can only be measured in terms of the standard resistances of the bridge itself, which are themselves subject to error. In a numerical example included as a test question to Chapter 1 it is seen that an error of $\pm$ 0·1% in the standard resistances can lead to an error of 0·3% in the measurement. However, in bridges made by H. W. Sullivan the standard resistance used for comparison is guaranteed to 1 part in 10^4 and the ratio arms do not differ from each other by more than 1 part in 5×10^4. Special standards can be used to give considerably higher accuracy.

Another factor to be taken into account in estimating the overall accuracy of the measurement, even if the bridge coils are of the requisite accuracy, is the fineness of subdivision of these bridge resistances. Taking as an example the familiar Post Office Box type of bridge shown in Fig. 3.4, the highest possible setting of the S arm is 11 110 Ω. The smallest subdivision is 1 Ω, which is 1/11 110 of the whole, but if the unknown resistance has a value around 1000 the best subdivision obtainable becomes 1/1000. Below this value the effect of greater subdivision can be produced by altering the ratio arms. Thus, to measure a resistance of about 500 Ω, by making the ratio arms 10:1 it can be regarded as 5000 so that a subdivision of 1 in 5000 is obtained. This order of accuracy is normally quite adequate for most electronic applications.

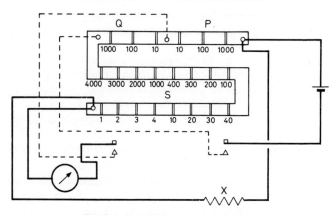

Fig. 3.4. Post Office box type bridge

There have been many improvements in bridge design directed towards greater ease and speed of operation. Clearly if an arbitrary group of plugs are removed from a Post Office Box, the total value of resistance in circuit will not be immediately evident. This difficulty is overcome in the Sullivan bridge by arranging the S resistance of the unit on the decade principle, so that the first set of plugs give 0 to 9 Ω, the second 10 to 90, and so on. The arrangement is of the form shown in Fig. 3.5.

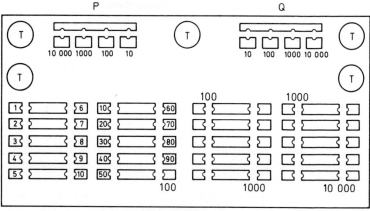

T are terminals
P and Q are the ratio arms

Fig. 3.5. Sullivan precision bridge layout

The reason for using plugs in these bridges is that it is in the operator's hands to ensure that the contact surfaces are clean, i.e. by rotation of the plug in the socket, and hence that the contact resistance is as low as possible. With modern switches and switch materials this is not so important, so nowadays there are very few plug arrangements used.

An obviously simpler method of selecting the required resistances is by means of a switch operated by a pointer knob with a dial to indicate the resistance value; the switch contacts must clearly have negligible resistance, and must not vary their resistance in use. In the Varley design, the studs have a slot cut in them and the moving contact takes the form of a two-sided brush, as shown in Fig. 3.6, so that any slight reduction of pressure on one side of the contact is automatically compensated for by an increase on the other. The studs and brushes are normally of silver or are heavily silver-plated to reduce the resistance to minimum and to reduce thermoelectric effects, which would tend to make the bridge impossible to balance correctly if the two sides of the contacts were of different metals. H. W. Sullivan make a bridge with four stud dials arranged in decade for the S arm and two more dials for the ratio arms; in other respects it is similar to the plug bridge previously mentioned.

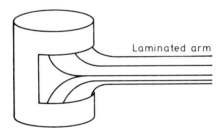

Laminated arm

Fig. 3.6. Varley switch contacts

The Cambridge Instrument Company make a Portable Decade Pattern having five dials in all, with a range of measurement from 0·01 to 10^6 Ω and an accuracy of adjustment of 0·1%. Another bridge made by this firm has four decade dials for the S arm but a set of plugs for the ratio arms. This model has a range of 0·01 to 10^7 Ω at 0·01%. In another of their bridges a Unipivot type galvanometer (Chapter 2) is included in the bridge box.

There are other factors affecting the available accuracy apart from the actual construction of the bridge. In Chapter 2 it was shown that to obtain the greatest sensitivity the galvanometer resistance should be equal to that of the circuit with which it is associated. In the case of a bridge the circuit resistance is the effective resistance of the four bridge arms.

Regarding galvanometer resistance, it is normally desirable to use an instrument already to hand. It is connected up with the bridge in the ordinary way with a variable shunt as a protection against an accidental heavy current due to the bridge being widely out of balance. The ratio arms P and Q in Fig. 3.4 or 3.5 are set to suitable values depending on the unknown resistance X and the arm S is adjusted to obtain an approximate balance. The galvanometer shunt is then removed, usually in stages, and the final balance point obtained. A change of one subdivision on the S arm should produce a noticeable deflection, but there should be a setting when there is none.

For example, to measure a 10-Ω coil the ratio arms P and Q could be set to 1000 and 10 and no deflection obtained with say 1001 in the S arm. The resistance of the coil would then be 10·01 Ω to within 1 part in 1000. When S is set at 1002 there would be a deflection of say 40 mm to one side and when S is at 1000 there might be 20 mm the other way. However, if the deflection in the latter case was only 2 mm, it would not be correct to assume that 1001 was the correct value since the galvanometer sensitivity would not be high enough to justify this assumption. If, on the other hand, the galvanometer was too sensitive there might be a deflection of 1·5 m one side, 1 m the other side and 50 mm for the 1001 setting. Thus an exact balance could not be obtained within the limits of setting possible on the bridge. The remedy is to shunt the galvanometer so that it just shows no deflection for the best setting.

Another possibility is to use the extra sensitivity to estimate the next significant figure in the result. If, with a setting of 1000, the deflection was 40 mm to the left but with 1001 it was 10 mm to the right then the difference between the correct result and 1000 is four times that between the correct value and 1001. Therefore the true resistance is 10·008. However, if the bridge coils are only accurate to within 5 parts in 1000 this method is undesirable since it tends to give a false sense of accuracy. It should be noted that when any result is calculated the number of figures in the answer should always show the accuracy obtained, e.g. if measurements are made to within 1% the answer should be given to not more than three figures.

It was shown in Chapter 1 that the Wheatstone bridge circuit can be analysed by means of Kirchhoff's Laws. Perhaps the most instructive method of doing this is to determine the galvanometer current in terms of the resistances of the four arms and the current in one of them when the bridge is slightly out of balance. It is obvious that at least one current must appear in the result and this can be either the total battery or that in one of the arms.

The advantage in choosing the latter is that normally there is a known maximum value depending on the allowable heating of the bridge resistance coils or of the coil being measured.

The Wheatstone bridge circuit of Fig. 1.3 should be referred to. Note that when the bridge is out of balance a galvanometer current I_g flows so that four different currents I_1, I_2, I_3 and I_4 flow in the resistance network if the resistances have different values. The positions of the galvanometer and battery can be reversed; the particular arrangement is ultimately decided by the relative values of the resistances, they may all be of the same order, when it does not matter, but if P and Q differ by a large amount from R and S it is best to connect the galvanometer from the junction of the two higher resistances to the junction of the two lower resistances.

Applying Kirchhoff's Laws to the circuit of Fig. 1.3,

$$I_g = \frac{I_4(QR - PS)}{R_g(P + Q) + P(Q + S)}$$

Alternatively, the galvanometer current can be expressed in terms of the battery current thus:-

$$I_g = \frac{I_b(QR - PS)}{R_g(P + Q + R + S) + (Q + S)(P + R)}$$

where I_b is the battery current and R_g the resistance of the galvanometer.

The above formulae show that the sensitivity can be increased indefinitely by increasing the current, but the safe loading of the coils sets a practical limit to this. Furthermore, there is no point in increasing the sensitivity beyond that required to obtain a definite balance with the smallest possible change in value of the bridge arms, since if this is done the effect is the same as using an over-sensitive galvanometer, as explained earlier.

In the first formula given above, write $S = S_0 + \delta S$ where S_0 is the value of the S arm required for perfect balance and δS is a small change in S. Then

$$\delta I_g = \frac{-I_4 P \delta S}{R_g(P + Q) + P(Q + S)}$$

Now dividing top and bottom by P, then

$$\delta I_g = \frac{-I_4 \delta S}{R_g\left(1 + \dfrac{Q}{P}\right) + S\left(1 + \dfrac{Q}{S}\right)}$$

From this equation it is evident that for maximum sensitivity Q/S should be small and P/Q large. The ratio arms should therefore be kept small and the unknown resistance should be large compared with the standard arm. Unfortunately, this last condition is the opposite of that required for the most accurate reading.

3.4.2. Carey Foster Bridge

This is a modification of the Wheatstone bridge which is very useful for comparing two resistances that are nearly equal, for example two that are supposed to be equal. It has the advantage of giving very accurate results with simple apparatus.

In the ordinary metre bridge it is possible to read to one millimetre on the slide wire with ease, but this is only one part in 500 of half the bridge wire. The degree of subdivision can be increased by adding resistance coils at each end of the slide wire, as shown in Fig. 3.7. This is tantamount to making the slide wire only a part of the ratio arms instead of the whole, as in the ordinary arrangement.

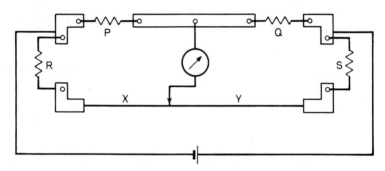

Fig. 3.7. Carey Foster bridge

The method devised by Carey Foster eliminates the effect of contact resistance. Referring to Fig. 3.7,
if L_c is the resistance of the connecting leads and contacts at C
L_d is the resistance of the connecting leads and contacts at D
then for balance
$$\frac{P}{Q} = \frac{R + X + L_c}{S + Y + L_d}$$
therefore
$$\frac{P}{P + Q} = \frac{R + X + L_c}{R + S + X + Y + L_c + L_d}$$
Now if the unknown R and standard S are reversed,
$$\frac{P}{P + Q} = \frac{S + X' + L_c}{R + S + X' + Y' + L_c + L_d}$$
Since $X + Y$ is constant being the resistance of the bridge wire, then
$$R + X + L_c = S + X' + L_c \text{ whence } R - S = X' - X$$

If s is the resistance per unit length and l and l' the lengths in use, then $R = S + (l + l')s$.

To determine s, the above procedure is repeated making $R = 0$. With all measurements of this type it is advisable to repeat with the battery reversed, and in this case with P and Q reversed. This reversal of supply current will correct for any thermoelectric effects when the mean value is taken.

3.5. HIGH RESISTANCE MEASUREMENT

The simplest method of measuring high resistance, e.g. insulation resistance, is by direct deflection using the circuit of Fig. 3.8. A very sensitive galvanometer is necessary, since only minute currents flow through an insulating material. As the circuit resistance is of the order of several megohms an instrument with a high resistance is usually chosen.

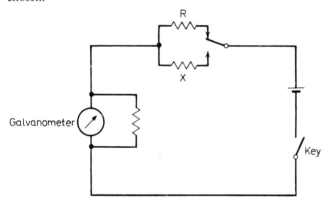

Fig. 3.8. Circuit for measuring high resistance

The galvanometer, suitably shunted, is connected in circuit with a standard resistance of one megohm or other suitable value R, and the deflection noted. The unknown resistance X is then switched into circuit in place of the standard and the deflection again noted. In a well-designed instrument the deflection is proportional to the current, therefore the resistance values are in the ratio of the deflections. A correction can easily be made for the resistance of the galvanometer and shunt if required, but since this is usually at most a few thousand ohms it is not usually necessary. It is obvious that this method gives the most accurate results when the resistance being measured is nearly equal to that of the standard, for then the direct proportionality of the deflection with current will be more nearly exact for small differences in deflection.

The ballistic galvanometer, described in Chapter 2, can be used to measure high resistance if a standard capacitor is available, using the circuit of Fig. 3.9. Let q_0 be the initial charge on the capacitor C and

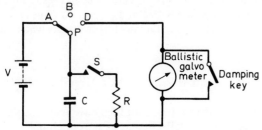

Fig. 3.9. Resistance measurement with ballistic galvanometer

q the charge after C has been allowed to discharge for t seconds through the high resistance R to be measured. Then

$$q = q_0 \, e^{(-t/CR)}$$

Initially switch P is at A and switch S is open so that C is charged up to V volts and the charge $q_0 = CV$. Then with switch P at D, capacitor C is discharged through the galvanometer, giving a throw θ_0. Then $q_0 = K\theta_0$ where K is constant for a given galvanometer.

Now switch P is again set to A so that the capacitor is recharged to $q_0 = CV$. Switch P is then set to B and switch S closed for t seconds so that the charge on the capacitor falls to q. Switch S is then opened and switch P set to D to give a galvanometer throw θ. Then $q = K\theta$.

Now

$$q = q_0 \, e^{(-t/CR)} \text{ therefore } e^{(-t/CR)} = \frac{q_0}{q} = \frac{\theta_0}{\theta}$$

Thus

$$\frac{t}{CR} = \log_e \frac{\theta_0}{\theta} \text{ whence } R \text{ can be found if } t \text{ and } C \text{ are known.}$$

3.6. MEASUREMENT OF LOW RESISTANCE

The main difficulty in the accurate measurement of low resistances arises from the fact that the resistances of leads and contacts are no longer negligible. It is clear that while contact resistances of the order of, say, 0·001 Ω are negligible when resistances of 100 Ω or more are to be measured, they are of great importance when the resistance to be measured is of the order of 0·01 Ω.

It is also essential with low resistances that the two points between which the resistance is to be measured shall be very carefully defined. For this reason the methods which are specially adapted to low resistance measurement employ connecting leads which form no part of the circuit whose resistance is to be measured but which connect two points in this circuit to the measuring circuit. These two points are known as the *potential terminals,* and serve to fix definitely the length of the circuit under test.

In the methods used for the precise measurement of low resistance, the unknown resistance is compared with a low resistance standard of the same order as the unknown, and with which it is connected in

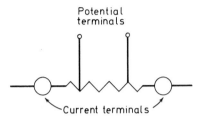

Fig. 3.10. Standard low resistance

series. Both resistances are fitted with four terminals — two *current terminals* for connection to the supply circuit and two *potential terminals* for connection to the measuring circuit (Fig. 3.10).

3.6.1. Kelvin Double Bridge

This is a development of the Wheatstone bridge and has the same advantages of quick and simple operation. An examination of the circuit (Fig. 3.11) shows that a current is passed through the standard resistance

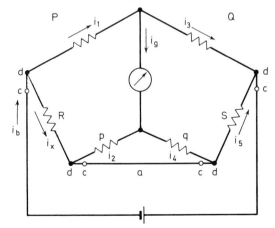

Fig. 3.11. Kelvin double bridge

S and the unknown resistance R in series and the potentials developed across these are balanced by means of the bridge network.

   This method can be regarded as a combination of bridge and potentiometer methods, having the advantages of both in that the actual balance is obtained by the instantaneous bridge method (i.e. not requiring any connections to be changed, as in the case of the potentiometer), but since the potentials are balanced against one another the contact resistance at the points of connection are not included in the measurement, as they would be in the Wheatstone method. In Fig. 3.11, cc represents the current terminals, and dd the potential terminals, of resistances R and S. At balance i_g is zero and the same current flows through P and Q, and this is also the case with p and q and R and S. Then $i_1 = i_3$, $i_2 = i_4$, and $i_s = i_x$.

By Kirchhoff's second law,

   for mesh (1), $\quad i_s R - i_1 P + i_2 p = 0$, or $i_s R = i_1 P - i_2 p$.

   For mesh (2), $\quad i_s S - i_1 Q + i_2 q = 0$, or $i_s S = i_1 Q - i_2 q$.

By division, $\dfrac{R}{S} = \dfrac{i_1 P - i_2 p}{i_1 Q - i_2 q} = \dfrac{\left\{ P\left(i_1 - i_2\left(\dfrac{p}{P}\right)\right)\right\}}{\left\{ Q\left(i_1 - i_2\left(\dfrac{q}{Q}\right)\right)\right\}}$

Now if it is arranged that p/P is always equal to q/Q, then $\dfrac{R}{S} = \dfrac{P}{Q}\left(=\dfrac{p}{q}\right)$. In commercial types of Kelvin bridge the dials are arranged to maintain this equality of the two ratios for all settings. The bridge is then almost as easy to use as a Wheatstone and great accuracy can be obtained.

3.6.2. Potentiometers

The basic principles of this instrument have been given in Chapter 1. When used for resistance measurements the two resistances being compared (i.e. the unknown and a standard resistance) are connected in series and a current passed through them of such a value that the e.m.f.'s across the resistances are of the order of one volt. These e.m.f.'s are then compared on the potentiometer, which for this purpose need not be calibrated by a standard cell. The advantage of this method lies in the fact that no current flows in the wires connecting the standard and unknown resistances to the potentiometer at balance, so that contact resistances are not included in the measurement.

   Modern developments of the potentiometer are concerned with increasing the degree of subdivision obtainable and within increasing the ease of operation. If a slide wire of 8 metres is used the subdivision amounts to 1 in 4000, but an 8 metre wire is obviously not a very convenient device, even if it is bent back upon itself several times. Furthermore, since no wire can be made perfectly uniform, if full use is to be made of its length it must be calibrated, and is therefore not direct reading. This difficulty is overcome by using a number of resistance coils in place of the wire, or in conjunction with a short wire which serves for fine adjustments. A further improvement is the provision of a resistance in the battery circuit so that the current may be adjusted until a certain setting of the coils and slide wire exactly balance against the standard cell. Thus the instrument is made to read directly in volts.

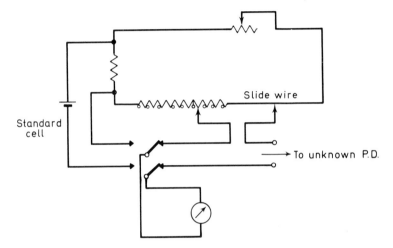

Fig. 3.12. Practical form of potentiometer

In the circuit of Fig. 3.12, as well as the features just mentioned a separate coil is provided for the standard coil connection, and the calibration of the potentiometer can therefore be instantly checked against the standard merely by operating the double-pole switch.

The Varley vernier is yet another refinement used on commercial instruments. A coil of resistance twice that between a pair of studs can be bridged across any pair of the main dial studs. The galvanometer contact is then made to some point on this second dial. The process can be repeated a number of times. In a typical five dial instrument the first has 10 coils of 100 Ω each, the next 10 of 20 Ω, 10 of 4 Ω, 10 of 0·8 Ω and lastly a slide wire of 0·16 Ω. With this five dial arrangement a subdivision of 1 in 180 000 is obtained.

With this fine subdivision, contact resistance must be taken into account. The resistance at the points where one dial makes contact with another, e.g. *H* and *L* in Fig. 3.13, is allowed for in the resistance of the vernier coil; however this initial allowance is useless unless the contacts are made so that their resistance will not vary with use or with age. The large silver contacts are of the type where the wiper moves in a slot in the stud, (Fig. 3.6).

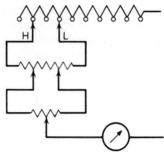

Fig. 3.13. Varley vernier

The circuit diagram of the Tinsley precision vernier potentiometer, is shown in Fig. 3.14. The first dial has 18 steps of 0·1 V, the second has 100 steps of 0·001, the third 101 steps of 0·00001 V. The degree of

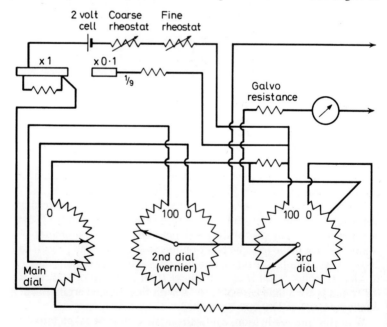

Fig. 3.14. Tinsley precision vernier potentiometer

subdivision is therefore 1 in 10 000. No special standard cell circuit is included since with this high degree of accuracy it is advisable to check the instrument itself. The potential contacts are of a silver gold alloy. The highest thermoelectric e.m.f. produced by the movement of the dial switches is one-fifth of the least count of the instrument. A galvano-meter series resistance to suit a meter of resistance about 10 Ω is fitted in the potentiometer.

It is because of its accuracy, even in its simpler forms, that the potentiometer is used as the standard method of calibrating voltmeters, ammeters and low resistances.

3.6.3. The Bonding Tester

Before leaving the subject of resistance measurement, mention should be made of the bonding tester used in aircraft servicing bays. An aircraft in flight acquires electrostatic charges or 'static' on the metal parts of the airframe and equipment. Any resistance between two adjacent metal parts charged to different potentials will cause a flow of current through that resistance; this current will cause interference in radio reception and if heavy may cause a spark with consequent risk of fire to the aircraft.

For this reason all metal parts of the aircraft are connected together by means of copper strips or braided wire, and the bonding tester, which is essentially an ohmmeter for reading up to about 0·1 Ω, is used to ensure that the bonding has been satisfactorily carried out. It works on the same principle as the Megger tester but uses a Nife cell instead of a hand-driven generator as the source. This is because, while the Megger tester is required to give a high voltage at low current, the bonding tester must supply a current heavy enough to cause a measurable voltage drop across the very low resistances under test. It is, of course, only a testing instrument and not a precision instrument.

WORKED EXAMPLE

Question. A resistance is measured by an ammeter and voltmeter method. The current passing the resistance-voltmeter combinations is 250 mA, the voltmeter resistance is 8·67 Ω and it reads 0·084 V. What is the 'true value' of resistance and to what order of accuracy is it measured?

Answer. Let R = unknown resistance and R_v = voltmeter resistance. Then resistance of combination is

$$\frac{R_v R}{R_v + R.}$$

The voltage across the combination is given as 0·084 and the current passing the *whole* is 250 mA. Hence

$$\frac{R_v R}{R_v + R} = \frac{0·084 \times 1000}{250}$$

But $R_v = 8·67 \, \Omega$.

Thus $\dfrac{8·67 \, R}{8·67 + R} = \dfrac{84}{250}$, whence $250 \times 8·67 \, R = 84 \, (8·67 + R)$

i.e. $2167·5 \, R = 84 \times 8·67 + 84 \, R$

Hence $R = \dfrac{84 \times 8·67}{2083·5} = \underline{0·349 \, \Omega.}$ *Answer.*

The order of accuracy is also required. It should be remembered that the accuracy of any measurement cannot be greater than that of the poorest instrument or other factor involved in the test.

The voltmeter reading is given to two figures only so that it can only be known to one part in 84, i.e. less than 1%. We should therefore be wise in giving our result as

$$R = 0·349 \pm 2\%.$$

Since the current is probably known to the nearest milliamp, i.e. 0·5%, and the voltmeter resistance to a much higher degree of accuracy these do not affect the result.

Note. This is a very important point on which students often go astray. It is very tempting to give the result as 0·3494 Ω but the last figure is 'false'. Had the voltage been given as 0·0840 it would be quite another matter.

EXERCISES

1. Describe with sketches the connection of a direct reading potentiometer and show how it may be used to measure (*a*) the e.m.f. of a primary IX battery, (*b*) to calibrate an ammeter reading to about 30 A. State what additional apparatus is required for this test.   (I.E.E.)

2. Describe a d.c. 'Test Set' suitable for electronic servicing work. Explain how such an instrument can be used to measure resistance and indicate the sphere of usefulness of such an ohmmeter. Mention the order of accuracy to be expected on the various ranges.

3. Describe a precision modification of the Wheatstone bridge network for the comparison of nearly equal resistances, stating the precautions to be observed for accurate results.

4. The resistances of the four arms of a Wheatstone bridge *ABCDA* are *AB* 1000 Ω, *BC* 1000 Ω, *CD* 749, *DA* 750 Ω. What current will flow

in a galvanometer of resistance 500 Ω between B and D if 20 V are applied between A and C. If the 749 Ω arm is highly inductive what precautions should be taken to safeguard the galvanometer? (B.Sc.)

Answer. 7·6 μA from D to B.

5. State the degree of accuracy to which the measurements in the above equation are made. If it was desired to increase that accuracy ten times what changes would you make in the bridge setting? For these changes to serve any useful purpose what guarantee of accuracy would you require from the bridge manufacturer? Would the same galvanometer do in this case?

6. Describe the Kelvin double bridge and deduce the equation expressing the unknown resistance in terms of the other resistances in the circuit at balance.

7. Describe the construction and principle of the Megger insulation tester.

CHAPTER 4

Alternating Current Measurements

4.1. UNIT ALTERNATING CURRENT

The value of an alternating current is normally stated in one of three ways, namely, maximum, r.m.s. or average.

Peak or maximum value is of particular significance when considering the permissible voltage across an insulator, since it is the actual maximum voltage that may cause breakdown. It is also of importance when considering the permissible input to a valve amplifier, for it is normally required that no part of the input signal shall encroach upon the curved part of the valve characteristic.

The r.m.s. (root-mean-square) value of an alternating current is the square root of the mean value of the squares of the instantaneous values taken over one complete cycle. It may also be defined as that current which has the same heating effect as the same value of d.c. current, and it is the value that must be taken into account whenever power is being considered.

Average value (= $2/\pi \times$ maximum value) is involved in any estimation of quantity, as in the charging of a capacitor.

The units of current and potential difference, as discussed in Chapter 1, are defined with reference to direct current. It is obvious that a definition based on the deposition of silver by electrolysis has no meaning for alternating current, nor can there be an a.c. standard cell. Therefore the measurement of a.c. must ultimately involve a comparison with d.c. One would therefore expect only to be able to measure a.c. quantities to a less degree of accuracy than the corresponding d.c.; in fact the attainable accuracy is very much less.

It should be mentioned that absolute a.c. voltage standards are available; these consist basically of an oscillator whose output voltage is held stable in amplitude to an extremely high degree (of the order of 1 part in 10^4) by appropriate electronic circuitry.

The same broad principles of measurement apply for a.c. as for d.c., i.e. deflectional and null methods, and again null methods, where applicable, are the more accurate. A.C. null methods are described in Chapter 8.

4.2. DEFLECTIONAL METHODS

Since the effective value of a current is defined in relation to its heating effect it is natural that the heating effect should be used as a basis of measurement.

4.2.1. Hot-wire Meters

In the hot-wire meter the current to be measured is passed through a fine wire, so heating it. The resultant expansion is taken up by a system of threads, under tension from a spring, in such a way as to rotate a pointer. The method of damping is usually by eddy currents induced in an aluminium disc moving between the poles of a permanent magnet.

In spite of its simple and straightforward construction, this type of instrument has several disadvantages. The main one is that, due to stretching of the wire and threads, the zero is uncertain. If the pointer returns to a different zero position after a reading it is difficult to determine what was the actual zero from which the reading should be reckoned. No zero adjusting screw can overcome this uncertainty, since it cannot compensate for any stretching in the system. Other disadvantages are: It is easily burnt out by excess currents; it is liable to temperature errors; the accuracy is seldom better than 2%; and it has a relatively high capacitance. The hot-wire instrument is now, however, virtually obsolete.

4.2.2. Thermocouple Meters

In the thermocouple instrument the current to be measured is passed through a heater which heats one junction of a thermocouple and the e.m.f. so produced is made to pass a current through a moving-coil instrument. Therefore most of the advantages of the latter are obtained, i.e. quick action, even scale and 'dead beat'.

The chief advantages of the hot-wire type are also obtained without its attendant disadvantages. Due to the fact that the instrument is connected electrically but not mechanically to the thermocouple, it is possible so to place the former that the capacitance across the heater is small. Skin effect is reduced to a negligible value by making the heater in the form of a flat strip or sometimes in the form of a thin wire. The actual design of the heater depends upon the magnitude of the current to be measured.

For large currents, the heater can be in the form of a strip with the junction fixed in close proximity to it or even soldered to it. The latter method gives an instrument that is quick in action but has the disadvantage that the moving-coil circuit is electrically connected to the heater circuit. Trouble may be experienced using this type due to the capacitance of the meter to earth. The capacitance can be reduced to a negligible value at all but the highest radio frequencies by insulating the actual junction from the heater with a small glass bead as shown in Fig. 4.1; this tends to make the action more sluggish, however. Heaters

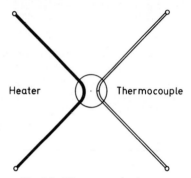

Fig. 4.1. Thermocouple element

of this type are normally made for currents over 0·1 A. For currents less than this the heater and junction together form four straight wires joined in the middle and enclosed in a vacuum to minimise loss of heat due to convection.

When measuring large currents at radio frequencies a special arrangement of shunts is employed. It is not desirable to use a large heater, as even the flat-strip type cannot be made reliable for very large currents. A number of fine wires are arranged symmetrically to form a cylinder, as shown in Fig. 4.2. As the wires are exactly alike any change in resistance or reactance with frequency affects them all equally, therefore the

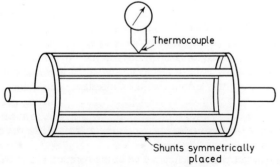

Fig. 4.2. Thermocouple shunts

multiplying power of the shunt is independent of frequency. Only one of the wires is used as the heater.

From the study of galvanometers given in Chapter 2 it will be realised that a low resistance meter is required for use with the thermojunction, since the latter also possesses low resistance. In other words, high voltage sensitivity is the predominating factor.

The main advantages of the thermocouple instrument as far as laboratory purposes are concerned are its great accuracy, freedom from frequency error, ability to be calibrated on d.c., and the fact that it reads r.m.s. values. The accuracy of a thermocouple (calibrated against direct current) can be better than 1%. A purely practical advantage is that heaters can be placed in convenient positions in a circuit and one moving-coil meter used to make the measurements, this meter being switched or plugged in as required. The Post Office use this arrangement in connection with facsimile (i.e. picture transmission) work. It avoids the necessity for a large meter panel since all the required measurements are made with reference to a single meter dial. If a heater burns out it can be easily replaced since for this class of work a standard heater will usually give the necessary accuracy without recalibrating with the meter.

The main disadvantage of thermocouple meters is that the heaters can easily burn out due to their small overload capacity. For this reason thermocouple instruments are not generally used for the kinds of tests described at the end of Chapter 2, where a greater current than expected is likely to pass through the meter. Their main use is in the laboratory, where the highest possible accuracy is required and where the instruments are used only by highly skilled personnel. For this purpose the meter is calibrated, together with its heater, on d.c. by the potentiometer method; it is then correct for any waveform and up to very high frequencies. The following brief details of some typical instruments on the market have been kindly supplied by the manufacturers.

The Cambridge Instrument Company supply a vacuum junction for use with their versatile galvanometer. The junction is insulated from the heater by vitreous material which will stand up to 100 V. The glass bulb is mounted in a moulded case fitted with a four-pin cap for insertion in a standard valve holder. The materials are well aged before delivery so that they will not deteriorate seriously with use. Their most sensitive model has a heater resistance of 1600 Ω, a junction resistance of 13 Ω, and a junction e.m.f. of 6 mV on open circuit for a current of 1·25 mA, the maximum safe current being 2·5 mA. The least sensitive model has corresponding figures of 0·2 Ω, 4 Ω, 1 A and 1·5 A. The versatile galvanometer has a coil resistance of 10 Ω and full scale deflection for 2·4 mV.

A number of instruments with self-contained thermo-junctions are made by the same firm. Pattern Y is made with a heater of 1600 Ω and gives full scale deflection with 0·5 mA. The movement is a Unipivot (Chapter 2). A smaller instrument with a scale length of 50 mm is made with a resistance of 100 Ω and requires 10 mA for full scale deflection. This meter is of the flush-mounting type so that it can be fitted flush with a control panel.

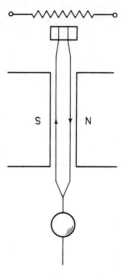

Fig. 4.3. Duddell thermo-galvanometer

The Duddell thermo-galvanometer (Fig. 4.3) takes the form of a moving-coil mirror galvanometer with the ends of the moving coil brought out to a thermo-junction which is suspended very close to a heater. The heaters can be easily changed; with a 1000-Ω heater a sensitivity of 2 μA per mm for a normal scale distance of one metre is obtained. A 1-Ω heater gives 60 μA per mm.

Since the galvanometer circuit itself is permanently closed the instrument is always critically damped — a great boon to the user. The inductance and capacity are negligible, therefore the instrument can be calibrated on d.c. very accurately and this calibration remains constant for any frequency.

4.2.3. Moving-iron Meters

These are of two kinds, namely, attraction and repulsion. The former type employs an eccentrically-mounted iron vane which is attracted into the current-carrying coil (Fig. 4.4). The latter has an iron bar fixed parallel to the axis of the coil, and a moving piece which is also parallel.

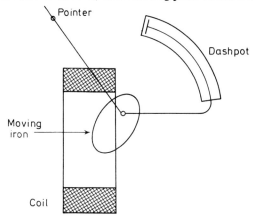

Fig. 4.4. Moving-iron meter (attraction type)

Both pieces are magnetised by the coil in the same direction and thus repel each other. The main constructional features are shown in Fig. 4.5. In both types damping is normally provided by means of a vane or a piston moving in an air chamber, i.e. 'dash-pot' damping.

Since the field in the coil is proportional to the current, the magnetic intensity in the iron is likewise proportional to the current. Now the

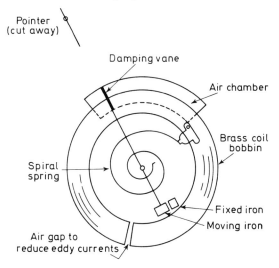

Fig. 4.5. Moving-iron meter (repulsion type)

force of repulsion is proportional to the product of the intensities, therefore it is proportional to the square of the current. For this reason the moving-iron meter is generally said to read r.m.s. values, but if it is arranged that the iron is worked near the saturation point, the reading becomes directly proportional to the current; the meter then reads average values and has a more even scale. This is sometimes an advantage, provided that distorted waveforms are not being measured, for the meter can still be calibrated in r.m.s. values for sine waves.

The attraction-type of meter tends to have a scale more crowded at the zero end because as the vane enters the coil the magnetic induction in it increases by virtue of its changing position as well as by virtue of increased current. This drawback can be turned to advantage in designing a meter with a very open scale in the middle and in the range of values most likely to be required.

At one time, moving-iron meters were prone to serious errors due to the effects of hysteresis, but these effects have been virtually eliminated in modern instruments. On d.c., moving-iron meters had a tendency to read low when the current was rising and high when it was falling. On a.c., error was caused due to the field in the iron lagging behind the current, as shown by an hysteresis curve for the material. This problem was most pronounced in the attraction type, for in the repulsion type both pieces of iron were similarly affected. The effect gave rise to a reverse 'pull' over part of the cycle, hence to low reading.

It will be seen from the foregoing that moving-iron meters cannot be calibrated on d.c. with any great accuracy and that they are prone to serious frequency error. When measuring power the frequency error is not serious since the frequency range will only be about 10 to 100 Hz at most, but the error is considerable at audio frequencies, and even greater on radio frequencies.

Eddy currents are reduced by having an air gap in the coil former on which the instrument coil is wound, by keeping the metal parts of the case well away from the coil and by using stranded wire for heavy current use.

Temperature errors are swamped to some extent by using a series resistance, as in the case of moving-coil voltmeters. This error may be of the order of 1% for $10°C$ rise in temperature. In the case of voltmeters the inductance also gives a frequency error but this is usually not greater than 1% for frequencies less than 100 Hz.

Moving-iron meters consume more power than moving-coil meters; the figures are 1 to 3 W for ammeters and 4 W for voltmeters. They are unsuitable for measuring values below 10 V or 1 A.

The design of moving iron instruments has been standardised by the makers, who specify fixed sizes of iron and coil with between 200 and 400 At.

In spite of the many disadvantages listed above, moving-iron meters are used a great deal for commercial frequencies (0-100 Hz), since they are cheap, robust and read r.m.s. values to the normal standard of accuracy required for this purpose.

4.2.4. Rectifier Meters

The instruments discussed so far in this chapter measure r.m.s. values directly; the metal rectifier instrument which is very commonly used in electronics work, measures average values. The current to be measured is passed through a bridge pattern full-wave rectifier and thence to a moving-coil meter, as shown in Fig. 4.6. A typical single unit comprising four rectifiers measures only about 25 mm in diameter and 12 mm long in the one mA size. Multimeters usually include a rectifier of this type for use with the existing moving coil meter on the a.c. ranges.

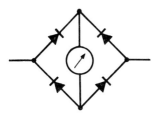

Fig. 4.6. Bridge rectifier meter

The main advantage of these instruments is that they will endure rough usage; the rectifier will normally stand as great an overload as the moving-coil meter to which it is connected. The rectifier is much cheaper than a thermo-junction, and meters can be easily made to give full scale deflection with one mA or less.

For laboratory use, however, these meters have certain serious disadvantages, i.e. waveform, leakage current and frequency error. The chief of these is perhaps the fact that they are only accurate on the waveform on which they are calibrated. For general electronic maintenance work this is not too serious a disadvantage as the output from a valve oscillator of reliable manufacture is practically sinusoidal, and in any case great accuracy is not normally required for this type of work.

The leakage current through the rectifier varies with temperature, giving rise to an error of the order of 0·015% per °C, which is less than the permissible error for Precision Grade moving-coil meters. For voltmeters with a full-scale reading of less than 10 V the change in total resistance due to the rectifier causes an increase in reading for a rise in temperature, but for meters reading 150 V and over the leakage current has a greater effect and they therefore read low for a rise in temperature.

Modern rectifier instruments have negligible frequency error up to 10 000 Hz but they are of little use on higher frequencies; this is due mainly to their considerable self-capacitance.

When rectifier meters are used for multi-range instruments some difficulty arises because the characteristic of the rectifier is such that its resistance varies with current, as shown in Fig. 4.7. The deflection is

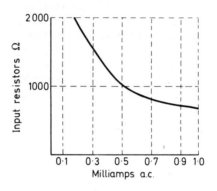

Fig. 4.7. Metal rectifier characteristics

proportional to the current for an unshunted ammeter but this is no longer the case if shunts are used, nor is it the case with voltmeters that the reading is proportional to the applied voltage. If a large series resistance is used with a high-range voltmeter it effectively swamps this effect. Therefore in multimeters the high voltage ranges and the unshunted current range use a uniform scale which is also used for the d.c. ranges, while the shunted current ranges use a scale cramped at the lower end. If a universal shunt is used, all the shunted ranges use the same scale. In order that one scale can be used for all the lower voltage ranges they are provided with an attenuator system, where a shunt is arranged to decrease in value as the series resistance increases. Typical scales are shown in Fig. 4.8 and the arrangement of resistances is shown in Fig. 4.9. Attenuators are fully dealt with in Chapter 13.

A typical example of an a.c./d.c. multimeter is the Model 7 Universal AvoMeter, which measures resistance from 0 to 40 megohms in five ranges and has a.c. ranges of 5, 10, 50, 100, 200, 400, 500 and 1000 V, 5, 10, 50, 100 and 500 mA, and 1, 5 and 10A. The d.c. ranges are the same but have additional lower ranges of 50 mV, 100 mV, 500 mV, 1 V, and 1 mA, 2 mA.

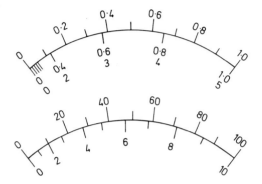

Fig. 4.8. Multi-range rectifier meter scales

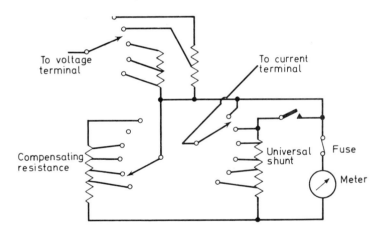

Fig. 4.9. Multi-range rectifier meter circuit

4.2.5. Dynamometer Instruments

Wattmeters are normally made on the dynamometer principle. The dynamometer consists of two fixed coils with a moving coil situated between them. The fixed coils consist of a few turns of heavy gauge wire with low resistance. The moving coil has many turns of small diameter wire with high resistance and is pivoted in jewelled bearings. The meter needle is attached to one end of the moving-coil shaft and the damping arrangement, usually a dash-pot, is attached to the other end. Springs provide the controlling force as in the ease of the moving-coil meter already described.

In use, the high-resistance moving coil is connected across the source of voltage and the fixed coils are connected in series with the load. The current through the load passes through the fixed coils so as to produce a magnetic field between them. The current through the voltage coil depends on the voltage across the load and tends to make the moving coil align itself with the stationary field due to the fixed coils. The rotation of the moving coil is directly proportional to the voltage across the load and also to the current passing through the load. Consequently, the meter registers the power consumption, or $E \times I$. Dynamometers can be used with either d.c. or low-frequency a.c.

For current measurement, the meter is so arranged that the fixed (heavy gauge) coils and the calibration resistor form the shunt for a shunted type ammeter, as shown in Fig. 4.10. In this case the field is

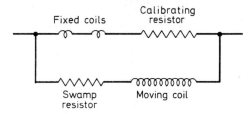

Fig. 4.10. Electrodynamometer arrangement for current measurement

proportional to the current hence the deflection is proportional to the current squared. The meter therefore reads r.m.s. values. Alternatively, with the fixed and moving coils connected in series, and additional series impedance if necessary, the movement is suitable for the measurement of r.m.s. voltages.

For ordinary use these meters have several disadvantages. Dashpot damping must be used as in a moving-iron meter, for any stray magnetic field will seriously affect the reading. They consume a relatively large amount of power and are liable to frequency error due to the reactance of the coils. In spite of these disadvantages they can be made very

accurate and with negligible error on low frequencies. For this reason
they are used in the laboratory to compare alternating currents with
direct currents, i.e. as 'transfer instruments'. This is necessary in the a.c.
potentiometer. However, thermocouple instruments are tending to
replace dynamometers for this purpose. For further details see Chapter 8.

4.2.6. Electrostatic Meters

Most voltmeters are really current-measuring instruments, an ammeter
calibrated in volts being used to measure the current in a known resistance across which the voltage under test is applied. The electrostatic
meter reads voltage directly, by measuring the electrostatic attraction
between two plates. This force, by the principles of electrostatics, is
proportional to the square of the charge and this again is proportional
to the square of the potential difference between the plates.

A typical example of a single-vane instrument is shown in Fig. 4.11.
The essential components are a spring-loaded pivot spindle on which

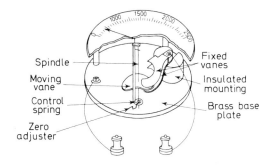

Fig. 4.11. Single-vane type electrostatic voltmeter

is mounted a pointer and a light aluminium vane, the latter being
positioned so that it can swing between two brass plates which are
electrically common, similar to a small air-spaced capacitor. The control
spring tends to hold the moving vane away from the fixed plates and
opposite poles of the supply are connected to fixed and moving plates
respectively. Damping is usually electromagnetic by means of an
additional vane, the rim of which rotates in the jaws of a small horse-
shoe magnet (not shown in the diagram).

The power consumption of electrostatic voltmeters is usually
negligible; there is always a minute leakage current and, on the lower
frequencies of a.c., a capacitive current of a few microamperes. Thus the
instrument is particularly valuable for use in a.c. or d.c. circuits of very

high impedance, where the current taken by an ordinary voltmeter would introduce considerable errors. Another form of electrostatic instrument, the double-vane type, is shown in Fig. 4.12. A special form

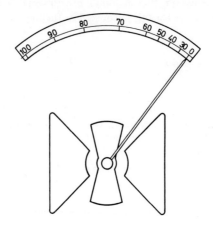

Fig. 4.12. Double-vane type electrostatic meter

of mechanical damping is employed, a wire passing through the case of the instrument. This type can be made for range from 1000–10000 V.

For ranges of 100–1000 V, a multicellular type as shown in Fig. 4.13 is used. As in the case of galvanometers increased sensitivity is obtained by utilising a fine phosphor-bronze suspension instead of pivots. There is a zero adjustment at the top of the suspension and a spring to protect the fine thread against damage from vibration. A vane moving in oil provides the damping.

For very high voltages the Abraham voltmeter shown in Fig. 4.14 can be used. This has two 'mushrooms', one of which forms one terminal while the other has a movable centre piece which is geared to the pointer. With this type of attracted disc instrument voltages up to 500 000 can be measured directly. The range can be varied by adjusting the distance between the mushrooms. The voltage range can be increased still further by connecting capacitors across the supply and placing the meter across one of them, so that the capacitors act as a voltage divider. It is desirable to use fairly large capacitors in order to swamp the effect of any leakage to earth.

Very high accuracies can be obtained with electrostatic meters but there is generally some trouble with 'creep' due to the low operating forces involved. For shielding against stray electrostatic fields the whole instrument is usually screened and the moving parts earthed whenever possible. It is undeniably the best method of measuring high

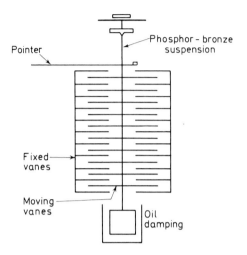

Fig. 4.13. Multicellular type electrostatic meter

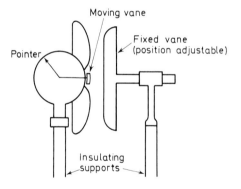

Fig. 4.14. Abraham type electrostatic voltmeter

values of a.c. and d.c. with accuracy, but is normally too delicate for low values. The instrument is free from frequency and waveform error but at very high frequencies the circuit under test may be influenced by the self-capacitance of the meter. The National Physical Laboratory uses an electrostatic voltmeter, shunt and transformer as a standard measuring device for a.c. current. It is in fact the standard 'transfer instrument' from d.c. to a.c.

Electrostatic instruments can be used to measure power. The circuit shown in Fig. 4.15 is employed to measure the power consumed in

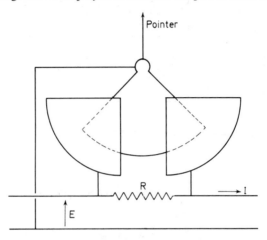

Fig. 4.15. *Measurement of power consumed in dielectrics*

dielectrics, since the current in an insulating material is so small that any other method is generally impractical. It can be shown that the deflection is given by $kREI$ if I is small and E large.

The theory of the instrument is simplified by assuming that the moving vane is a sector of a circle moving between two plates. Let C_θ be the capacitance between the moving and fixed vanes for an angular deflection θ. If E is the p.d. between the vanes then the electrical energy of the charge on the instrument is $\frac{1}{2}C_\theta E^2$ and the charge is $Q_\theta = C_\theta E$. Now for a small increase in deflection $d\theta$ the increase in potential energy is $\frac{1}{2}d(C_\theta)E^2$ but since the increase in charge is $d(Q) = d(C_\theta)E$ the energy gain from the source of supply is $d(Q_\theta)E = d(C_\theta)E^2$.

Hence the work done by the supply exceeds the potential energy gained by $\frac{1}{2}d(C_\theta)E^2$.

Now the capacitance of a parallel plate capacitor is given by $C = \dfrac{A\varepsilon_0}{t}$

where A is the area of the plates and t the distance between them.

In the case under consideration the plate is a sector of a circle whose area is $\frac{1}{2}r^2\theta$. Therefore, since both sides of the moving vane are employed, $C_\theta = \dfrac{r^2\theta\,\mathcal{E}_0}{t}$

The work done by the supply against the restoring couple of the suspension for a small angle $d(\theta)$ is

$$dW = \frac{1}{2}d(C_\theta)E^2 = \frac{\mathcal{E}_0 r^2}{2t}E^2\,d\theta \text{ whence } \frac{dC_\theta}{d\theta} = \frac{\mathcal{E}_0 r^2}{t}$$

If τ is the torque per unit angle due to the suspension, then

$$\tau\theta\,d\theta = \frac{\mathcal{E}_0 r^2}{2t}E^2\,d\theta \text{ whence } \theta = \frac{\mathcal{E}_0 r^2}{2\tau t}E^2 \text{ and torque } \tau\theta = \frac{1}{2}\frac{dC_\theta}{d\theta}E^2.$$

Thus it is seen that the deflection is proportional to the square of the voltage. The electrostatic meter therefore reads r.m.s. values on a.c.

In low-reading electrostatic instruments there is the difficult problem of designing a coiled hair spring for control purposes that is delicate and reliable enough for this application, unless the suspension method is used. However, the latter produces an instrument that is normally too delicate for industrial purposes.

4.2.7. Current Transformers

Current transformers are used to enable very heavy currents to be easily measured on meters of convenient range and to isolate the meter circuit from high-voltage supplies. They have only a few primary turns (sometimes only one in the shape of a bus-bar) and a secondary, wound to give about 5 A. The transformer often consists solely of an insulated secondary winding which is permanently fitted around the heavy cable in which flows a current that requires to be measured at regular intervals.

An increase in frequency causes an increase in rate of change of flux linkages and consequently an increase in secondary e.m.f. As the secondary reactance will also rise, the current will not change in the same proportion; however, it is clear that there will be a variation of transformation ratio with frequency. This can be made negligible for any likely changes at commercial frequencies but the same apparatus would not be used at audio frequencies. One precaution that should be mentioned is that the iron-cored current transformer should never have its secondary on open circuit.

Radio frequency current transformers are also made. From Fig. 4.16 the secondary current is given by

$$I_s = \frac{j\omega M I_p}{R_s + j\omega L_s}$$

and the transformation ratio is therefore

$$\left|\frac{I_p}{I_s}\right| = \frac{L_s}{M}\sqrt{1 + \left(\frac{R_s}{\omega L_s}\right)^2}$$

where M is the mutual inductance between primary and secondary, R_s the total resistance of the secondary circuit including the meter, and L_s the inductance of the secondary circuit.

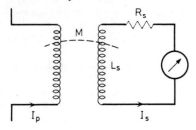

Fig. 4.16. Instrument transformer circuit

If R_s is made small, the ratio becomes simply L_s/M which is independent of frequency, provided that there are negligible hysteresis or eddy current losses. The former difficulty is overcome by using an air core and the latter by careful construction. At high radio frequencies the self- and mutual-capacitance of the windings introduces another frequency error.

If there is plenty of power available to operate the measuring device as a whole it is possible to design a current transformer with loose coupling so that it reflects negligible reactance from secondary into primary, with the obvious advantages.

4.2.8. Impedance Meter

The basic circuit for a direct-reading impedance meter employing the same principle as the ohmmeter used on d.c. but operating on a single a.c. frequency is shown in Fig. 4.17.

The impedance at the left-hand side, made up of an inductor, capacitor and variable potentiometer, gives practically constant impedance of variable phase measured between the junction of the L and C and the tap on the potentiometer, as the slider of the potentiometer is moved. With an inductance of Q 10, and a similar 10% resistance in series with the capacitor, the variation of impedance value can be maintained within plus or minus 2% for a phase variation from 63° inductive to 63° capacitive. The potentiometer is calibrated in terms of phase. The input potentiometer serves as a zero adjustment. Frequency must be accurately adjusted to that for which the impedance standard is designed, and should be a pure sine wave. The transformer with its associated switch serves as a range change device, enabling the instrument

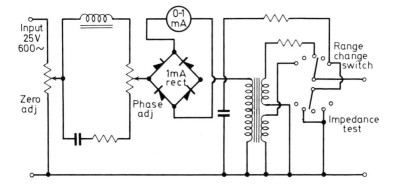

Fig. 4.17. Impedance meter

to be used directly over a range from 0·05 ohm to 1 megohm, with fairly high accuracy between 0·2 ohm and 0·2 megohm. The frequency used is an audio one — 600 or 1000 Hz are suggested. The scale is similar to that obtained with an ordinary ohmmeter, and is read in conjunction with × 100, × 1, and ÷ 100 multipliers. The procedure is to rotate the phase knob until the phase of the standard impedance agrees with that under test, as evidenced by a maximum impedance reading on the instrument scale. This reading is the value required, while the phase knob calibration indicates the phase of the impedance measured.

WORKED EXAMPLE

Question. A hot-wire meter, thermocouple, metal rectifier and repulsion type moving iron meter are all connected in series. The waveform of the current is given by

$$i = 100 \sin \omega t + 20 \sin 2\omega t + 10 \sin 5\omega t.$$

State which of the meters would be said to give a correct reading and give the percentage error in the case of the other(s).

Answer. The hot-wire and thermocouple meters read r.m.s. values and that without serious frequency error so they can be said to read 'correctly', sine r.m.s. is the standard value for measurement purposes.

The moving-iron meter also reads r.m.s. values, assuming its irons are not saturated. There may however be a frequency error but as the fundamental frequency is not given there is no means of knowing. It must therefore be assumed that this instrument also reads 'correctly'. The rectifier meter however reads average values, which on this waveform will be very different.

The r.m.s. value of the given current is given by

$$I = \sqrt{\frac{1}{2\pi} \int_0^{2\pi} i^2 \, d(\omega t)}$$

Since $i = 100 \sin \omega t + 20 \sin 3\omega t + 10 \sin 5\omega t$, then

$$I^2 = \frac{1}{2\pi} \int_0^{2\pi} \left[\begin{array}{l} 100^2 \sin^2 \omega t + 20^2 \sin^2 3\omega t + 10^2 \sin^2 5\omega t + 4000 \\ \sin \omega t \sin 3\omega t + 2000 \sin \omega t \sin 5\omega t + 400 \sin 3\omega t \\ \qquad\qquad\qquad\qquad\qquad\qquad\qquad\qquad \sin 5\omega t \end{array} \right] d(\omega t)$$

Now $\sin A \sin B = \dfrac{\cos (A - B)}{2} - \dfrac{\cos (A + B)}{2}$ and $\sin^2 A = \dfrac{1 - \cos 2A}{2}$

Hence all the terms under the integral can be expressed as sine and cosine terms together with the terms

$$\frac{100^2}{2}, \frac{20^2}{2} \text{ and } \frac{10^2}{2}.$$

Since the average value of a sine and cosine over one or more complete cycles is zero, then

$$I^2 = \frac{1}{2\pi} \left[\frac{100^2}{2} \cdot 2\pi + \frac{20^2}{2} \cdot 2\pi + \frac{10^2}{2} \cdot 2\pi \right]$$

$$= \frac{1}{2} \left[100^2 + 20^2 + 10^2 \right]$$

whence $\qquad I = \dfrac{1}{\sqrt{2}} \sqrt{100^2 + 20^2 + 10^2} = 72 \cdot 4 \text{ A.}$

The average value is given by

$$I_{\text{av}} = \frac{1}{\pi} \int_0^{\pi} i \, d(\omega t)$$

$$= \frac{1}{\pi} \int_0^{\pi} \left[100 \sin \omega t + 20 \sin 3\omega t + 10 \sin 5 \omega t \right] d(\omega t)$$

$$= \frac{1}{\pi} \left[100 \cos \omega t + \frac{20}{3} \cos 3\omega t + \frac{10}{5} \cos 5\omega t \right]_0^{\pi} = \frac{1}{\pi} \left[200 + \frac{400}{3} + \frac{20}{5} \right]$$

$$= 69 \cdot 5 \text{ A.}$$

If the rectifier meter is calibrated in average values then it will read

$$\frac{72 \cdot 4 - 69 \cdot 5}{72 \cdot 4} \times 100 = 4\% \text{ low.}$$

If the meter is calibrated in r.m.s. values for a pure sine wave it will read

$$69\cdot5 \times 1\cdot11 = 77\cdot1 \text{ A}.$$

The error is then $\dfrac{77\cdot1 - 72\cdot4}{72.4} \times 100 = \underline{5\cdot1\% \text{ high}}$. *Answer*.

Note. This is a very instructive question for it shown that even with 20% third harmonic the error obtained with a rectifier is not serious, if it is required for say an output meter or for general testing.

EXERCISES

1. Show that the torque of an electrostatic voltmeter is $\tfrac{1}{2}V^2 (dC/d\theta)$ joule/radian where V is in volts, C in farads and θ in radians. An electrostatic voltmeter having spring control gives a full-scale deflection of 80 deg. when 2·0 kV is applied. The capacitance increases uniformly with angular deflection from $20\,pF$ at zero deflection to $100\,pF$ at 80 deg.
Calculate
   (*a*) the angular deflection corresponding to a scale mark of 1·5 kV;
   (*b*) the capacitance required in series with the instrument to increase the full-scale range to 6 kV;
   (*c*) the actual voltage applied to the combination in (*b*) when a reading of 1·2 *k*V is observed on the voltmeter.
Why is the arrangement described in (*b*) unsatisfactory? Suggest a better method of increasing the range. (L.U.B.Sc. (Eng.) Part III, 1967)

Answer. (*a*) 45°, (*b*) 50 *pF*, (*c*) 2·4 kV.

2. Two similar electrostatic voltmeters, having a maximum scale reading of 500 V and negligible leakage, are joined in parallel and then connected across a 200 V d.c. supply. After disconnection from the supply the pointer of one instrument is moved to full-scale deflection by means of an insulated probe. Describe the resulting effect on the other instrument, given reasons.   (C. & G. 1950)

Answer. Neglecting the initial capacitance of each instrument and assuming that each has a square-law scale, when the pointer of one instrument is moved to full-scale deflection, that of the other will register approximately 64 V.

CHAPTER 5

Electronic Voltmeters

5.1. INTRODUCTION

The previous chapters have dealt mainly with ordinary meters, which are electrical rather than electronic instruments. However, since many electronic measuring devices use meters as the ultimate indicating method, a knowledge of meter principles is important to the electronic engineer. Most of the valve voltmeters described in this chapter use meters of the moving-coil type to indicate the value of the quantity being measured.

The first use of a valve to measure voltage was in 1915 by R. A. Heising.[1] Most of the pioneer work in the U.K. was done by E. B. Moullin of Oxford University. In fact, at one time, valve voltmeters were usually referred to as Moullin voltmeters. American workers in particular have done much to develop their use; in the U.S.A. these meters are known as 'vacuum tube voltmeters' usually abbreviated for convenience in descriptive matter as 'vtvm'.

5.2. TYPES OF VOLTMETER

Electronic voltmeters are made in two basic forms, which may be classified as a.c. amplifier types and d.c. amplifier types. In the a.c. amplifier configuration, the voltage to be measured is applied directly to the input terminals of a wide-band gain-stabilised amplifier, whose output is rectified and applied to a moving-coil meter. In the d.c. amplifier construction, the input voltage is applied directly to a diode detector, and the resulting d.c. is amplified and monitored. It is generally accepted that the a.c. amplifier type is usually the more sensitive of the two, but the usable frequency range is restricted by the amplifier bandwidth.

The d.c. amplifier form permits voltage measurement up to frequencies approaching the resonance of the diode unit. Sensitivity, however, is restricted by the linearity of the diode and the stability of the d.c. amplifier. The first of these limitations is reduced considerably by the use of semiconductor diodes, which maintain their low forward resistance down to very small voltage levels. High gain d.c. amplification is obtained by the use of an a.c. coupled amplifier in conjunction with a chopper and synchronous detector.

The first part of this chapter deals with the basic principles only of voltage measurement using valves and transistors.

5.2.1. True r.m.s. Voltmeter

This instrument is so named because it measures the true r.m.s. voltage of the input signal whatever its waveform. One type of commercial true r.m.s. instrument is shown in Fig. 5.1. The input signal is amplified and

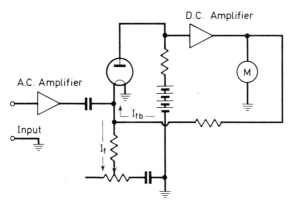

Fig. 5.1. True r.m.s. voltmeter

fed into the directly-heated filament of a high-vacuum diode valve, thus furnishing part of the filament heating power. The filament must have a small thermal time constant if the instrument is to respond to rapid changes in signal level. An emission operating point is established in the thermal saturation region by means of a d.c. filament current I_f, which consists of a constant component I_f and a feedback current I_{fb} from the d.c. amplifier.

After amplification of the a.c. input signal a cathode follower is used to obtain an impedance match between the amplifier and the low-impedance filament. The signal current will tend to raise the temperature of the filament, which will cause the anode current to rise and the anode-to-cathode voltage to fall. This drop in anode voltage is amplified by the d.c. amplifier. The output of this amplifier supplies the component of current I_{fb} to the filament. The feedback circuit is adjusted so that the decrease in $I_{fb}^2 R_f$ equals the signal power, $I_s^2 R_f$, in the filament, where I_s is the r.m.s. signal current. The meter reads the output voltage of the amplifier, which is proportional to the feedback current I_{fb}. (Feedback is dealt with later in this chapter). The total power dissipated in the filament is

$$P_F = (I_f + I_{fb})^2 R_f + I_s^2 R_f$$

whence

$$I_f + I_{fb} = \left(\frac{P_F}{R_f} - I_s^2\right)^{\frac{1}{2}} \qquad (5.1)$$

Expanding equation (5.1) by Taylor's theorem gives

$$I_f + I_{fb} = \left(\frac{P_F}{R_f}\right)^{\frac{1}{2}} - \frac{1}{2}\left(\frac{P_F}{R_f}\right)^{-\frac{1}{2}} I_s^2 + \ldots .$$

If I_s is small compared to I_f, then the first two terms of this series only need be considered. The constant terms on each side of the equation must be equal; thus

$$I_f = \left(\frac{P_F}{R_F}\right)^{\frac{1}{2}}$$

The variable terms must also be equal, hence

$$I_{fb} = -\frac{1}{2}\left(\frac{P_F}{R_F}\right)^{-\frac{1}{2}} I_s^2$$

or

$$I_{fb} = KI_s^2$$

The feedback current is proportional to the square of the r.m.s. signal current. The meter reading is, therefore, proportional to the r.m.s. signal current, and the meter will have a linear power scale.

5.2.2. Peak Voltmeter

Fig. 5.2 shows the basic circuit of a peak-reading voltmeter. For high-frequency response and low-level signals the diode is placed in a probe, i.e. a screened case at the end of a flexible lead.

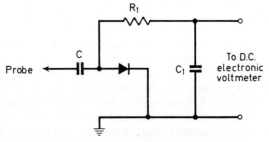

Fig. 5.2. Peak-reading electronic voltmeter

When used in this manner, very little stray capacitance is introduced
into the circuit under measurement. The diode permits the a.c. signal
to charge C to the peak value of the signal voltage. The network $R_1 C_1$
is a simple filter to remove all ripple voltage from the rectified d.c. that
is delivered to the d.c. amplifier in the instrument.

5.2.3. Anode Bend Meters

The simple anode-bend rectifier is shown in Fig. 5.3. The use of this
circuit for rectifying signals in a radio receiver is well known, but the

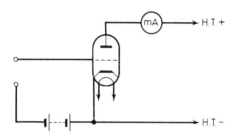

Fig. 5.3. Anode bend type valve voltmeter

problems involved in its use for measurement purposes are rather
different because it is not an audio-frequency envelope but a d.c.
component that has to be considered. This of course is also the case
when a diode is used to obtain automatic gain control, but here the
exact relationship between the alternating e.m.f. input and the steady
output current is of no great importance. In the case of a voltmeter,
however, this relationship must be known with some definiteness, for
on it depends the question of whether r.m.s., average or peak values are
being measured.

Fig. 5.4 shows the characteristic curve for a small receiving triode.
The grid is biased to about the mid-point of the curved part of the
characteristic. The waveform of the anode current, resulting from a
sinusoidal grid voltage, is shown. Now the curved part of a valve
characteristic (or indeed of any rectifier) is very nearly parabolic.
Therefore the anode current is proportional to the square of the grid
volts and the meter reads r.m.s. values. Naturally some valves have
curves which more nearly approach a parabola than others. If a rectifying circuit is set up in this way and grid volts squared plotted against
anode current a straight line is obtained from zero up to say 2 V r.m.s.

This fact is of considerable value in calibrating such a meter, for only a sufficient number of points need be checked to establish the straight line, which in any case passes through the origin.

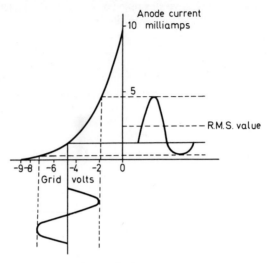

Fig. 5.4. *Triode characteristic*

Using an obvious notation the anode current is given by

$$i_a = a(v_a + \mu_0 v_g)^2 = a(v_a^2 + 2 v_a \mu \cdot v_g + \mu^2 v_g^2).$$

Now since the resistance of the meter in the anode circuit is small compared with the valve impedance, v_a is constant and equal to the voltage of the h.t. battery. The grid voltage is given by $v_g = V_g \sin \omega t$. Thus the average value of the anode current is given by

$$I_{av} = \frac{1}{2\pi} \int_0^{2\pi} i_a \, d(\omega t) = \frac{a}{2\pi} \int_0^{2\pi} (v_a^2 + 2\mu v_a V_g \sin \omega t + \mu^2 V_g^2 \sin^2 \omega t) d(\omega t)$$

$$= \frac{a}{2}(2v_a^2 + \mu^2 V_g^2)$$

since the average value of a sine curve is zero.

In practice, arrangements are made to balance out the component due to the steady anode voltage, so that the meter reading is

$$I = \frac{1}{2} a\mu^2 V_g^2$$

which is the condition for obtaining r.m.s. values.

If now the circuit of Fig. 5.3 is again employed but the bias is increased to 9 V the situation is similar to that of a Class B amplifier using only one valve instead of two in push-pull, as is normally the case. From the curve of Fig. 5.4 it is clear that the negative half-cycles are entirely suppressed and half-wave rectification takes place. It should be noted that with this adjustment the meter does not read r.m.s. neither does it read the same average values as the metal rectifier meter; it gives half and not full wave rectification.

The practical effect of this adjustment, called half-wave square law, is that the waveform of the voltage being measured has a considerable effect upon the reading. Even the phase of the harmonics has some effect. There is one particularly interesting effect when even harmonics are present: reversing the connections will produce a different reading, since the two parts of the wave are not symmetrical. This effect is known as turnover.

Under these circumstances it might appear that this type of voltmeter is of very little use, but this is not the case. Valve voltmeters are normally used on radio frequencies and these are of very pure waveform. Even the modulated output from a broadcasting station has a very small amount of harmonics, for obvious reasons. Any oscillation taking place in lightly damped resonant circuits is necessarily sensibly sinusoidal, thus the peculiar behaviour of half-wave square law meters is not a serious disadvantage for most purposes. This property must however be borne in mind when a valve voltmeter is required for audio-frequency measurements.

The anode-bend meter can be further modified by increasing the bias to say 12 V. Then only a small part of the cycle (about 15%) will produce any effect. In this condition the meter will read peak values (or nearly so).

Turnover effect is most marked with peak voltmeters. In fact there is no point in using this modification except in circumstances where the measurement of peak voltages is definitely required, for example in examining audio-frequency apparatus for overload conditions.

A practical difficulty with anode bend meters is that some anode current still flows when no signal is applied. This difficulty is easily overcome by balancing out this residual current as shown in Fig. 5.5, a separate cell B_4 with a variable series resistor R_2 being connected across the indicating meter. The same device can be used with a grid rectifier meter described later.

Much time and attention has been spent in designing valve voltmeters in order to make their calibration remain practically constant. In the types just described there are power supplies, grid batteries and the valve itself which are all liable to variation. If the valve is 'aged' or preferably run under its normal rating, i.e. with a heater voltage about 20% below that specified by the maker, its characteristics remain constant over a long period. However, it is not easy to reproduce the setting of the various voltages so as to always work on the same part of the characteristic curve.

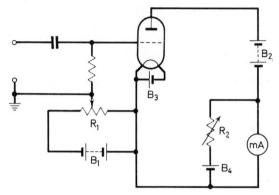

Fig. 5.5. Anode bend voltmeter with backing-off circuit

5.2.4. Grid Rectifier Meter

It is assumed that the reader is already familiar with the principles of grid rectification and also with the use of a grid capacitor and leak to obtain automatic bias in radio transmitters. These two techniques depend, of course, upon exactly the same phenomenon: when the grid is driven positive it draws current which charges the capacitor so as to restore the grid voltage to the required biasing value.

In the case of the Class C amplifier a state of equilibrium is reached when the current passing through the leak just balances the amount of charge taken during that part of the cycle in which the grid is positive. The bias which the valve acquires will therefore depend upon the values of the leak and capacitor: the larger the product RC the smaller the part of the cycle in which the grid has to go positive, and consequently the greater the bias it acquires.

In a transmitter a reasonable part of the cycle must be conducting, else the valve will not provide the necessary power to drive its anode circuit and will have a very distorted waveform. In radio reception, however, the nearer the condition can be approached where the grid current does not flow at all, the better; other things being equal.

If this condition is approached in a valve voltmeter it will read peak values; therefore to build a voltmeter that will measure average values the grid leak must be fairly low in value and the capacitor no larger than is necessary to obtain a reasonable freedom from frequency error. The full analysis of the situation is rather involved and beyond the scope of this book.

It may be mentioned that the only way of estimating the accuracy of many instruments on radio frequencies is by comparing the behaviour of two or more pieces of apparatus that do not work on exactly the same principle; if they agree over a wide range of frequencies, both can be considered as free from frequency error. It might also be mentioned that the grid and diode patterns have the advantages of not requiring a conducting path between the terminals and of being able to measure an a.c. potential which is superimposed on a steady one.

5.2.5. Electronic Voltmeters for D.C. Measurements

Fig. 5.6 shows a simple transistor d.c. voltmeter. The operation of this circuit can be understood by remembering that, in the grounded

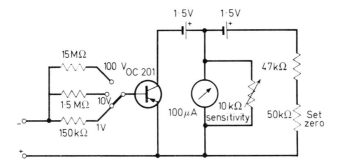

Fig. 5.6. Transistor voltmeter

emitter connection, a very small input current is required by the transistor. The input resistance on the highest range is 15 M Ω which is comparable with that of a valve voltmeter. Before use the zero should be adjusted with input short circuited. The sensitivity can then be adjusted by connecting a known voltage to the input terminals. Because transistors are temperature sensitive, they should be fitted with heat sinks, otherwise the variation in $I'_{c(o)}$ with temperature tends to unbalance the meter. The heat sink can take the form of a metal cooling fin which fits round the transistor and makes a good thermal contact with some larger mass of cool metal, or the transistor can be fitted into a hole drilled in a brass bar.

The elementary anode-bend type meter shown in Fig. 5.3 can be used to measure steady potentials but it is liable to 'drift' due to varia-tions in supply voltage. If the instrument is required for measurements over 100 volts these drifts are not likely to cause serious error.

Because of the possibilities of obtaining a meter of virtually infinite ohms per volt, several devices have been evolved to obviate the errors due to the drift of supply voltages. Variations in base-to-emitter bias and collector cut-off current due to changes in ambient temperature may also cause the output of transistorised d.c. amplifiers to drift. However, when a differential circuit is employed in the first stage of these amplifiers, equal variations in the parameters of both transistors are not amplified because of the rejection of common-mode signals. For maximum reduction of d.c. drift, matched transistors should be selected. They should be mounted in close proximity on a common heat sink.

The use of germanium transistors above room temperature in d.c. amplifiers is not recommended. Fig. 5.7 shows a d.c. amplifier used as

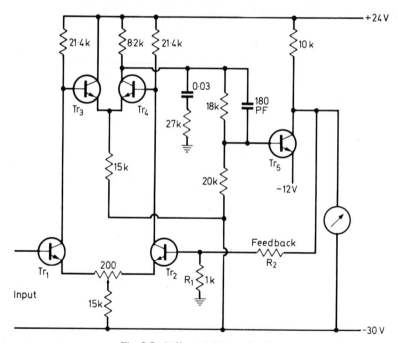

Fig. 5.7. Differential d.c. voltmeter

voltmeter employing *n-p-n* silicon transistors which perform satisfactorily at 93°C or higher. By employing a differential circuit in the second as well as in the first stage, a worthwhile increase in common-mode rejection and a decrease in overall amplifier drift is obtained. Power-supply regulation of from 2 to 5% is adequate. Amplifier internal gain is about 2500, and the overall gain is set by adjusting R_2 in conjunction with R_1 to give the required negative feedback for gain stability purposes (see next section). Transistors Tr_1 and Tr_2 are type 905, Tr_3 and Tr_4 type 904, and Tr_5 type 904 or 903 made by Texas Instruments Inc., U.S.A.

5.3. NEGATIVE FEEDBACK

This important technique has had a great effect on both a.c. and d.c. electronic voltmeter design. A brief account of its effect in increasing gain stability and reducing distortion follows.

Assume an amplifier of gain A units and fed with a signal e_s. If now a fraction β of the output voltage E is fed back to the input, then the actual input will be $e_s + \beta E$. (Note that both A and β are complex quantities).

Hence
$$A \cdot e_s = E(1 - A\beta).$$

Therefore the actual gain $A_f = \dfrac{E}{e_s} = \dfrac{A}{1 - A\beta}$ \hfill (5.2)

If the feedback is negative, i.e. such as to oppose the signal voltage, β is negative and the gain is reduced. Now if $A\beta$ is considerably greater than unity then

$$\text{Gain} = \frac{1}{\beta}$$

Hence the remarkable conclusion that the gain of the amplifier is independent of the amplification due to the valves or transistors used and therefore it must be independent of small changes in the supply voltages or ambient temperature. Therefore it must be independent of small changes in the operating voltages.

Now let d be the amount of distortion generated in the amplifier without feedback, and let D be the distortion actually present in the output voltage with feedback. Then the distortion fed back to the grid circuit is βD. This is amplified A times, hence the total distortion in the output is $d + \beta DA$.

Therefore $D = d + \beta DA$ or $D = \dfrac{d}{1 - A\beta}$

Again if $A\beta$ is great compared with unity, then $D = -\dfrac{d}{A\beta}$

Thus the distortion is very considerably reduced by the feedback.

The application of feedback to rectifiers is a much more complicated problem. Stated simply, the effect is to straighten out the bend in the rectifier characteristic so as to make this characteristic straight right down to zero anode current. This is the ideal rectifier. In the case under consideration, however, the most important effect of the feedback is again to make the mean anode current for a given signal sensibly

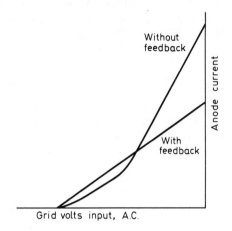

Fig. 5.8. Effect of negative feedback

independent of changes in the operating voltages. The effect of feedback on a rectifier curve is shown in Fig. 5.8. The relation between anode current and input volts is obviously constant down to the lowest values.

In Fig. 5.9 a simple feedback circuit is shown to illustrate the general principle. R_F is the feedback resistor.

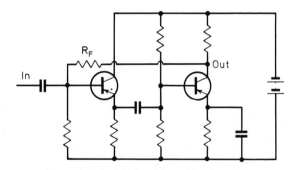

Fig. 5.9. Negative feedback circuit

Perhaps the most well-known circuit employing negative feedback is the cathode follower circuit. This uses negative current feedback, which is easily applied to any amplifier stage by employing a cathode bias resistor which is not decoupled to earth, i.e. the usual decoupling capacitor is omitted. The effect of negative current feedback is to greatly increase the input resistance of the stage in which it is used, in fact the input resistance is several times the value of the grid input resistor of the stage. A high input resistance is most desirable in an electronic voltmeter to ensure, in the ideal case, that the circuit under test is unaffected by the addition of the voltmeter. However, cathode followers are little used in electronic voltmeter circuits since the first stage of the voltmeter is usually a diode on the end of a flexible lead, as will be described in the next section.

Negative feedback circuits are obviously a great boon to the electronic voltmeter designer. An indirectly-heated valve can be used and all the operating potentials derived from the mains without the likelihood of error due to these quantities varying. Not only can a battery-less meter be produced but one that can be made to read high voltages by providing a high anode voltage. Very small voltages are measured by employing high-gain amplifiers in addition to the rectifier.

Another important effect of negative feedback is that it straightens the overall characteristic, thereby reducing harmonic distortion. Since most rectifiers are subject to waveform error it is most important that an amplifier used in measurement applications shall not introduce harmonics.

5.4. SPECIAL REQUIREMENTS AT HIGH FREQUENCIES

It has been stated several times that valve voltmeters have no frequency error and cause negligible disturbance to the circuit to which they are connected. However, with the very high frequencies used in connection with television and short range communication the situation is not so simple. The capacitance between grid and heater of an ordinary triode is alone sufficiently high at these frequencies to disturb the circuit, while the capacitance of the input leads to a voltmeter can be great enough to act as a virtual short-circuit.

The first difficulty is overcome by using an acorn valve, which is specially designed for u.h.f. work. The second difficulty is overcome in an ingenious yet simple manner by taking the valve to the source of high frequency instead of vice versa. The valve is contained in a screened case at the end of a flexible lead and when a measurement is to be made the grid pin of the valve is connected directly to the circuit under test. Instead of a valve, a semiconductor diode can be used as shown in Fig. 5.2.

5.5. CALIBRATION OF ELECTRONIC VOLTMETERS

A suitable circuit for calibration of an electronic voltmeter is shown in Fig. 5.10. The supply is obtained from the 50-Hz mains as this is most

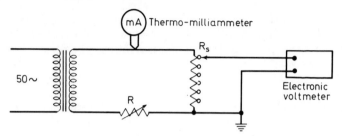

Fig. 5.10. Circuit for calibrating electronic voltmeter

convenient and the electronic voltmeter is presumed to be without frequency error. The output from the transformer secondary is taken, via a thermo-couple milliammeter and rheostat R to a standard variable resistance R_s. The current is measured by the milliammeter so the voltage across R_s is known and, since it is accurately sub-divided, the voltage applied to the electronic voltmeter is known.

A thermo-milliammeter is chosen because it is accurate and likely to be available in an electronics laboratory, but a really good moving-iron or dynamometer instrument could be used equally well.

The potentiometer described in Chapter 2 is for d.c. only and electronic voltmeters must be calibrated on a.c. supplies. A form of a.c. potentiometer could be used but the accuracy required in this case does not warrant the use of so complicated a piece of apparatus.

5.6. DIGITAL VOLTMETERS

An electronic measuring device which is becoming widely used due to its high accuracy and ease of read-out is the digital voltmeter, where the result of a measurement appears in the form of a series of figures. Its operation is usually based on one of the two following principles:

(*a*) The comparison principle, where the voltage to be measured is compared with a voltage developed step-by-step within the measuring instrument. This voltage development ceases as soon as both voltages are equal. The number of steps is a measure of the voltage being investigated.

(*b*) The converter principle, where the voltage to be measured is converted into a pulsed voltage whose *frequency* is proportional to the amplitude of the voltage being measured. This frequency is measured by means of an electronic counter.

As method (b) is most used, only this method will be considered in detail. Referring to Fig. 5.11 (a), the voltage to be measured is fed, via

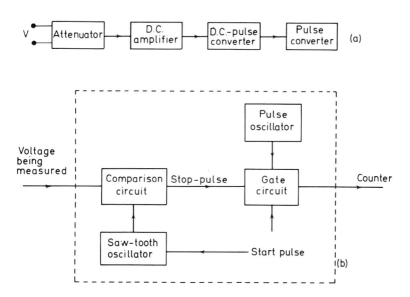

Fig. 5.11. Converter-type digital voltmeter

a high-resistance attenuator or range switch (which can be switched automatically according to the input voltage in some instruments) and a simple d.c. amplifier, to a converter. Fig. 5.11 (b) gives a block diagram of a practical 'analogue-to-digital' converter circuit. The voltage being measured is compared with a saw-tooth voltage whose value varies linearly with time as shown in Fig. 5.12. At the moment when the saw-tooth voltage begins, a gate-circuit is opened which passes the signals from a pulse generator to a counter. The gate is closed again as soon as the saw-tooth voltage is equal to the voltage being measured. The number of pulses transmitted is a measure of the value of the voltage being observed. The following example will make this clear.

Suppose that the saw-tooth voltage rises by 1 V per ms and that the frequency of the pulse generator is 100 kHz. If the voltage being measured in the comparison circuit is 6·37 V, for instance, the counter will operate for 6·37 ms. During this time the oscillator will have delivered 637 pulses and the counter therefore indicates 637. The range switch automatically indicates the position of the decimal point.

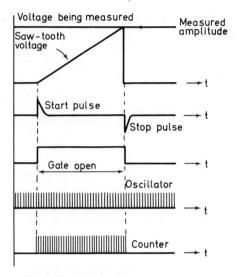

Fig. 5.12. Digital voltmeter operation

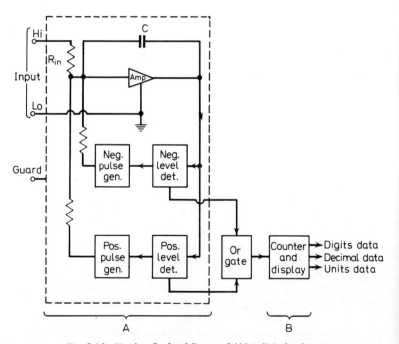

Fig. 5.13. Hewlett Packard Dymec 2401A digital voltmeter

It is clear from this numerical example that the time required for this measurement is only 6·37 ms. A commercial instrument of this type made by the Hewlett-Packard Co. of California, U.S.A. is described below.

The basic circuit arrangement is shown in Fig. 5.13. The d.c. voltage to be measured causes the section A enclosed by the dotted line (representing a screening box) to generate a train of pulses whose repetition rate is made to be directly proportional to the input voltage. The section marked B then counts the number of these pulses occurring during a preselected time interval to obtain the time integral of the input voltage.

Section A includes an analogue integrator consisting of a high-gain d.c. amplifier (AMP) with input resistor R_{in} and feedback capacitor C, and this integrator is provided with two special feedback circuits. When a d.c. voltage to be measured is applied to the integrator, the integrator output voltage rises at a slope and polarity that depend on the magnitude and polarity of the voltage to be measured.

The integrator output is connected to two pulse-generating channels, one triggered by a negative-going voltage, the other by a positive-going voltage. When the integrator output reaches a predetermined level, it triggers the appropriate pulse generator and a pulse of proper polarity is supplied to the integrator input to cancel the integrated voltage and return the integrator output to its zero condition. As long as the external d.c. voltage is applied to the voltmeter, the process repeats itself. The total integral of the input voltage over any given time interval is thus equal to the integral of the feedback pulses over that same time interval.

Since the feedback pulses are of constant voltage-time area, their integral and hence that of the input voltage is given by a count of the pulses.

The function of the counter in section B is to totalise the pulses over a precise time interval. By making the pulse repetition rate of section A an integral decimal multiple of the input voltage (i.e. 100 000 pps for 1 V input) and totalising over an integral decimal multiple of one second, the counter registration needs only correct positioning of the decimal point to display a direct reading of the input voltage.

The voltmeter display consists of a five-digit numerical read-out with indication of decimal point, units (e.g. volts or millivolts) and polarity, the latter information being obtained by sensing the active pulse generator. Binary-coded-decimal recording outputs are provided for the displayed reading, range, measurement units and polarity.

A ± 1 V internal standard is provided for self-calibration. This voltage reference is derived from a specially aged, temperature stabilised Zener diode; some digital voltmeters use a standard cell (Chapter 17) for this purpose. This voltmeter can be supplied with a converter unit to enable it to measure a.c. voltages up to 750 V peak and resistance up to 10 M Ω. It should be mentioned here that some makes of digital voltmeters have frequency limitations imposed by a relatively high total input capacitance (around 120 pF including the capacitance of the leads).

The foregoing details and Fig. 5.11 are based on information given in the Hewlett-Packard Journal, Vol. 13, No. 6, February, 1962, by kind permission of the Hewlett-Packard Co., U.S.A. For details of a book devoted entirely to this type of instrument, see Ref. 3.

WORKED EXAMPLE

Question. What do you understand by a negative feedback amplifier? For what purposes is this type of amplifier employed, and what are its advantages? If the overall gain of a feedback amplifier is 60 dB, and the attenuation of the feedback path is 61 dB, what gain has the amplifier without the feedback?   (Grad. I.E.E.)

Answer. The descriptive parts of the question may be fully answered by reference to the text.

Equation (5.2) for the case of negative feedback, namely

$$A_f = \frac{A}{1 + A\beta}$$

(where A_f and A are the respective gains with and without feedback, and β is the coupling attenuation), is used in solving the numerical part of the example, but first the data expressed in decibels must be converted to voltage ratios.

Since the overall gain of the feedback amplifier is 60 dB, then

$$20 \log_{10}\left(\frac{E_{of}}{E_i}\right) = 60,$$

where E_i and E_{of} are the input and output voltage respectively.

$$\therefore \ \log_{10}\left(\frac{E_{of}}{E_i}\right) = 3$$

$$\therefore \ \frac{E_{of}}{E_i} = \text{antilog}_{10} \ 3 = 1000$$

$$\therefore \ A_f = 1000 \ .$$

Since the attenuation of the feedback path is 61 dB, then

$$20 \log_{10}\left(\frac{E_{of}}{E_f}\right) = 61$$

where E_f is the fed-back voltage.

$$\therefore \log_{10}\left(\frac{E_{of}}{E_f}\right) = \frac{61}{20} = 3.05$$

$$\therefore \frac{E_{of}}{E_f} = \text{antilog}_{10} \ 3.05 = 1122$$

$$\therefore \beta = \frac{1}{1122}$$

Substituting in the original equation to determine the value of A gives

$$1000 = \frac{A}{1 + \dfrac{A}{1122}}$$

$$\therefore \ 1000 + \frac{1000A}{1122} = A$$

$$\therefore A = \frac{1000}{1 - \dfrac{1000}{1122}}$$

$$= \frac{1000 \times 1122}{122} = 9196$$

$$\therefore \frac{E_o}{E_i} = 9196,$$

where E_o is the output voltage without feedback.

Gain without feedback $= 20 \log_{10}\left(\frac{E_o}{E_i}\right)$

$$= 20 \times \log_{10} \ 9196$$

$$= 20 \times 3.9636$$

$$= 79.3 \ \text{dB. } Answer.$$

EXERCISES

1. Explain why the electronic voltmeter is such a useful measuring instrument.

2. Describe a form of electronic voltmeter with which you are familiar, outlining its advantages and limitations.

3. Explain the principles of negative feedback and their application to electronic voltmeters.

4. Give circuit diagrams of simple electronic voltmeters of the r.m.s., peak and 'average' types. Indicate briefly why each type measures these

particular values. What is 'turnover' and to which of the above types does it apply?

5. Draw a diagram of a circuit suitable for calibrating an electronic voltmeter. Indicate clearly the type of 'standard' measuring device used as a comparison, stating reasons for its choice, and also the source of the necessary current.

6. Describe the operation of a digital voltmeter.

REFERENCES

1. HEISING, R. A., *Historic First: Vacuum-tube Voltmeter,* Bell Lab. Rec., **24**, 270, (July, 1946).
2. CAMPBELL, R. D., *Electronics,* **23**, 93, (July, 1950).
3. LENK, JOHN D., *Direct Readout Meters.* W. Foulsham & Co. Ltd. (1967).

CHAPTER 6

Alternating Current Galvanometers and Oscillographs

In Chapter 4 the measurement of alternating currents and potential differences by various methods was considered; each method having its own special advantages and sphere of usefulness. These were all deflectional methods and were concerned with mean readings, i.e. r.m.s. or average readings. Null methods of measuring a.c. quantities and methods for studying instantaneous values will be dealt with in Chapter 8.

An instrument for measuring instantaneous values is called an oscillograph or oscilloscope, although the latter term should be reserved for an instrument used more for waveform examination than for actual measuring purposes. Null methods require some form of indicator to show the absence of alternating current at balance and the only reason for associating these quite different types of measurement is that the principle commonly used in a.c. galvanometers is also used in one form of oscillograph. Also the cathode-ray tube, whose chief use is in an oscilloscope, is sometimes used as a null indicator.

6.1. VIBRATION GALVANOMETERS

If an alternating current is passed through a moving-coil instrument, or a moving-magnet galvanometer, no deflection is obtained because the moving parts do not have time to move an appreciable distance before the current reverses and they are forced back again. It will be remembered that for all ordinary a.c. measurements it was necessary to use an instrument whose direction of deflection was independent of the direction of current. A moving coil or moving magnet instrument could, however, be of some use if the moment of inertia of its moving parts was so low that it could follow the reversals of current.

Consider a moving mirror galvanometer with a very light movement. The spot of light on the scale would move to the left during one half cycle and to the right during the other half cycle. The effect of the persistence of vision would be such as to make this movement of the spot of light have the appearance of broadening out into a line. The length of this line would increase with the current and the amount of this increase would bear some relation to the amplitude of the current. Such a device could be used as an a.c. galvanometer if it could be made sufficiently sensitive. Exact proportionality between current and length of line would not matter for null indicator purposes. The necessary sensitivity is obtained by making use of the principle of resonance. The moving system of the galvanometer is tuned, by adjusting the tension of the supporting fibres, so that the natural frequency of mechanical vibration is the same as that of the current concerned – hence the name vibration galvanometer.

Not only will the amplitude of vibration be some indication of the strength of the current (a necessary feature in making rapid null measurements) but also it will have a large amount of frequency discrimination. This latter is a very useful feature. If a bridge is being used it is quite possible that it may be balanced at 250 Hz but by no means balanced for 750 (the third harmonic). The vibration galvanometer would only show the balance for the 250 if it was tuned to that frequency. This will be referred to again in Chapter 8.

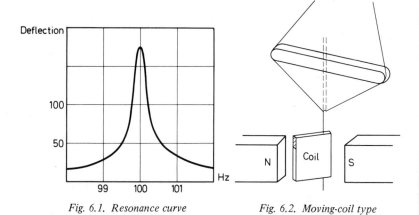

Fig. 6.1. Resonance curve
for vibration galvanometer

Fig. 6.2. Moving-coil type
vibration galvanometer

A typical resonance curve for a vibration galvanometer is shown in Fig. 6.1. One method of construction is shown in Fig. 6.2. Here a light coil with mirror is suspended by two threads. A bridge piece can be moved for tuning, or entirely taken out, when the position of the threads is as shown dotted.

The full mathematical treatment of vibration galvanometers is rather involved and beyond the scope of this book. The general idea, however, can easily be seen by referring back to Chapter 2, where equation (2.14) gives the general equation of motion and it is shown, by comparison with an electrical circuit, that the condition for critical damping is

$$\frac{\tau}{P} = \left(\frac{k^2}{R}\right)\frac{1}{4P^2}.$$

In the case of the vibration galvanometer the damping is required to be small in which (again by analogy with the electrical case) the natural period is given by

$$f = \frac{1}{2\pi}\sqrt{\frac{\tau}{P}}.$$

6.2. MOVING-COIL OSCILLOGRAPHS

It has already been mentioned that an oscillograph is a device for measuring instantaneous electrical values. It is the only way of observing what are commonly called transients, e.g. sudden discharges due to atmospherics or pulses of current in a radio receiver due to the striking of a drum or piano in the broadcasting studio. It is also the only satisfactory way of examining waveforms; this is of the greatest import-ance where audio frequencies are concerned. Thus the oscillograph is an instrument of the very highest importance to the electronic engineer.

Duddell developed a moving-coil galvanometer which would follow the instantaneous values of current. The principle is the exact opposite to that of the vibration galvanometer, in that the movement is detuned so as to prevent any swing due to natural period over the range of frequencies to be examined. The inertia is very low due to the natural period being made very high, and the movement is able to follow the changes of current in much the same way as does a moving-coil loud-speaker.

The galvanometer may be diagrammatically represented by Fig. 6.3. The single-turn loop is stretched over two ivory bridge pieces. The natural period can be altered either by tightening up the suspension as a whole, by means of a screw which pulls on the top spring, or by alter-ing the distance apart of the bridge pieces, also by a screw adjustment. The principle is exactly the same as that used in tuning a stringed musical instrument. A soft iron core is placed in the loop so that each part of the loop moves in its own air gap, as in an ordinary D'Arsonval instrument. The core has to be cut away for the mirror. The magnetic field is provided by permanent magnets or even by electromagnets where extreme sensitivity is required. In this case the magnet is worked beyond saturation, to ensure constancy of field strength. Damping is obtained by placing the whole moving system in oil.

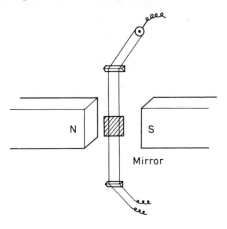

Fig. 6.3. Duddell oscillograph element

As might be expected, there is a frequency error. For example, as regards an instrument whose natural frequency is 1000 Hz the error at say 550 Hz is about 0·3%, assuming the reading at 50 Hz is correct. When the natural frequency is approached the instrument is much less satisfactory and it will not follow a wave of frequency higher than its natural period. Hence it is only of use at commercial and low audio frequencies.

The expected error in the Duddell instrument can easily be calculated, but it is hardly worth while investigating it, since the instrument has become virtually superseded at high frequencies by the cathode-ray oscilloscope. The U.V. recorder which is now widely used for low-frequency work is a development of the older Duddell oscillograph.

The galvanometer just described requires a 'time base'. The movement follows the variations of the current but the spot of light becomes a line as in the case of the vibration galvanometer. To reveal the actual wave shape it is necessary to provide a movement at right angles to that of the galvanometer mirror, i.e. vertical. The difficulty is overcome by providing a mirror which oscillates vertically. The beam of light impinges on the galvanometer mirror and is reflected across to the time base mirror where it is further reflected on to a screen. Fig. 6.4 shows the general scheme. The synchronous motor operates a cam which tilts the

mirror continuously for nearly two cycles. The mirror then returns
quickly to its initial position, under the action of a spring, ready to
repeat the movement exactly two cycles later. The synchronous motor
must be driven from the supply under examination then by virtue of
persistence of vision a 'standing wave' is seen on the screen. To avoid
confusing the image an opaque screen obstructs the light during the brief
return period.

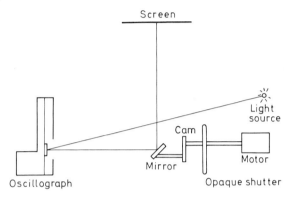

Fig. 6.4. Moving-coil oscillograph

The string or Einthoven galvanometer is perhaps deserving of mention.
In this instrument the 'moving coil' consists of a single filament of
silver-plated glass situated in a very narrow air-gap between the poles of
a powerful electromagnet. This filament is viewed by a microscope
which passes through one of the pole pieces. In this way a sensitivity
of several mm/μA at a scale distance of one metre can be obtained. It
is also possible to project a shadow of the filament onto a photographic
plate for obtaining a permanent record; even larger deflections can then
be obtained using the principle of an optical multiplier. The tension on
the string can be adjusted to suit the frequency under examination but
it is evident that only the lowest radio frequencies can be followed even
by so light a mechanical system as this.

The string galvanometer has been used for measuring atmospherics,
being placed directly in an aerial circuit. It is much more sensitive than
a cathode-ray tube, so can be used without an amplifier. This is an
advantage as no tuned circuits are employed and the waveform of the
transient is not smoothed out by low damping in the measuring
apparatus.

It has been suggested that a two-stringed galvanometer could be used
for comparing frequencies. One is excited from a 1000 Hz tuning fork

circuit and the other from a low radio frequency. The number of oscillations of the latter that occupy the same time as a number of the former can then be counted from a photographic record.

6.3. THE CATHODE-RAY OSCILLOSCOPE

The cathode-ray tube has been developed to a high degree of perfection, largely because of its application to radar and television. Tubes are now made with screens from about 2½ in dia. up to the large tubes used in television of diameter up to the order of 21 in.

The general principles of construction of an electrostatically focused and deflected cathode-ray tube are shown in Fig. 6.5. (The *actual* construction is partly shown in Fig. 6.8.)

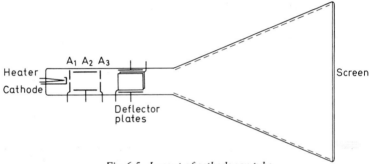

Fig. 6.5. Layout of cathode-ray tube

The source of electrons is a cathode consisting either of a filament of hairpin shape, the top of which is coated with barium and strontium oxides, or a small cup-shaped indirectly heated cathode activated by the same substances. The emitting source is made as small as possible. The electrons emitted from the cathode pass through a first disc accelerator A_1, a cylinder A_2, and a final disc A_3. The outer discs are maintained at a high positive potential and the cylinder at a lower value. A_1, A_2 and A_3 form an electron lens. The exact function of the lens will be described later in this chapter. The outer electrodes attract the electrons, giving them such a velocity that those, which happen to be in line with the centre holes, pass right through on to the end of the tube where they strike a fluorescent screen and produce a spot of light. The cylinder, being more negative, repels the electrons and tends to confine them to its axis.

The combined effect of these potentials is that a large proportion of the electrons form a narrow beam and pass through the hole in the final disc or anode. If the negative potential on the cylinder is reduced, the repelling action will also be reduced. Most of the electrons will then spread out and, missing the hole, will strike the anode. The cylinder can, therefore, be used to control the strength of the electron beam, and hence the brightness of the spot on the screen; for this reason it is usually known as the 'grid'.

Any residual traces of air in the tube will be ionised by the electron beam, and the positive ions will be attracted to the negative cathode and tend to damage it by bombardment. This can be overcome by the use of 'ion traps', i.e. small permanent magnets fitted to the neck of the tube in order to deflect the ions on to an internal graphite coating.

6.3.1. Focusing

For focusing, it is possible to employ a magnetic field parallel to the direction of the beam but in practice it is found difficult to obtain the uniform field required. Electrostatic focusing is now generally used.

The electrostatic fields are made of such a shape that the electrons converge onto a common axis. This is shown in Fig. 6.6 at 'a'. It is often

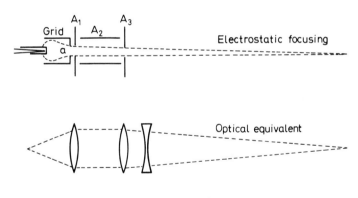

Fig. 6.6. Electron lens

assumed that the cylinder has no focusing action. In fact, its potential does control the direction of electrons passing to the accelerator but the behaviour of electrons passing through the accelerator is independent of grid potential; in effect then it only controls the intensity of the beam though it does so by a type of focusing action.

The simplest method of further focusing is to place a second disc anode some distance from the first and give it a potential of several thousand volts, the first having only a few hundred. The lines of electric force are more or less parallel between the plates but, near holes, they will be far from parallel. In fact there is 'edge effect' which, as is well known, makes the actual value of a parallel plate capacitor slightly different from the value calculated from the simple formula.

A more usual form of 'electron lens' consists of three electrodes, the first disc accelerator, a cylinder and a final disc. The outer discs are maintained at a high positive potential and the cylinder at a lower value. The precise theory of electron lenses involves rather complicated problems in electrostatics but an idea can be obtained by drawing the lines of force as shown in Fig. 6.7. A beam of electrons entering through A_1

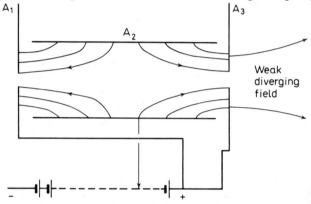

Fig. 6.7. Cathode-ray tube focusing action

will be deflected towards the axis, since the electrons are travelling against the lines of force. On approaching A_3 they will be further converged, since they are now travelling with the lines. On emerging from A_3 they will diverge slightly but as the field to the right of A_3 is comparatively weak the effect will not be nearly great enough to neutralise the converging effect.

It will be clear that the amount of convergence produced will depend upon the velocity of the electrons and upon the *relative* potentials of A_1, A_2 and A_3. The focus of the tube can therefore be controlled by the anode potentials.

The general principle of the electron lens can be seen by supposing the electron approaches an electrode with a velocity, v, at an angle, i, to the normal to the electrode. This velocity can be resolved into components $v \sin i$ parallel to the electrode and $v \cos i$ normal to it. Now, on passing the electrode, suppose the electron enters a region of higher potential, the force being parallel to the axis. The force on the electron is $e \, (\mathrm{d}E/\mathrm{d}s)$ where e is the charge on the electron and $\mathrm{d}E/\mathrm{d}s$ the potential gradient.

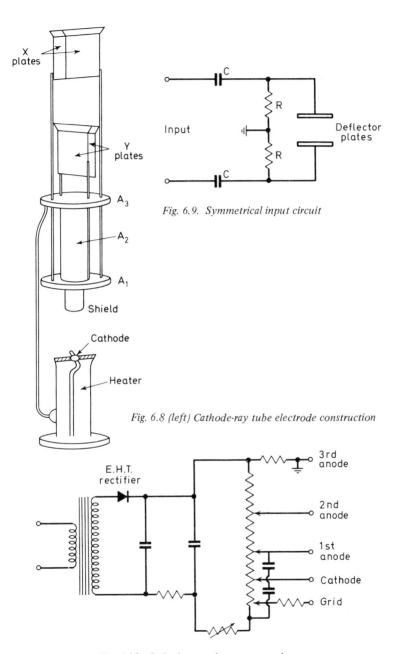

X plates

Y plates

A_3

A_2

A_1

Shield

Cathode

Heater

Fig. 6.8 (left) Cathode-ray tube electrode construction

Input

C

R

R

C

Deflector plates

Fig. 6.9. Symmetrical input circuit

E.H.T. rectifier

3rd anode

2nd anode

1st anode

Cathode

Grid

Fig. 6.10. Cathode-ray tube power supply

Then if m is the mass of the electron, $\dfrac{d(mv)}{dt} = e\dfrac{dE}{ds}$

or $dv = \dfrac{e}{m} \cdot \dfrac{dE}{ds} \, dt = \dfrac{e}{m} \cdot \dfrac{1}{v} \, dE$ whence $v \cdot dv = \dfrac{e}{m} \, dE$

On integrating and neglecting constants the change in velocity is

$$v_1 = \sqrt{2\dfrac{e}{m}E}$$

The velocity change is parallel to the axis. If the new velocity is v' and the angle i', then $v' \sin i' = v \sin i$ or $\dfrac{v'}{v} = \dfrac{\sin i}{\sin i'}$

Students of optics will recognise this as Snell's law of refraction. In other words an electron passing into a region of greater potential gradient behaves in a manner analogous to a ray of light passing into a denser medium, say from air into glass.

The refractive index in electron optics is rather difficult to derive in the general case but if the angles are small the ratio $\dfrac{v'}{v}$ is practically equal to $\dfrac{v' \cos i'}{v \cos i}$ and it has already been shown that the velocity is proportional to the square root of the potential. Hence, for small angles, the refractive index of the equipotential surface can be expressed as

$$n = \frac{v'}{v} = \frac{\sin i}{\sin i'} = \sqrt{\frac{E_1}{E_0}}$$

The comparatively small hole in the anode corresponds to the stop in a photographic lens. It ensures that only the middle part of the lens is used thus avoiding aberrations or distortions which occur when a wide aperture is used. One effect of such aberration is that a spot which appears circular at the middle part of the screen is seen to be elongated when deflected to the side. This is an extreme case but in general the smaller the stop the finer the focus that can be obtained.

The method of deflecting the beam is by a pair of plates known as X and Y plates (Fig. 6.8). Hard tubes do not suffer from origin distortion but they have certain other defects. If one of the pair of deflector plates is connected to the anode, the potential through which the beam passes, will vary for different parts of the signal wave. Consequently the focus will be impaired over part of the cycle. This is easily remedied by connecting the plates so that their potentials vary symmetrically on either side of the anode potential, as shown in Fig. 6.9. This difficulty, of course, does not arise with low voltages on the deflector plates.

Fig. 6.10 shows a typical supply unit for a cathode-ray tube and is self-explanatory. The final anode is earthed to reduce the pick-up of interference by the deflector plates.

6.3.2. Screens

The colours obtainable with cathode-ray tube screens are very numerous, depending upon the material used. For the nearly white images produced by television tubes the basic screen material is zinc sulphide and zinc-cadmium sulphide. For measurement purposes blue or green traces are usual while a screen rich in ultra-violet rays is an advantage for photographic work.

Some screens are of the long-persistence type, i.e. they continue to glow for several seconds after the signal has passed. This is useful when comparing transients such as atmospherics and in several radar applications.

In recent years, tubes with 'infinite persistence' or storage tubes have been developed. These are of two main kinds, namely, those in which the trace is maintained by continuously playing an electron beam on to the screen, and those in which the trace remains on the screen indefinitely even if the apparatus is switched off. It is of interest to mention that in an American oscilloscope used by the National Physical Laboratory employing this kind of tube a signal is put on the screen in the U.S.A. and is still there when the instrument arrives at the N.P.L.

6.3.3. Magnetic Deflection

With magnetic deflection a coil is used to produce a magnetic field at right angles to the axis of the tube. This field produces a deflection of the electron beam at right angles to the direction of the field.

The force on the beam is Bev where B is the magnetic flux density (assumed uniform), and e and v are the charge and velocity of the electrons. The acceleration 'a' is therefore given by $a = Bev/m$ where m is the mass of the electrons. The beam is acted upon for a time $t = l/v$, where l is the length of the field (Fig. 6.11a) and the deflection is thus

$$\tfrac{1}{2}at^2 = \tfrac{1}{2}(Bev/m)(l/v)^2.$$

At the screen this deflection is multiplied by the ratio $\dfrac{L}{l/2}$, so that the deflection is $(Bev/m)(Ll/v^2)$. But by applying the laws of mechanics the energy of an electron is $Ee = \tfrac{1}{2}mv^2$, where E is the accelerating anode voltage, so that $v^2 = 2Ee/m$, whence by substitution

$$\text{Deflection} = \frac{BLl}{\sqrt{2E}}\sqrt{\frac{e}{m}}$$

In SI units, B is in tesla, L and l in metres, E in volts, and e/m is 1.76×10^{11} coulombs/kilogramme.

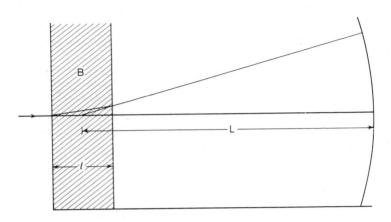

Fig. 6.11a. Magnetic deflection

The actual deflection produced by the coils is therefore dependent upon the length of the tube from the deflecting point to the screen, the length of the field, and the flux density, the latter being of course proportional to the energising current in the coils.

6.3.4. Electrostatic Deflection

It can easily be shown that when a charged particle in a cathode-ray tube is deflected by means of an electric field, the deflection is independent of the mass of the particle. In the analysis which follows, relativistic variations in mass and interaction of particles within the beam are assumed negligible and the initial velocity of electrons from the cathode is assumed zero.

Referring to Fig. 6.11*b*, let a stream of particles of mass *m* and charge *e* enter the electric field *E* between two parallel electrodes (the

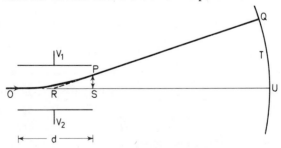

Fig. 6.11b. Electrostatic deflection

deflector plates) at potentials V_1 and V_2. Then the force acting on a particle at right angles to its direction of motion is eE, and this is its mass $\times$ acceleration.

Therefore $ma = eE$ or acceleration $a = \dfrac{e}{m}E$.

If the force remains constant until the particle leaves the electric field at time t, the particle will move a distance $SP = \frac{1}{2}at^2$ at right angles to its original direction.

Therefore the deflection $SP = \frac{1}{2}\dfrac{e}{m}Et^2$.

But the particle of mass m derived its original speed from the accelerating potential V between the cathode and the final anode. Thus its speed along the axis is $v = \sqrt{\dfrac{2Ve}{m}}$.

Now the deflection is small, and therefore if the length of the deflecting path is d, the particle will traverse d at speed v, whence the time it is between the plates $= t = \dfrac{d}{v}$ and $t^2 = \dfrac{d^2}{v^2} = \dfrac{d^2}{2Ve/m}$.

Hence the deflection $SP = \frac{1}{2}\dfrac{e}{m}Et^2 = \frac{1}{2}\dfrac{e}{m}E\dfrac{d^2}{2Ve/m} = \dfrac{Ed^2}{4V}$ \hfill (6.1)

This expression for SP does not contain m, showing that the deflection will be the same for all particles originating at the cathode, no matter what their charges and masses may be.

PQ is the path of the electron beam extended to where the beam impinges on the screen T. The actual screen deflection is UQ, and the deflection $SP = Ed^2/4V$. Producing the straight line QP to cut the axis OSU at R, the deflection at the screen $UQ = PS \times RU/RS$. Let $RU = D$, then $UQ = \dfrac{Ed^2 D}{4V(d/2)} = \dfrac{EdD}{2V}$

Hence the deflection is

(1) proportional to E, the electric field strength,
(2) proportional to d, the length of the deflector plates,
(3) proportional to D, the distance between the plates and the screen,
(4) inversely proportional to V, the final anode voltage.

Since $UQ = \dfrac{EdD}{2V}$, and assuming that $E = \dfrac{Vx}{b}$ where $Vx = (V_2 - V_1)$ is the voltage between the plates and b their distance apart, then $UQ = \dfrac{Vx \cdot d \cdot D}{2Vb}$. The *deflection sensitivity* of the cathode-ray tube is defined as

$$\frac{UQ}{Vx} = \frac{dD}{2Vb}$$

This is rarely greater than 0·4 mm/V for normal tubes.

The methods of using the cathode-ray oscilloscope are fully dealt with in Chapter 7. A vertical movement of the beam is obtained by applying the potentials under examination to one pair of deflector plates (usually the Y plates) while a horizontal deflection is obtained by applying potentials of known waveform to the other pair of plates. If desired the latter can be left unused and a moving strip of photographic film employed.

6.3.5. Other Types of Tubes

Von Ardenne brought out a cathode-ray tube that would give a 'curve' in polar co-ordinates instead of rectangular as just described. Two pairs of plates at right angles are given potentials $90°$ out of phase: this produces a circular motion of the spot. The diameter of the spot is then controlled by the voltage under test, which is applied to a cylindrical accelerator anode thus varying the electron velocity which, in turn, alters the sensitivity of the beam to subsequent deflection.

The principle of the tube is the same as the more usual type but, to avoid defocusing the actual structure is distinctly different, as shown in Fig. 6.12. The test potential is applied to a central 'core' electrode

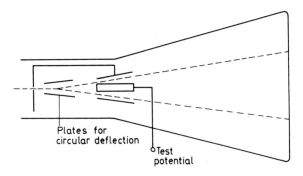

Fig. 6.12. Von Ardenne tube

round which the beam rotates. This tube has certain disadvantages for examining pulses of short duration which occur at long intervals, e.g. the synchronising pulses in television.

Another development is the double-beam tube. In the Cossor double-beam tube, an extra plate is situated between the first pair of deflector plates. This extra plate is at zero potential and splits the as yet wide beam into two. The next pair of plates – the X plates – deflect both beams equally. In this way it is possible to use one Y plate as a 'voltage' plate and the other as a 'current' plate and so obtain on one screen the waveforms of current and voltage, one above the other on the same time scale. A practical use of this tube is comparing the resonance curves of primary and secondary of the same i.f. transformer. These uses are referred to again in Chapter 13.

6.3.6. Sampling Oscilloscopes

Signals to be measured with an oscilloscope often require considerable amplification before they can be applied to the deflection systems of the c.r.t., since they are usually of the order of a few millivolts or at the most a few volts. For signals of frequency up to about 150 MHz this does not raise serious problems if distributed amplifiers are used, i.e. amplifiers so constructed that the active and passive components form a type of transmission line so as to minimise losses. However, if signals above 150 MHz have to be given sufficient noise-free amplification the difficulties are considerable.

In order to obviate the necessity of dealing with these higher frequencies in the amplifiers, the signal in the sampling oscilloscope is reduced in frequency at the input of the oscilloscope before it enters the amplifiers. After frequency reduction the signal can then be amplified in the normal manner (a similar technique is used in the superheterodyne receiver). In the sampling oscilloscope, the method of frequency reduction is based on the stroboscopic principle. By this means considerable improvement in bandwidth and sensitivity is achieved.

In the following description the bracketed letters refer to the waveforms shown in Fig. 6.13. The display of the signal at point 3 in Fig. 6.13 will be examined. The input signal (a) is first applied to a trigger take-off stage where 1/9 part is tapped off (b) and brought to a trigger isolation stage. The signal is then given a 35 ns delay in a delay line, (c) in order to allow sufficient time for the trigger pulse to start the time base generator. A trigger pulse (d) is derived from the triggering signal which may be either a part of the input signal (b) or an external signal. This pulse starts a fast ramp generator (e) whose output voltage is compared with a staircase voltage (f) in a voltage comparator stage. As soon as the amplitude of the fast ramp voltage equals the staircase voltage, the comparator produces a pulse which enters a pulse shaper. The shaped pulse resets the fast ramp generator to zero, and causes the staircase voltage to be increased by one step. The horizontal deflection is coupled to this staircase voltage. The magnitude of the steps of the staircase voltage can be set in such a way that either 10, 100 or 1000 steps are made for every centimetre of the display.

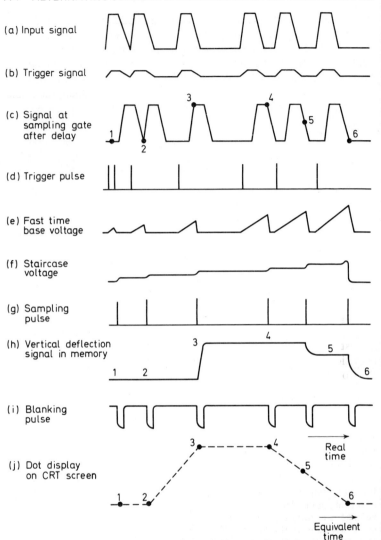

(a) Input signal

(b) Trigger signal

(c) Signal at sampling gate after delay

(d) Trigger pulse

(e) Fast time base voltage

(f) Staircase voltage

(g) Sampling pulse

(h) Vertical deflection signal in memory

(i) Blanking pulse

(j) Dot display on CRT screen

Fig. 6.13. Waveforms in a sampling oscilloscope

The pulse is also fed to the vertical amplifier, where it is transformed into a very steep sampling pulse in a sampling pulse generator (*g*). This sampling pulse opens the sampling gate at moment 3 (*c*). As already stated, the value of the signal amplitude at the moment that the gate is opened is stored in the memory (*h*). Simultaneously a blanking pulse (*i*) is generated which suppresses the electron beam in the cathode-ray tube during the transient. The memory voltage is applied to the vertical deflection plates after amplification in the main vertical amplifier.

Summarising, the display is obtained by making the vertical deflection proportional to the memory voltage and by coupling the horizontal deflection (the time axis) to the staircase voltage. In this way a time-stretched analogue of the input signal is obtained, the display on the cathode-ray tube being made up of a number of dots, called 'samples' (j).

The sampling oscilloscope made by Philips has a bandwidth from d.c. up to 1000 MHz. The above description is based on details of this oscilloscope given in Phillips Electronic Measuring and Microwave Notes 1967/1 by kind permission of Philips Ltd.

6.4. CONCLUSION

The cathode-ray oscilloscope has many advantages. Its moving system is inertia-less, so that it has no frequency error until the situation arises where the time of electron transit is considerable compared with that of a cycle. It cannot be damaged by overload since the spot merely goes off the screen, and it imposes no load on the circuit under test.

The cathode-ray tube is not without some disadvantages, however. Among these may be mentioned its cost, its bulkiness, the need for high operating voltages, and its fragility. Concerning the latter aspect, it must be mentioned that when the large tubes such as are used in television are fractured they implode due to their high vacuum. The electron gun may be shot through the screen of the imploding tube at high velocity and for this reason television sets are fitted with safety glass in front of the screen. Hence large cathode-ray tubes must be handled with care.

At the time of writing, much work is being done on a solid-state device that may eventually replace the cathode-ray tube. This is the electroluminescent panel, which consists of a mosaic of cells each of which emits light when an alternating current is passed through it. If this device can be made to have the same sensitivity and fineness of focus of the cathode-ray tube, then since it has none of the drawbacks mentioned in the last paragraph (except, most probably, that of cost!) it is possible that electroluminescent devices will become as widely used for display purposes as transistors are for low power applications which were formerly the exclusive domain of the thermionic valve. Further information on c.r.o. design and applications is given by Rider and Ulsan[1]

WORKED EXAMPLE

Question. In a cathode-ray tube a beam of electrons is accelerated through a potential difference V_1, before passing between a pair of parallel deflecting plates. The distance between the plates is s and the effective axial length of the plates is l. If a steady p.d. V_2 is maintained between the plates, derive an expression for the angular deflection of the electron beam. It may be assumed that the electric field between the plates is constant over the effective length. Hence calculate the angular deflection of an electron beam when V_1 = 3000 V, V_2 = 150 V, 1 = 60 mm and s = 20 mm.

(I.E.E. (Advanced Electrical Engineering) 1957)

Answer. Referring to Fig. 6.11, angular deflection θ is given by

$$\tan \theta = \frac{SP}{RS}$$

and from equation (6.1),

$$SP = \frac{Ed^2}{4V} = \frac{El^2}{4V_1}$$

using the symbols given in this question, where $E = V_2/s$ = field between plates.
Also $RS = 1/2$.

$$\therefore \ \tan \theta = \frac{lV_2}{2s \ V_1} = \frac{60 \times 150}{2 \times 20 \times 3000} = 0.075 \text{ whence } \underline{\theta = 4° 18'}.$$

EXERCISES

1. Describe one form of a.c. galvanometer and mention an advantage it has over headphones when used with a.c. bridges.

2. Describe the general principles of the cathode-ray oscilloscope. Mention two possible faults of operation (i.e. errors due to the design of the tube or circuit, not faulty adjustment) and state what methods have been used to overcome them.

3. Explain what is meant by an electron lens and show with the aid of diagrams how such a device works.

4. Obtain from first principles the equation for the deflection sensitivity of an electrostatically focused cathode-ray tube.

5. Repeat Question 4 for the case of a magnetically focused cathode-ray tube.

6. Discuss the advantages of the cathode-ray oscilloscope over electro-mechanical types.

REFERENCE

1. RIDER, JOHN F. and ULSAN, SEYMOUR D., *Encyclopaedia on Cathode-ray Oscilloscopes and their Uses.* (U.K.) Chapman and Hall Ltd. (1959).

CHAPTER 7

Use of the Cathode-Ray Oscilloscope

The principles and construction of the cathode-ray tube were described in Chapter 6. The present chapter covers the various uses of the cathode-ray tube. Cathode-ray oscilloscopes often have provision for various plug-in units for different types of measurement.

7.1. THE CATHODE-RAY TUBE AS VOLTMETER

As the deflection of the beam in a cathode-ray tube is proportional to the potential applied to the deflector plates (Chapter 6), the tube can be used as a voltmeter. If a fixed d.c. potential is applied to one pair of plates the spot will move to a position which can be definitely measured by providing the screen with a series of vertical and horizontal lines like graph paper. Manufacturers provide a ruled celluloid sheet or 'graticule' which fits into guides in front of the tube, for this purpose. However, it is undesirable to allow the spot to remain stationary on the screen, except at very low electron beam intensities, as a hole may be burnt in the screen. Moreover, the cathode-ray tube has no particular advantages for d.c. measurement except that it can be conveniently calibrated by a direct current.

If an alternating potential difference is applied to a pair of plates the spot will move in a straight line so that its distance from the undeflected position is at any instant proportional to the instantaneous voltage. Owing to the persistence of vision, further aided by the afterglow of the screen, the trace will be seen as a straight line of length equal to twice the peak value of the applied voltage. Thus peak values of voltage can be measured with no frequency error; however, for ordinary measurements, the c.r.t. has no particular advantages over a good electronic voltmeter (see Chapter 5). Since the tube sensitivity varies considerably with the operating voltages, calibration is essential. This can be quickly carried out by applying a 50-Hz potential which can be accurately measured.

While the cathode-ray tube has little application as an ordinary voltmeter, the principle is of value since, when it is used as an oscilloscope, the actual values can be obtained from the oscillogram by measuring the heights of the points concerned; the vertical movement being directly proportional to the applied p.d. quite independently of any time base applied to the X plates.

7.2. CATHODE-RAY TUBE AS NULL INDICATOR

The cathode-ray tube with an amplifier for the deflecting voltage has two main advantages over other instruments such as the vibration galvanometer for null indicating purposes. It is often the case that the oscillating voltage used to feed a measuring bridge has not as pure a waveform as could be desired. Also, stray voltages are easily picked up from other apparatus and power supplies in the laboratory, if the bridge components are not very well screened. The result is that the null point of the bridge is far from definite. Headphones therefore become difficult to use while an electronic voltmeter cannot distinguish between the frequency deliberately applied to the bridge and stray pick-up.

When a cathode-ray oscilloscope is used, its time base can be set to show a clear picture of the wanted frequency, so that the effects of all others can easily be ignored by the user. Thus, by this method a bridge can be balanced quite easily in spite of a large number of stray voltages.

7.3. MEASUREMENT OF PHASE ANGLE

The phase angle between two sinusoidal voltages may be determined by applying the two voltages respectively to the X and Y plates. The resulting figure is a special case of a Lissajous figure (Chapter 9), in which the frequency ratio is unity, and is an inclined ellipse in the general case (Fig. 7.1(a)). Limiting cases are an inclined line, when the voltages are in phase, and an ellipse with its axes vertical and horizontal, when the voltages are in quadrature. If the X and Y sensitivities are equal, the straight line will be at $45°$ to the horizontal for the in-phase case, and the figure for the quadrature case will be a circle.

For any other phase angle, measurement of the ellipse will yield a value of the phase angle. For this purpose the horizontal and vertical axes are required; these may be obtained by removing in turn the Y and X deflecting voltages. Let $v_1 = v_1 \sin \omega t$ be the voltage applied to the

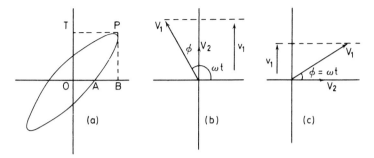

Fig. 7.1. Measurement of phase angle

X plates, and $v_2 = v_2 \sin(\omega t - \phi)$ be the Y voltage (i.e. lagging by ϕ). Then TP (Fig. 7.1(a)) represents the value of v_1 when v_2 is a maximum, i.e. $TP = S_x V_1 \cos \phi$ (Fig. 7.1(b)), where S_x is the sensitivity of the tube in the X direction. Now OB represents the maximum value of v_1, i.e. $OB = S_x V_1$.

Hence
$$\frac{TP}{OB} = \frac{S_x V_1 \cos \phi}{S_x V_1} = \cos \phi.$$

Thus the phase angle between the two voltages is obtained. If v_2 is the voltage drop across a non-inductive shunt carrying the current in a circuit and v_1 is the voltage applied to the circuit. TP/OB gives the circuit power factor directly.

The length of the tangent TP is not obtainable with great accuracy, and it is usually more accurate to obtain a value of $\sin \phi$. OA represents the value of v_1 at the instant when v_2 is zero, i.e.

$$OA = S_x V_1 \sin \phi \text{ (Fig. 7.1c)}$$

Hence
$$\frac{OA}{OB} = \frac{S_x V_1 \sin \phi}{S_x V_1} = \sin \phi \qquad (7.1)$$

It will be seen that the ellipse method of phase-angle determination is independent of the tube sensitivities; it is quite immaterial whether or not the X and Y sensitivities are equal.

7.4. IMPEDANCE MEASUREMENT

The phase ellipse may be used for the measurement of impedance. A known non-inductive resistance R is placed in series with the unknown impedance Z, as shown in Fig. 7.2. The peak values of V_1 and V_2 are obtained from the ellipse on the c.r.o. screen. Now the peak current

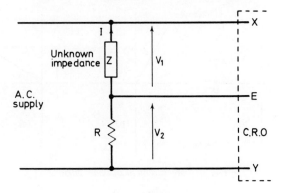

Fig. 7.2. Impedance measurement

$$I = \frac{V_2}{R} = \frac{V_1 + V_2}{R + Z} \qquad (7.2)$$

whence Z can be calculated.

Power can be measured in a similar manner. This is dealt with in Chapter 12.

7.5. TIME BASES

The Lissajous figure method of using an oscilloscope as described in Chapter 9 has its limitations because the figures can be very complicated and require interpreting. It is obviously preferable to employ a time base as mentioned in Chapter 6 in connection with the moving-coil oscillograph. The moving photographic film time base has much to recommend it, since it is a simple matter to construct mechanical devices that will produce an even movement to a very high degree of uniformity.

Moreover, for many applications the photographic record is required; this is especially so in the case of phenomena of short duration. Brief circuit transients, atmospherics and the echo signals used in measuring the height of the ionised layers can be studied in this way. The method is, however, limited to comparatively low frequencies, furthermore the requirement in most cases is for a single stationary figure the changes in which can be immediately observed by the user. Thus it would be absurd to use a photographic method when tuning the i.f. transformer of a radio receiver to obtain the required response curve. On the other hand, in measuring the height of an ionospheric layer, since the echo signals appear once only for each pulse, a permanent record is essential so that the analysis can be performed at leisure.

When studying atmospherics the photographic method is indispensable. It is sometimes desirable to combine both methods so as to obtain a record and yet avoid the risk of the spot being stationary on the screen.

The simplest form of time base is, of course, the sine wave, as discussed in Chapter 9 when dealing with Lissajous figures, but it can be modified so as to produce figures which are easier to study. If the amplitude of the X-sweep is increased so that only the central part of the wave is effective while the spot is on the screen, the time base will be nearly linear, i.e. the distance the spot is from the centre will be proportional to time.

Unfortunately there will be a return stroke of the wave $180°$ out of phase, so that a double curve will be traced out, but this can easily be overcome by arranging to bias the grid of the tube so as to cut off during this part of the wave. With a linear time base and the return sweep cut off, the spot moves across the screen in one direction linearly with respect to time. Any wave applied to the other plates will then be traced out in the same way as it would be drawn on a sheet of graph paper with a linear time scale as one coordinate and the amplitude of the wave as the other. Each cycle of the wave under examination will only occupy the same position on the screen if the frequency is an exact multiple of the timing wave.

The usual timing wave is of 'saw-tooth' form, which provides a truly linear sweep in one direction with a sudden 'fly-back'. The fly-back will of course produce a trace on the screen but, as the speed of travel is so much faster than in the forward direction, this trace will appear as a faint straight line and will cause little inconvenience. If desired, the fly-back trace can be completely blacked out using the method already mentioned for the case of a sine wave time base.

Saw-tooth time bases are produced by charging a capacitor slowly and then suddenly discharging it. An early form used a gas-filled triode or thyratron in parallel with the capacitor to discharge it. The capacitor C was charged from the h.t. supply through a resistance R. The equation of the charging process may be written in the form $V = V_m\left(1 - e^{\frac{-t}{CR}}\right)$, where V is the instantaneous voltage across C and V_m is the maximum value of V, i.e. the value of V when C is fully charged.

The discharge equation is then $V = V_m \; e^{\frac{-t}{CR}}$

Note that since 'e' represents the base of natural logarithms, both the charge and discharge equations are exponential in form. It is therefore undesirable (and theoretically impossible!) that C should be charged to the full h.t. voltage or discharged to zero. When C is charging, its potential rises until it is high enough to make the thyratron 'strike', i.e. its anode voltage reaches a value which draws sufficient electronic current from the cathode to ionise the gas, which is usually argon. The ionised gas forms a conductor of low resistance, thus discharging the capacitor down to a voltage at which the gas again becomes non-conducting.

As already stated, this simple time base is not very linear since the charging process follows a logarithmic law. This can be overcome by replacing R with a pentode valve, which has the property of passing a constant anode current. In this circuit (Fig. 7.3) the thyratron bias is

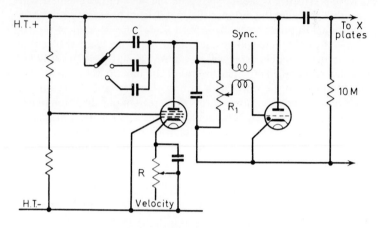

Fig. 7.3. Thyratron time base

used for amplitude control while the pentode grid bias controls the charging current and hence the frequency.

In order to avoid having to adjust the amplitude by altering the bias, which also affects the frequency, the output is sometimes fed to a push-pull amplifier of variable gain. This also facilitates the use of symmetrical deflection, as mentioned in the previous chapter.

7.6. HARD VALVE TIME BASES

Gas discharge valves have several disadvantages, the most important being the time lag due to the finite time required for the gas to become de-ionised and the fact that the whole circuit is sensitive to changes of temperature due to draughts, heating of other components in the oscilloscope, etc. These drawbacks are especially important at high frequencies, and to overcome them many circuits using hard valves throughout have been designed and patented. A number of time base circuits are described by Puckle[1].

Many hard-valve circuits use the principle of the squegging oscillator; an ordinary oscillator is tightly coupled and the grid leak is replaced by a pentode. The oscillations cause an accumulation of charge on the capacitor, which eventually stops the oscillation. The capacitor then discharges through the pentode. In these circuits the discharge is the forward part of the stroke and the charging by the oscillator is the fly-back. Very rapid fly-back is obtained with these circuits and they can work up to several megahertz.

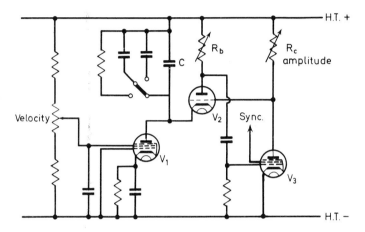

Fig. 7.4. Puckle time base

The circuit of the Puckle time base is shown in Fig. 7.4. The charging capacitor C is again in series with a pentode but the thyratron is replaced by a two-valve multivibrator circuit, the action of which will be dealt with in Chapter 9. The frequency is governed by the pentode bias as before, but it can be synchronised by a suitable potential applied to the valve V_3 so as to 'trigger' the discharge by stopping the anode current of V_3.

One modern form of time base is the transitron-Miller circuit shown in Fig. 7.5. This is basically a combination of two circuit arrangements. The sawtooth voltage is generated by the transitron, and the application of the 'Miller effect' permits the use of considerably smaller charging capacitances. The transitron circuit takes advantage of the fact that at particular values of voltage on the screen and suppressor grids of a pentode the screen-current/screen-voltage characteristic has a very steep *negative portion.* Thus the transitron characteristic is very similar to the dynatron characteristic of a tetrode.

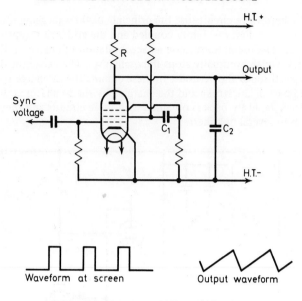

Fig. 7.5. Transistron-Miller time base

In the dynatron, however, the falling portion of the Va-Ia characteristic is due to the effect of secondary emission at the anode. As this does not occur evenly and in the standard makes of valve is not controlled and certainly not sought after, this circuit has fallen into disfavour. With a transitron, on the other hand, use is made of the current distribution between the suppressor and screen grid. Since this current distribution essentially depends only upon the geometric form of the grids and the voltages applied to them, no fundamental objection is raised against their use.

Referring to Fig. 7.5, the voltage for the suppressor grid appears automatically across the capacitor as a result of oscillation. If, as a starting point, C_2 is taken as discharged, then as the charge builds up through R the voltage rises until anode current begins to flow. Owing to the anode current, which is controlled by the screen and suppressor grids, C_2 will now discharge rapidly. This produces a sawtooth voltage at the anode and an asymmetrical rectangular voltage on the screen grid. A sawtooth voltage of the order of 30 V peak-to-peak can be taken off at the anode.

In principle, the charging capacitor with its resistor could be connected in the grid circuit. The discharge would then take place as grid current, and the voltage variation across the charging capacitor would then appear amplified at the anode. Thus, only a small variation in grid volts suffices to produce a fundamentally improved linearity and enables a still larger sawtooth voltage to be taken off at the anode, which must now be connected to the voltage source via a coupling resistor. It is large enough to deflect the beam in the cathode-ray tube without subsequent amplification.

If, however, the charging capacitor is connected between grid and anode instead of between grid and cathode, then for a rise in grid voltage of, say, 1 V, there will be a voltage drop at the anode of G volts, where G is the gain of this stage. A certain voltage variation between grid and cathode thus produces a $(1 + G)$ times greater variation of the voltage across capacitor C_2. For a given charging current to produce a certain voltage variation across the charging capacitor, only $1/(1 + G)$ times the capacitance needed it was connected between grid and cathode is now required.

This effect became known as the *Miller effect* at a time when the influence of the grid-anode capacitance of a triode was being investigated. It does not influence by itself the linearity of the voltage rise, as is sometimes assumed, but merely makes it possible to use considerably smaller capacitances to obtain a nevertheless satisfactory amplitude of voltage.

A circular time base can be produced simply by introducing a phase difference between the voltages applied to the two pairs of deflector plates, as shown in Fig. 7.6. The signal deflection can then be super-imposed either upon the Y or the X deflection, as in Fig. 7.7(a), in which case the trace at the ends becomes somewhat confused so that full advantage of the increased length is not obtained, or it can be

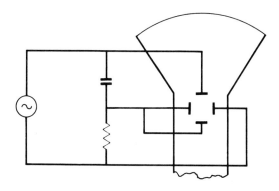

Fig. 7.6. Circular time base

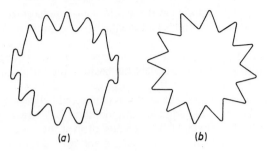

(a)   (b)

Fig. 7.7. Circular traces

injected in series with the final anode potential so as to produce a modulation of the deflection amplitude due to the time base voltages, giving a trace of the form shown at Fig. 7.7(*b*).

An alternative method is to apply the phase-differing potentials to the grids of two pairs of multi-electrode valves in push-pull used to provide push-pull deflection of the X and Y plates, while the signal potential is applied as a modulation on another of the grids of each of the four valves, all four of the signal control grids being connected in parallel. If, in addition to the signal voltage, a sawtooth potential is fed in series with it, the trace can be still further lengthened into a spiral, of the form shown in Fig. 7.8, without signal applied.

The circular time base enables the period of the trace to be lengthened without closing up certain parts of it by reducing its velocity, as is the case when the frequency of a linear time base is adjusted. Thus, circular time bases lengthen the actual trace so as to utilise the maximum amount of available screen space. Against the advantage of increased

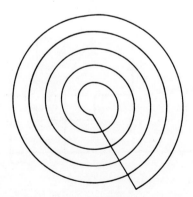

Fig. 7.8. Spiral trace

length of trace must be set the disadvantage, for many measurement applications, of lack of precision in determining actual time or amplitude indications over different parts of the screen. Also, it is obvious that it is not so easy to arrange synchronisation, where periodic signals are being examined, as with the simple sawtooth type time base.

7.7. EXPANDED TIME BASES

A time base is expanded when a part of it is spread out on the screen of the cathode-ray tube. When this is done, the speed of the electron beam is not constant for the duration of the sweep. Instead, the beam moves rapidly when the expansion occurs and more slowly at all other times. Occasionally, an expanded time base is produced in which the expansion is gradual so that the speed of the spot is constantly changing.

Expansion of the time base is useful for a number of reasons. It permits a waveform which occurs at a particular location along the time base to be examined more closely. This can be done without removing other signals which appear at different locations along the sweep. Also, an expanded time base is useful in certain radar displays. When very long sweeps are used, the scale on the indicator screen can become too large to measure range accurately. If a target signal can be placed in that part of the sweep which has been expanded, its characteristics and exact range can be determined more readily. Methods of expanding time bases are known in the U.K. as 'strobe' techniques.

7.8. SYNCHRONISATION

The most common signal used for synchronisation is the signal to be observed. The usual practice is to apply part of this signal to the time base in such a way that synchronisation results as described in the previous section, In this way, the sweep frequency is synchronised with the incoming signal frequency. This is known as *internal synchronisation* and the sync voltage is obtained from the vertical deflection amplifier.

It is sometimes desired to operate the time base at the frequency of the a.c. mains or a submultiple thereof. A low-amplitude voltage from a.c. mains input to the oscilloscope power supply is then used as the sync signal. When this is done, the saw-tooth generator frequency is accurately locked-in with that of the power source. This type of synchronisation, sometimes called 'line sync' is useful when the signals to be observed recur at the frequency of the a.c. mains or its harmonic.

When the nature of the signal to be observed is such that it will not synchronise the time base properly, some external source of sync signal must be used. Also, it is sometimes required that the time base be synchronised with some remotely located oscillator or other device. For example, in a television display it is necessary that the time bases used in the receiver operate at exactly the same frequency as is used in the original scanning process. To accomplish this, synchronising signals from the transmitter are used to control the operating frequency of the time bases in the receiver.

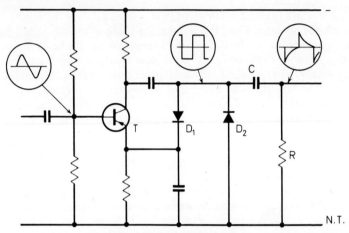

Fig. 7.9. Sync. pulse circuit

A typical synchronising circuit is shown in Fig. 7.9. The sinusoidal input is first amplified by T so as to make it more steep-sided. The top and bottom of this wave are then 'clipped' by diodes D_1 and D_2 to produce a square wave which is converted into positive and negative pulses by the differentiating circuit C and R. Since the sync pulses are normally required to be of only one polarity, a further diode clipper stage may follow the differentiating circuit to remove either the positive or the negative pulses. The waveforms at each point in the circuit are shown.

Some C.R.O. applications employing linear time bases will now be described.

7.9. MODULATION

If the output from a radio transmitter is applied to one pair of deflector plates and the other pair shorted, a line of a length proportional to the peak amplitude will appear on the screen. The screen can be easily calibrated in terms of the length of line for 100% modulation, when any over-modulation can be seen immediately.

If the other pair of plates are fed from a linear time base the actual waveform will be traced out. If a high-frequency time base is used, the waveform of the carrier can be examined; this can also be done using the Lissajous figure method, applying a pure sine wave of the same frequency to the other plates. If an audio-frequency time base is used the r.f. waves will not be seen but the modulation envelope will be visible. The timing frequency should be the same as that of the fundamental of the a.f. under examination. In the case of music this does not of course remain constant, but since the greater power is involved in the low notes the timing wave should be set to about 100 Hz, so that any overloading by low notes is easily seen.

For testing either receiving or transmitting radio apparatus, a pure sine wave should be applied and the output waveform examined by adjusting the time base until the waveform is stationary. Then any harmonics can be seen at once and both their order and amount noted.

In the trapezium method of examining amplitude-modulated waves, the modulating wave is applied to the X plates and the modulated wave to the Y plates. The sort of trace obtained is shown in Fig. 7.10. At 'a'

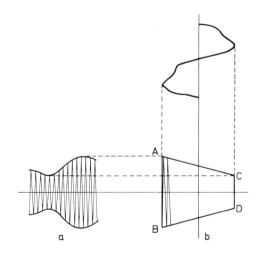

Fig. 7.10. Modulation measurement

is seen the trace obtained with a linear time base; in practice, of course, the r.f. waveform is seen as only a faint luminescence within the envelope. At 'b' is seen the figure obtained by applying the modulating voltage instead of a linear time base. If there is no distortion a perfect trapezium is formed. The modulation factor K is given by $\dfrac{m-n}{m+n}$ where $m\,(=AB)$ is the length of the largest vertical side of the trapezium and $n\,(=CD)$ is the length of the smallest side.

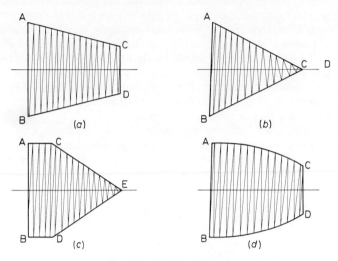

Fig. 7.11. Modulation patterns

Fig. 7.11 shows some traces obtained when distortion is present. The trace seen at (b) indicates 100% modulation, CD indicating that the r.f. amplitude remains zero for an appreciable fraction of the modulation cycle. The trace shown at (c) appears when the modulator is overloaded during the positive peaks of the modulating wave, i.e. between CD and AB; the modulation is distortionless over the part of each cycle of modulation represented by the triangle CDE. Trace (d) shows one effect of non-linear distortion. AC and BD may be unsymmetrical with respect to the zero line.

Using this method the waveform produced by a particular musical instrument can be observed, using a microphone with linear response.

The distortion produced by an a.f. amplifier or by an output transformer can also be examined. For observing the actual distortion produced, the linear time base method is preferable, whereas for merely detecting the presence of distortion, the Lissajous figure method is better. In this method, by adjusting the phase until a straight line trace is obtained, the slightest distortion is at once seen as a bending over of the ends of the line. For examining a complex waveform such as that of the human voice, the moving photographic film is obviously the best method to employ.

Filters or smoothing circuits can be examined in the same manner. For example, a d.c. voltage obtained by rectification of a.c. mains can be observed using a battery in opposition to compensate for the d.c. component. Some a.c. ripple will normally be observed and if the time base frequency is set to 50 Hz, it can be instantly determined whether the ripple is 50 Hz, 100 Hz or higher harmonics.

The method can also be applied to r.f. filters but a rather different technique is usually employed for this purpose.

7.10. CRYSTAL RESONATORS

The piezo-electric crystals used to maintain frequency stability in oscillators can be tested by feeding the crystal with a d.c. potential which is also applied to one pair of oscilloscope plates. The output from the valve (or transistor) to which the crystal is connected goes to the other pair of plates.

When resonance is obtained the ellipse shows a maximum. Any harmonic resonances are at once detected by the distortion of the ellipse.

7.11. RESPONSE CURVES

The behaviour of resonant circuits is usually illustrated by plotting the current or voltage against frequency. This can be done, for example, by measuring the voltage on an electronic voltmeter and compiling a table of readings for different frequency settings. This process is very laborious and its cost is prohibitive in mass production testing.

The response curve of any apparatus can be obtained on the cathode-ray tube instantly by applying to the input of the apparatus an oscillation whose frequency is being continually varied about a mean value in a definite way. The time base is then adjusted so that its cycle corresponds exactly with the cycle of frequency variation.

Special rotary capacitors driven by a synchronous motor may be used to vary the resonant frequency of a tuned circuit. A contact is fixed on the capacitor shaft so that, at a particular point in the cycle of frequency change caused by the rotating capacitor, the time-base circuit can be triggered. By this method it is possible to obtain curves of r.f. circuits under operating conditions, superheterodyne i.f. circuits including the associated valve or transistor, frequency response of a.f. amplifiers, impedance of loudspeakers with change of frequency, etc. In fact any electrical quantity can be instantaneously plotted against frequency.

The rather clumsy apparatus just described is rarely used in modern practice since an all-electronic device is available for the same purpose. This is the frequency-modulated oscillator or 'wobbulator' which is described in Chapter 9.

An alternative method, which has definite advantages as far as calibration of the results is concerned, is to obtain the horizontal deflection from a rectified output derived from the source frequency, after passing through an amplitude limiting or clipper stage followed by an integrating or differentiating network giving some known relation between frequency and output amplitude. The output from this stage is rectified and filtered by a circuit with known time constant, while the output from the apparatus under test is also rectified and filtered with an identical circuit. The position of the spot on the screen at any instant is an accurate representation of the frequency and amplitude response of the equipment being tested at some specified short time interval previous to the instant of observing the trace. If transient effects are being examined, the frequency may be slowly changed for comparison with faster rates of change. The trace should follow the same course with increasing as with decreasing frequency, and failure to do so will again indicate faulty transient response, in addition to the frequency response indicated on the screen.

7.12. DAMPED OSCILLATIONS

The cathode-ray tube can show the waveform of an oscillatory circuit which has been charged up by d.c. and allowed to oscillate. The recharging can be arranged to take place periodically and the timebase synchronised accordingly so that a continuous trace is obtained. From the resulting display, the logarithmic decrement and the natural frequency can easily be measured. If the capacitance is known the inductance and r.f. resistance can be obtained from the equations

$$\delta = \frac{R}{2fL} \text{ and } f = \frac{1}{2\pi} \sqrt{\frac{1}{LC} - \frac{R^2}{4L^2}}.$$

7.13. MAGNETIC MEASUREMENTS

It will now be shown how the oscilloscope can be used to display the hysteresis loop of a magnetic material. As the reader will be aware, this is a question of representing magnetic induction B as a function of the field strength H, i.e. the interdependence of two quantities is to be shown.

Provided that the iron core is sufficiently well closed (there must be no air gap), the field strength H can be taken as proportional to the number of ampere-turns. This means that the primary current can serve to represent the field strength. Two windings are arranged on the specimen core. A resistor R_s is connected in series with the primary winding and the voltage drop across it is used as the deflection voltage for the X plates, as indicated in Fig. 7.12.

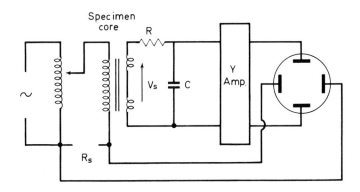

Fig. 7.12. C.R.O. display of hysteresis loop

The vertical deflection is to be proportional to the magnetic induction B. The secondary winding on the specimen core serves for this, the voltage on it being:

$$V_s = k \frac{dB}{dt}$$

where k is a constant. This voltage is electrically integrated by feeding it via a large resistor R (approx 2 megohms) to a capacitor C (approx 2 μF) in such a way that $R \gg \frac{1}{\omega C}$. The voltage on the capacitor is then:

$$V_c = k' \frac{B}{RC}.$$

Due to integration the amplitude of the voltage is small and must be amplified to produce satisfactory deflection.

The secondary winding is divided in two parts and arranged so that both ends lie outside and have approximately the same capacitance to the primary winding and to the core. Screening is provided between primary and secondary so that the secondary voltage is entirely due to magnetic induction.

7.14. NETWORK ANALYSER

Practically any characteristic of a component or network can be measured with this instrument, or rather set of instruments, one of which is the network analyser itself. The following data refer to the Hewlett Packard equipment, which can be used on frequencies from 110 MHz to 12·4 GHz. The reason for including this equipment in the present chapter is that the output is conveniently displayed on a cathode-ray tube, which displays amplitude and phase data in polar coordinates, Cartesian coordinates, or in the form of a Smith Chart. The reader requiring further details of the Smith Chart technique should consult the book by A. H. Morton[2]

The signal source is a frequency-swept oscillator feeding into a transmission test unit. The latter unit splits the r.f. input signal from the source into reference and test channels for connection directly to a converter for the reference channel and via the device under test for the test channel. The converter unit converts the two 0·11 and 12·4 GHz input signals into 20 MHz i.f. signals and feeds them to the network analyser unit itself. The latter unit includes tuning circuits, i.f. amplifiers, precision i.f. attenuator and provision for a plug-in module. This module may provide meter display of relative amplitude and phase between input signals or may include a c.r.t. display as described above.

An automatic version (Hewlett Packard Model 8540A) of the above equipment is available. The system is controlled by a small instrumentation computer with an 8192 word memory. In addition to controlling the measurement, the computer also operates on the data to calculate the desired read-out parameter and to calibrate out system errors. The computer programs the signal source to the desired test frequencies. The signal source r.f. output is introduced to the unknown through transducers which isolate the signals required to characterise the unknown. The complex ratio of these high-frequency signals is then measured by the r.f. and microwave network analyser unit. The magnitude ratio of the two signals, amd the phase angle between them, is fed to the computer through an analogue to digital converter. The computer receives instructions either from a teleprinter or tape reader, and provides data outputs on either a teleprinter, paper or magnetic tape, or a c.r.t.display. This equipment can measure 50 different network or component characteristics.

7.15. THE SPECTRUM ANALYSER

Spectrum analysis may be defined as the study of energy distribution across the frequency spectrum for a given electrical signal. From this

study comes valuable information about bandwidths, effects of various
types of modulation on oscillators and spurious signal generation
enabling engineers to design and test r.f. and pulse circuitry for
maximum efficiency.

A spectrum analyser is an instrument designed to graphically present
amplitude as a function of frequency in a portion of the spectrum. The
most common and best known approach to this incorporates a narrow
band superheterodyne receiver and all oscilloscope. The receiver is
electronically tuned in frequency by applying a sawtooth voltage to the
frequency control element of a voltage tuned local oscillator. The same
sawtooth voltage is simultaneously applied to the horizontal deflection
plates of the cathode-ray tube in the oscilloscope. The output signal
of the receiver is applied to the vertical deflection plates thus producing
a plot of signal amplitude versus frequency on the screen. A block
diagram of a basic analyser is shown in Fig. 7.13.

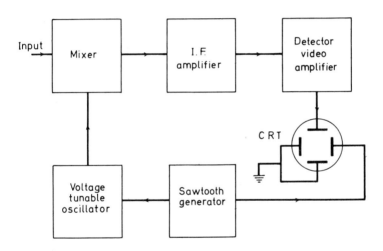

Fig. 7.13. Block diagram of spectrum analyser

The reception and display of a signal by the instrument is easily
explained. Referring to Fig. 7.13, an r.f. signal is applied to the input
of the mixer. As the local oscillator is swept through the band by the
sawtooth generator it will pass through a frequency that will beat with
the input signal producing the required i.f. This i.f. signal is then
amplified, detected, and applied to the vertical deflection plates of the
c.r.t. producing a plot of amplitude versus frequency. Frequencies
from 10 MHz to 40 GHz can be dealt with in this way.

The maximum sweep width of various oscillator types is reasonably well fixed by their inherent design. Klystron local oscillators have long been employed because they offer fundamental frequencies in the radar band and are capable of limited electronic sweep. Using a klystron local oscillator in the arrangement shown in Fig. 7.13, reflector voltage sweep will typically produce maximum spectrum widths of 50 to 80 MHz.

Typical modern applications of spectrum analysers include pulse radar performance checks, parametric amplifier tuning, varactor multiplier tuning, f.m. deviation measurement, radio frequency interference testing, and aerial pattern measurements.

7.16. MEASUREMENT OF TIME DELAY

Fig. 7.14 illustrates one effective technique which may be used to measure the time delay associated with networks such as filters. The signal generator should be modulated with a similar type of signal expected in practice for a band-pass or band-rejection filter. Generally no carrier is used for band-pass filter testing unless it is a characteristic of the normally applied signal. Signals applied to the input and output terminals of the filter under test should drive separate channels of a dual-channel oscilloscope. Impedance matching networks are connected in series with the filter terminals in order to simulate normal operating conditions.

Time delay is determined directly by comparison of leading edges and/or maximums or minimums of the two traces appearing on the oscilloscope. Polaroid or equivalent cameras may be used to photograph the resultant traces if a permanent record is desired. Note in Fig. 7.14 that if the oscilloscope input impedance Z is not much greater than R_g, the leads to the upper channel of the oscilloscope should be connected to the points XX.

WORKED EXAMPLE

A two-terminal network is connected in series with a non-reactive 5-kΩ resistor to an alternating voltage of sinusoidal wave-form. The voltage across the two-terminal network is applied between the two Y-plates of a cathode-ray oscillograph, and that across the 5-kΩ resistor between the two X-plates. The oscillograph has equal deflection sensitivities along the two axes.

The oscillogram is an ellipse contained within a rectangle 60 mm wide (i.e. in the X-direction) and 72 mm high (i.e. in the Y-direction), and the intercept made by the ellipse on the X-axis is 36 mm. Deduce the impedance and the power factor of the network at the supply frequency.   (B.Sc., Part II, 1949)

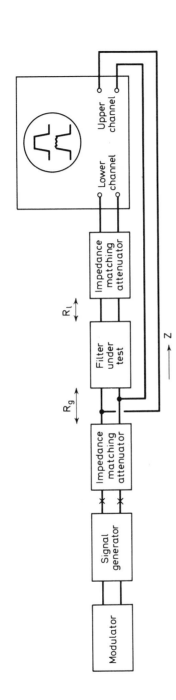

Fig. 7.14. Measurement of filter time delay

From equation (7.1) and Fig. 7.1(a), $\dfrac{OA}{OB}$ = sin ϕ whence

$\sin \phi = \dfrac{36}{60} = 0\cdot 6$. Thus $\phi = \sin^{-1} 0\cdot 6 = 36°52'$.

And power factor = cos ϕ = $\underline{0\cdot 8}$.

From equation (7.2),

$$I = \frac{V_2}{R} = \frac{V_1 + V_2}{R + Z} \text{ whence } \frac{SV_2}{R} = \frac{S(V_1 + V_2)}{R + Z}$$

where S is the deflection sensitivity for both pairs of plates.
Thus

$$\frac{60}{5000} = \frac{132}{5000 + Z} \quad \therefore \ 300\,000 + 60\,Z = 660\,000$$

$$\therefore \ Z = \frac{360\,000}{60} = \underline{6000\ \Omega}$$

EXERCISES

1. Discuss the use of the cathode-ray tube as (a) a voltmeter, (b) a null indicator. In the latter case, describe the advantages of the cathode-ray tube over other methods for this application.

2. Does a pentode, as a charging resistance, produce a perfectly linear time base? What steps can be taken to further improve linearity?

3. State the reason why synchronisation is applied to the time base of a cathode-ray oscilloscope. Sketch and describe a typical synchronising circuit.

4. Show how a cathode-ray oscilloscope can be used for the following applications:

(a) modulation measurements,
(b) response curve tracing,
(c) magnetic materials evaluation.

5. What are the advantages of a circular or spiral type time base? Explain why you think such types of time base are not more used.

REFERENCES

1. PUCKLE, O. S., *Time Bases.* Chapman and Hall Ltd. (1955).
2. MORTON, A. H., *Advanced Electrical Engineering.* Pitman. (1966).

CHAPTER 8

Alternating Current Null Methods

8.1. INTRODUCTION

In Chapter 1 the advantages of null methods for measuring direct-current quantities were considered, but so far their use for alternating-current work has not been described. The general principle holds good that, other things being equal, a null method is more accurate but requires more care to carry out.

Alternating current null methods are more troublesome than direct current ones due to the fact that phase angles as well as magnitudes enter into the problems. A lesser degree of accuracy than in the d.c. case is also to be expected since ultimately an a.c. has to be compared with a d.c. quantity because the standard definitions of units are based on direct currents and an 'alternating-current standard cell' is clearly an impossibility.

The need to balance phase angles as well as magnitudes can be shown in the following way. Suppose that there are two potential differences $E_m \sin \omega t$ and $E_m \sin(\omega t + \phi)$ and that one is being balanced against the other just as the e.m.f. of a cell is balanced against the p.d. along a length of potentiometer wire. The resultant e.m.f. applied to the galvanometer or other indicator will be

$$E_m \sin \omega t - E_m \sin(\omega t + \phi) = E_m \{\sin \omega t - \sin(\omega t + \phi)\}$$

The r.m.s. value, E, of this is found as follows:-

$$E^2 = \frac{E_m{}^2}{2\pi} \int_0^{2\pi} [\sin \omega t - \sin(\omega t + \phi)]^2 \, d.\, \omega t$$

$$= \frac{E_m{}^2}{2\pi} \int_0^{2\pi} [\sin^2 \omega t + \sin^2(\omega t + \phi) - 2 \sin \omega t . \sin(\omega t + \phi)] \, d.\, \omega t$$

$$= \frac{E_m{}^2}{2\pi} \int_0^{2\pi} \left[\frac{1 - \cos 2\omega t + 1 - \cos 2(\omega t + \phi)}{2} \right.$$

$$
-2\,\frac{\cos{(-\phi)}-\cos{(2\omega t+\phi)}}{2}\Bigg]d\,.\,\omega t
$$

$$
=\frac{E_m{}^2}{4\pi}\int_0^{2\pi}[2-\cos 2\omega t-\cos 2(\omega t+\phi)-2\cos\phi-2\cos{(2\omega t+\phi)}]\\ d\,.\,\omega t
$$

$$
=\frac{E_m{}^2}{4\pi}\Bigg[2\omega t-\tfrac{1}{2}\sin 2\omega t-\tfrac{1}{2}\sin 2(\omega t+\phi)-2\omega t\cos\phi-\sin\\ -\sin{(2\omega t+\phi)}\Bigg]_0^{2\pi}
$$

The average value of the second, third and fifth terms is zero; therefore

$$
E^2=\frac{E_m{}^2}{4\pi}\Bigg[2\omega t-2\omega t\cos\phi\Bigg]_0^{2\pi}=\frac{E_m{}^2}{4\pi}\Bigg[4\pi-4\pi\cos\phi\Bigg]=E_m{}^2\,(1-\cos\phi).
$$

This obviously cannot be zero unless $\cos\phi=1$, i.e. unless the voltages are in phase.

The practical applications of this fact are seen in any a.c. bridge, where it is necessary to balance the phase angles of the impedances as well as their magnitudes; in the a.c. potentiometer the fact is made use of in order to measure phase angles and magnitudes simultaneously.

8.2. A.C. POTENTIOMETERS

These instruments are a natural extension of the d.c. potentiometer and they are used for similar purposes, namely, calibration of instruments where great accuracy is required and the accurate measurement of potentials in circumstances where it is essential that no current shall be taken from the circuit under test. A few other uses will be mentioned later.

There are two main types of a.c. potentiometer: the polar type, which measures voltage in terms of a magnitude and a phase angle E/θ, and the co-ordinate type, which measures two components at right angles, i.e. it gives the voltage in the form $a+jb$.

The basic circuits of these two types are described below. Both types are now somewhat obsolete for practical purposes but serve to show the operating principles. Refined versions of the two instruments are still used in the laboratory.

8.2.1. Drysdale Potentiometer

The Drysdale potentiometer is shown in Fig. 8.1. The potentiometer itself is much the same as a d.c. instrument and is provided with a standard cell E and moving-coil galvanometer M in the usual way. There is, however, also in circuit a dynamometer milliammeter D whose

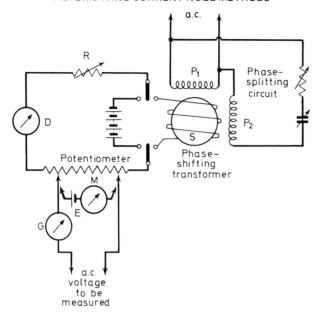

Fig. 8.1. Drysdale potentiometer

purpose is to show when the r.m.s. value of potentiometer current is exactly equal to the direct current that flows when the standard cell is connected. This can be done very accurately for no attempt is made to read the value of the current, but only to adjust rheostat R until the pointer coincides with a particular mark. This point is stressed so as not to give the impression that the advantage of a null measurement is lost by making it dependent upon a deflectional measurement.

The phase-shifting transformer consists of two primaries P_1 and P_2 which are geometrically at right angles and are fed with currents in exact phase quadrature, and a secondary S which can be rotated between the two primaries. The position of the secondary is thus a measure of the phase angle of its output but its magnitude does not vary with position.

In using the instrument the standard cell is first connected and the potentiometer calibrated with a known current flowing, as recorded by D. The switches are then thrown and the a.c. supply adjusted until the same current is obtained. The unknown voltage is then measured by setting the potentiometer sliders and the phase-shifting transformer so that the vibration galvanometer G gives no deflection. It requires a little practice to make both adjustments quickly.

8.2.2. Gall Potentiometer

The circuit is given in Fig. 8.2. This instrument consists of two exactly similar potentiometers. One is supplied with current in phase with the supply and the other is supplied with current in exact quadrature with that in the first. Each potentiometer is provided with a reversing

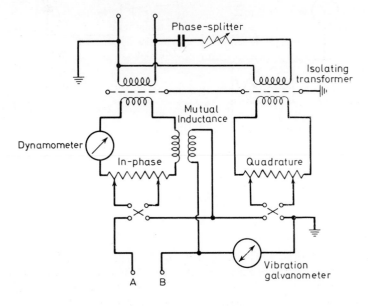

Fig. 8.2. Gall potentiometer

switch to deal with a voltage 180° out of phase, which corresponds to the cell being connected the wrong way round in a d.c. instrument.

To use the instrument, the in-phase potentiometer is balanced against the standard cell in the usual way and the torsion head of the dynamometer instrument turned until that instrument indicates zero. The d.c. supply is then replaced by the a.c. and the current adjusted until the dynamometer again reads exactly zero. Next the voltage-drop on the quadrature potentiometer is balanced against the e.m.f. induced in the mutual inductance shown. In this way the quadrature current is made exactly 90° out of phase, since the mutual inductance e.m.f. must be in exact quadrature.

The blank contacts *A* and *B* are brought out to a pair of terminals to which is connected the unknown voltage. Each potentiometer is then balanced for minimum.

The chief application of these instruments is the measurement of impedances with speed and accuracy. Instrument transformers can be tested by measuring the secondary voltage when the primary is supplied from the same source as the potentiometer. In this way not only can the output voltage be measured but also any phase shift. Iron losses can be measured, again by noting the magnitude of in-phase voltage across an inductance.

Attempts have been made to use this type of instrument at high frequencies, but since, in this case, it is standardised by a valve voltmeter its accuracy is not great. Moreover, a dynamometer instrument is of no use at high frequency. One further criticism of a.c. potentiometers is that the dynamometer instrument used in standardisation indicates the r.m.s. value of the current flowing, whereas the vibration galvanometer responds only to the fundamental component. Therefore, if the supply has any harmonics, standardisation is on an r.m.s. basis but the final balance is achieved on the fundamental only. Thus the a.c. potentiometer will never achieve the accuracy possible with the d.c. potentiometer.

8.3. A.C. BRIDGES

Alternating-current bridges, of which there are a great many types, are all based on the principle of the Wheatstone bridge, which has been dealt with in some detail in Chapter 3.

The general case is shown in Fig. 8.3. Headphones are shown as the balance indicator but a vibration galvanometer, 'magic eye' or cathode-ray tube may be used.

The equation of balance is clearly

$$\frac{Z_a}{Z_b} = \frac{Z_c}{Z_d}$$

The impedances are phasor quantities, thus it is evident that the above equation emphasises the need for phase balancing. In the simplest a.c. bridge Z_a and Z_b are pure resistances; Z_c and Z_d are then of the same kind, e.g. an unknown capacitor is compared with a standard capacitor, or an unknown inductor with a standard inductor. The phase balancing is done by means of a resistance which can be varied in value and put into either the Z_c or the Z_d arm as required. Fig. 8.4 shows such a bridge arranged for comparing inductors, say for testing smoothing chokes. This is one form of Maxwell bridge, another form which compares the unknown inductor with a standard capacitor and resistance will be described later. The procedure is as follows.

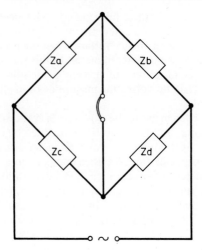

Fig. 8.3. General a.c. bridge

With the bridge, oscillator and headphones connected, the ratio arms and/or the standard inductor are varied until the minimum sound is heard. The resistance R_c is introduced into first the Z_c arm and then the Z_d arm and its value adjusted until even less sound is heard. The side in which R_c gives the best results must be found by trial. The original variable is then adjusted again until a perfect balance is obtained. The equations of balance are

$$L_x = \frac{R_a}{R_b} L_s \text{ and } R_x = \frac{R_a}{R_b} (R_s \pm R_c)$$

where L_s and R_s are the inductance and resistance of the standard.

When two capacitances are to be compared the procedure is the same. The standard capacitor may be variable or fixed; in the latter case all the balancing has to be done by the ratio arms. In the case of capacitances the value of R_c required is usually very small and at power frequencies may be negligible.

The balancing operation is much simpler if a variable standard capacitor or inductor is used because obviously any alteration of the ratio arms upsets the resistance balance, and thus the ratio arms and R_c have to be adjusted alternately a great number of times before perfect balance is obtained. If, however, the ratio arms are not varied after the initial setting, any change in R_c will not necessitate a change in L_s.

When working with any but the lowest frequencies trouble will be experienced due to earth currents. Some part of the source will have a capacitance to earth and so will the headphones via the wearer's head. Circulating currents will therefore be set up which are not removed at the point of balance required. False balances may then be obtained. The obvious solution is to earth one side of the headphones but this does not have the desired effect because the stray capacitances which are causing the trouble are then put across the bridge arms and will alter their effective ratio. The remedy is to use an artificial or Wagner earth, shown in Fig. 8.4 at W.E.

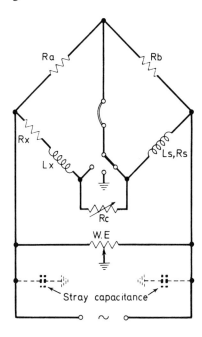

Fig. 8.4. Use of Wagner earth

To use the Wagner earth, the bridge is first balanced in the usual way then the headphones are earthed at one end, by means of the special switch contact shown, and the adjustment of W.E. made until no sound is heard. The bridge is then rebalanced. The need to obtain a resistance balance at the same time is actually an advantage, for it enables the a.c. resistance of a coil to be measured at the same time as its inductance. The resistance of the standard inductor is, of course, specified by the makers. The bridge may obviously be used to measure resistances at any frequency within its range and, by replacing the headphones by a moving-coil galvanometer, it can be used as a d.c. Wheatstone bridge.

The accuracy obtainable with an a.c. bridge of this type depends upon the accuracy of the standard, the purity of waveform of the supply and the stray inductance and capacitance of the wiring and the bridge arms. If the bridge possessed no reactances other than the intended ones its adjustment for balance would be independent of frequency, and therefore of waveform but, in practice, the correct setting of W.E. may be slightly different for different frequencies and the inductance and capacitance of the ratio arms may play a part. The extent of these effects depends upon the care with which the bridge is designed and constructed, and because of these effects a vibration galvanometer will give a more definite balance when the supply is not a pure sine wave. The bridge may be perfectly balanced at the fundamental but not at the harmonics, a situation which will render balancing by headphones difficult for unskilled operators and make magic-eye indicators liable to error.

The use of bridges at radio frequencies is not very common, for the stray reactances mentioned above then assume values comparable with the quantities being measured. However, r.f. bridges are made, and Fig. 8.5 indicates the manner in which screening is carried out. The aim

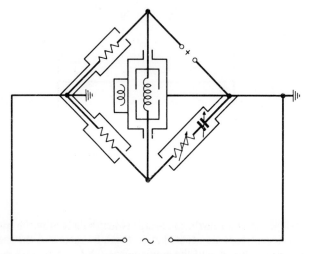

Fig. 8.5. R.F. bridge

is to make the bridge symmetrical so that the stray reactances balance themselves out as much as possible. Even the output transformer, leading to the indicator, must be specially designed to avoid throwing unbalanced capacitance across one of the arms. To obtain symmetry, the ratio arms are generally made exactly equal. For the detection of balance a rectifier is necessary; this can be provided by listening to the bridge with a radio receiver, which must be provided with a beat frequency oscillator if the supply to the bridge is unmodulated.

In radio frequency work, and for measuring small inductances at audio frequencies, the method of substitution is to be preferred. In this method the apparatus under test is replaced by a standard piece of apparatus of similar type. The practical application of the method may have to be modified somewhat, however. Suppose it is desired to measure a small capacitance by means of a bridge such as that shown in Fig. 8.6. A small capacitance is specified because it is here that the

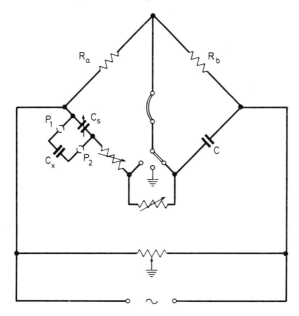

Fig. 8.6. Substitution method

stray bridge and wiring reactances will cause most trouble. In parallel with the capacitor under test a standard variable capacitor is connected and the bridge is balanced in the usual way. Then the capacitor under test is disconnected, say by removing the plugs P_1 and P_2 (which are as close to C_x as practicable so that the stray capacitances shall not be appreciably changed by the removal of the plugs) and the value of the standard is increased until balance is again obtained. The required increase in the standard variable capacitor is equal to the value of the unknown capacitor; the measurement is made *without altering any other part of the bridge.*

This last point accounts for the accuracy of the method, for any strays present when the first balance is obtained are still present when the second balance is made and hence have no effect on the result.

The resistance of the capacitor under test is determined by connecting a resistance in series with the X arm. Then, when the capacitor C_x is disconnected, this resistance is adjusted to compensate. If the resistor is carefully made the change of reactance caused by adjusting it will be quite negligible. The same principle is used for measuring inductances by the method of substitution. A sense of proportion is required when using these instruments.

In testing filter chokes or power transformers the ordinary method is quite satisfactory. For such work a standard inductor is used and balance obtained by means of the ratio arms. For testing coils for use in an oscillator and for tuning coils generally this method is not nearly accurate enough. In the last mentioned case, the main requirement is often that all coils shall be equal within close limits.

To test the degree of equality, a bridge can be set up and adjusted with a standard coil in the X arm, then the coils (or capacitors) to be tested are connected in place of the standard, and the amount of re-adjustment required is noted. If it exceeds a certain amount the component is rejected.

8.4. MUTUAL INDUCTANCE

There are several methods of measuring mutual inductance. The total inductance of two coils of inductances L_1 and L_2 can be measured by connecting them first in 'series aiding' and then in 'series opposing'. The mutual inductance M is then one-quarter of the difference between the total values L_a (series aiding) and L_o (series opposing) as can be seen from the following equations.

$$L_a = L_1 + L_2 + 2M$$
$$L_o = L_1 + L_2 - 2M$$
$$\text{whence} \quad M = \frac{L_a - L_o}{4}$$

Alternatively, the mutual inductance may be evaluated if the voltage induced in the 'secondary' by a 'primary' current of known frequency and magnitude is measured, since the magnitude of the induced voltage is equal to $\omega M I_p$. The mutual inductance between two windings of an auto-transformer (Fig. 8.7) is found by determining Z_{12} when terminals 3 and 4 are open-circuited, and repeating the measurement when they are short-circuited; finally the value of Z_{34} is found when terminals

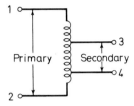

Fig. 8.7. Auto-transformer

1 and 2 are open-circuited. Let L_p, L_s, M be the primary, secondary and mutual inductances respectively. Let Z_{12}, Z_{12}', be the impedance between terminals 1 and 2 when the secondary is open or short-circuited. Then

$$Z_{12} = j\omega L_p \tag{8.1}$$

If I_p and I_s denote the primary and secondary currents when the applied voltage is E_p and the secondary is short-circuited, then assuming the primary and secondary resistances are negligible,

$$E_p = j\omega L_p I_p + j\omega M I_s \tag{8.2}$$

$$O = j\omega L_s I_s + j\omega M I_p \tag{8.3}$$

From (8.3)

$$I_s = \frac{-j\omega M I_p}{j\omega L_s} = \frac{-M I_p}{L_s}$$

Substituting for I_s in (8.2) gives:

$$E_p = j\omega L_p I_p - \frac{j\omega M^2 I_p}{L_s}$$

Therefore

$$\frac{E_p}{I_p} = j\omega L_p I_p - \frac{j\omega M^2}{L_s} = Z_{12}' \tag{8.4}$$

Also, when terminals 1 and 2 are open-circuited, the impedance measured between the secondary terminals is given by

$$Z_{34} = j\omega L_s \tag{8.5}$$

Substituting equations (8.1) and (8.5) in (8.4) gives

$$Z_{12} - \frac{\frac{j\omega M^2}{Z_{34}}}{j\omega} = Z_{12}' \text{ whence } Z_{12}' - Z_{12} = \frac{\omega^2 M^2}{Z_{34}}$$

Therefore

$$M = \sqrt{\frac{(Z_{12}' - Z_{12})Z_{34}}{\omega}}$$

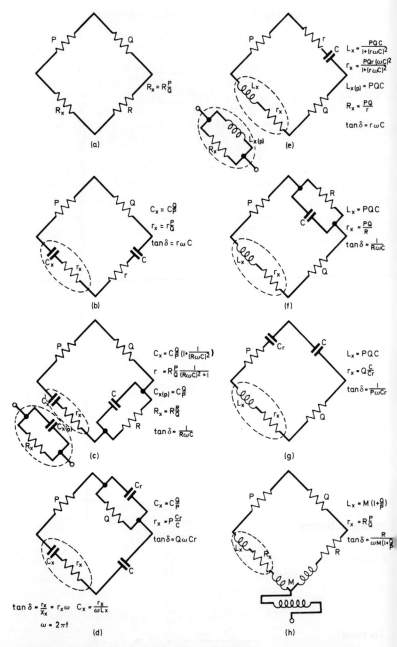

Fig. 8.8. Bridge circuits (a) Wheatstone; (b) De Sauty (with series resistance); (c) Wien; (d) Schering; (e) Hay; (f) Maxwell; (g) Owen; (h) Heaviside-Campbell (mutual inductometer)

8.5. SPECIAL TYPES OF BRIDGE

So far only the simple and obvious development of the d.c. Wheatstone bridge shown in Fig. 8.8 (*a*) has been considered. There are, however, a great many special types of a.c. bridge which have been evolved from time to time to facilitate particular measurements. Only a few of these can be mentioned here: the circuits of the best-known types are shown in Fig. 8.8. In many of them balance is *directly* dependent upon frequency: in the bridge previously considered the frequency effect was due to stray reactances and was not a deliberate part of the design. Fig. 8.8 (*b*) shows a capacitor version of the De Sauty bridge shown in Fig. 8.4.

8.5.1. Wien Bridge

The balance conditions for the Wien bridge circuit shown in Fig. 8.8 (*c*) are found by equating the real and imaginary parts of the general equation for balance, namely $Z_a Z_d = Z_b Z_c$, where in this case

$$Z_a = P \quad Z_b = Q \quad Z_c = r_x - \frac{j}{\omega C_x} \quad Z_d = \frac{\dfrac{-jR}{\omega C}}{R - \dfrac{j}{\omega C}}$$

$$\therefore Q\left(r_x - \frac{j}{\omega C_x}\right) = P \frac{\dfrac{-jR}{\omega C}}{R - \dfrac{j}{\omega C}}$$

$$\therefore Q\left(r_x - \frac{j}{\omega C_x}\right)\left(R - \frac{j}{\omega C}\right) = -\frac{j}{\omega C} RP$$

$$\therefore Q r_x R - \frac{j}{\omega C_x} QR - \frac{j}{\omega C} Q r_x - \frac{1}{\omega^2 C_x C} Q = -\frac{j}{\omega C} RP$$

Equating real parts gives

$$r_x R - \frac{1}{\omega^2 C_x C} = 0 \text{ or } r_x = \frac{1}{\omega^2 C_x C R} \tag{8.6}$$

Equating imaginary parts gives

$$\frac{1}{C_x} QR + \frac{1}{C} Q r_x = \frac{1}{C} RP \quad \therefore \frac{1}{C}\left(Q r_x - RP\right) = -\frac{1}{C_x} QR$$

$$\therefore C = \frac{(RP - Q r_x) C_x}{QR} \quad \therefore C_x = \frac{C}{\left(\dfrac{P}{Q} - \dfrac{r_x}{R}\right)}$$

Substituting for r_x from equation (8.6),

$$C_x = \frac{C}{\left(\dfrac{P}{Q} - \dfrac{1}{\omega^2 R^2 C_x C}\right)} \qquad \therefore \quad C_x \frac{P}{Q} - \frac{1}{\omega^2 R^2 C} = C$$

$$\therefore \quad C_x = \left(C + \frac{1}{\omega^2 R^2 C}\right)\frac{Q}{P} = C\frac{Q}{P}\left(1 + \frac{1}{\omega^2 C^2 R^2}\right)$$

Substituting for C_x in equation (8.6),

$$r_x = \frac{1}{\omega^2 CR \cdot \dfrac{Q}{P}\left(1 + \dfrac{1}{\omega^2 C^2 R^2}\right)} = \frac{\omega^2 C^2 R^2}{C^2 R \dfrac{Q}{P}\left(1 + \omega^2 C^2 R^2\right)} = R\frac{P}{Q}\left(\frac{1}{1 + \omega^2 C^2 R^2}\right)$$

Also, from equation (8.6),

$$\omega^2 = \frac{1}{C_x C r_x R}$$

This bridge may be used for measuring audio frequencies in terms of resistance and capacitance. For the most accurate results the four quantities should be of the same order of magnitude. The bridge can also be used for the accurate measurement of capacitance. In this case the resistances and the supply frequency must be known. Both of these can be determined to a high order of accuracy, hence the value of the bridge for capacitance measurement. It will be seen that r_x (or R_x in the parallel case) might be due to the leakage in the capacitor being tested.

8.5.2. Schering Bridge

The circuit diagram is shown in Fig. 8.8 (d). The conditions for balance give:

$$C_x = \frac{Q}{P} C \quad \text{and} \quad r_x = \frac{C_r}{C} P.$$

This bridge is very useful for measuring valve inter-electrode capacitances. This is because the capacitances between the electrodes other than the pair being measured are arranged to be in the position of C_r, or across the detector, where they do not affect the capacitance balance. For example, to measure the grid-anode capacitance of a triode the anode is connected to the junction of C and r_x, the grid to the junction of C and the parallel combination of Q and C_r, and the cathode to the junction of this parallel combination and P. In this way the detector and supply are so arranged that the cathode and one side of the detector are earthed. This bridge is also very suitable for measurement of the capacitance and leakage of electrolytic capacitors; Q would then represent the leakage and C_r the capacitor under test.

8.5.3. Hay Bridge

Fig. 8.3 (e) shows the circuit diagram and the conditions for balance are as follows:

$$L_x = \frac{PQC}{1 + (r\omega C)^2}$$

$$r_x = \frac{PQr(\omega C)^2}{1 + (r\omega C)^2}$$

$$\tan \delta = r_x/\omega L_x = r\omega C$$

This bridge is useful for measuring what is called incremental inductance, i.e. the inductance of a choke with respect to a.c. when its is also carrying a d.c. component. Resistors r and Q are adjusted for balance and, in practice, r_x can usually be neglected in comparison with L_x and hence r is small and the equation for L_x can be simplified to

$$L_x = PQC \text{ (approximately)}.$$

Of course, provision for sending a direct current through L_x must be made. The only satisfactory way to do this is to feed it in series with the detector arm. The actual detector must therefore be fed by a choke-capacitor filter. Usually no great accuracy is required for these tests but reasonable speed in carrying them out is essential.

A similar problem is involved in testing electrolytic capacitors but as the polarising current is small it can usually be provided by a battery in series with the detector; a microammeter in series with this arm will indicate the leakage current. The type of bridge used is the Schering type shown in Fig. 8.8 (d).

8.5.4. Maxwell Bridge

This is used for inductance measurement and testing magnetic materials, and the basic circuit is shown in Fig. 8.8 (f). If it is assumed that the losses in the inductor may be represented by a series resistance, which is usually the most convenient assumption, then the condition for balance may be found by applying the equation $Z_a Z_d = Z_b Z_c$, whence

$$\left(\frac{1}{\frac{1}{R} + j\omega C}\right)(r_x + j\omega L_x) = PQ.$$

Cross multiplication gives

$$R(r_x + j\omega L_x) = PQ(1 + j\omega CR)$$

Equating real parts:

$$Rr_x = PQ, \text{ or } r_x = \frac{PQ}{R}$$

Equating imaginary parts:

$$L_x = PQC.$$

$$\tan \delta = r_x/\omega L_x = \frac{1}{R\omega C}$$

Thus it is seen that, provided all values are constant with frequency, the result is independent of frequency, which is not true of the solution for the Hay bridge. As stated earlier, the Maxwell bridge is widely applicable for inductance measurement, and also for the testing of magnetic materials, where the sample to be tested is used as a core piece to a standard coil. A further refinement can be added which, in addition to giving information concerning the iron losses, will also give information concerning the shape of its magnetisation curve as it affects harmonic generation at various flux densities. This refinement can be added by measuring the amplitude of residual signal at balance across the bridge in relation to the a.c. in the test arm. In this circuit, it is essential that the impedance of arms Z_a and Z_c should be small compared to Z_b and Z_d respectively, so that the voltage across the sample coil shall be sensibly sinusoidal when the current through it departs from sinusoidal.

8.5.5. Owen Bridge

The circuit is shown in Fig. 8.8 (g). The conditions of balance are:

$$L_x = PQC, \quad r_x = Q\frac{C}{C_r} \text{ and } \tan \delta = \frac{1}{P\omega C_r}$$

This bridge may be considered as a modification of an ideal Maxwell bridge, as will be shown later.

8.5.6. Heaviside-Campbell (Mutual Inductometer) Bridge

The Campbell standard mutual inductometer, made by the Cambridge Instrument Co., is a high-precision instrument and is provided with facilities enabling it to be used for measuring mutual inductance, self-inductance from fractions of 1 μH to thousands of henrys, with superimposed d.c. if necessary, and capacitance over a wide range. In the Heaviside-Campbell bridge shown in Fig. 8.8 (h) the ratio resistances P and Q are equal, and this is preferred for high accuracy.

The inductometer fixed coils are connected in the other two arms, and having equal self-inductance they balance. L_x is balanced by mutual inductance M, injected by adjusting the moving coil, which is in series with the source. Up to rather more than an ohm, the r_x balancer R is provided in the inductometer by a slide wire at the junction of the coils, so additional R, where shown, need not be varied in smaller steps. Coils are provided for ratios of $10:1$ and $100:1$, and to suit these P and Q should include the values 10, 90, and 990 Ω. With unequal ratios the slide wire is out of action and the external R must be continuously variable.

8.5.7. Derivation of Owen from Maxwell Bridge

A disadvantage with the Maxwell bridge for wide range application is the almost unlimited range of values that P must have to accommodate varying combinations of Q and L_x. The Owen bridge overcomes this difficulty by a modification based upon an ideal Maxwell bridge. Considering a Maxwell bridge in which arms Z_a and Z_d are purely reactive, Z_a being capacitance and Z_d being inductance, then balance will be obtained for the single condition $L_x = P\dot{Q}\dot{C}$, Fig. 8.9 (a), since

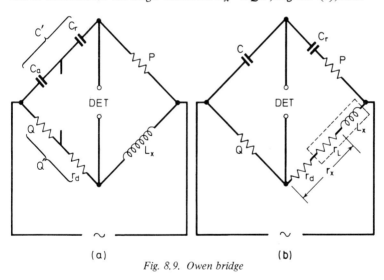

(a)   (b)

Fig. 8.9. Owen bridge

R and r_x are absent, one being infinity and the other zero. If now the impedance arms Z_a and Z_c are tapped a fraction along, equal in each case, then balance will be equally correct if the detector arm is connected across these tapping points. Fig. 8.9 (*a*) and (*b*) illustrate this point. From this treatment the conditions for balance for the Owen bridge of Fig. 8.9 (*b*) may be deduced as $r_x = QC/C_r$ and $L_x = PQC$, as before. Note that r_x can be made up of the inductance losses r_L and a calibrated resistance forming part of the instrument, r_d, so that $r_x = r_L + r_d$, whence,

$$r_L = \left(\frac{QC}{C_r}\right) - r_d.$$

This method requires a far smaller range of r_d than for R in the Maxwell type bridge of Fig. 8.8 (*f*).

8.5.8. Anderson's Bridge

This modification of Maxwell's bridge enables the double balance to be obtained by the variation of resistances only, the standard capacitance being of a fixed value. The modification consists in connecting a non-inductive resistance r in series with the capacitor, this combination being in parallel across S, as shown in Fig. 8.10. The method is used for

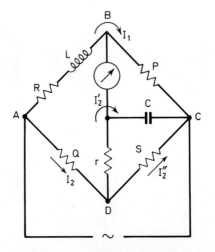

Fig. 8.10. Anderson's bridge

the precise measurement of inductances over a wide range of values, and is one of the commonest and best bridge methods.

Referring to Fig. 8.10, at balance there is no potential difference across the indicator. Thus

$$I_1(R + j\omega L) = I_2 Q + I_2' r \tag{8.7}$$

$$I_1 P = \frac{-I_2' j}{\omega C} \tag{8.8}$$

$$I_2'' S = I_2'\left(r - \frac{1}{\omega C}\right) \tag{8.9}$$

Also $$I_2 = I_2' + I_2'' \tag{8.10}$$

Substituting for I_2 from (8.10) into (8.7) gives

$$I_1(R + j\omega L) = I_2'(Q + r) + I_2'' Q \tag{8.11}$$

Substituting for I_2'' from (8.9) into (8.11) gives

$$I_1(R + j\omega L) = I_2'\left(Q + r + Q\frac{r - \dfrac{j}{\omega C}}{S}\right)$$

Substituting for I_2' from (8.8) gives

$$I_1(R + j\omega L) = -\left(Q + r + Q\frac{r - \dfrac{j}{\omega C}}{S}\right)\frac{P\omega C}{j} I_1$$

Therefore cancelling I_1 and multiplying by j gives

$$jR - \omega L = -\left(PQ\omega C + rP\omega C + \frac{PQr\omega C}{S} - \frac{jPQ}{S}\right)$$

Equating real and imaginary parts:

$$R = \frac{PQ}{S}$$

$$L = CP\left(Q + r + \frac{Qr}{S}\right)$$

These are the equations of balance.

8.5.9. Transformer Turns Ratio Bridge

In a transformer, the fluxes due to primary and secondary currents balance, except for the magnetising flux of the core, which takes a magnetising current from the primary. If primary and secondary are simultaneously provided with magnetising currents whose net magnetising effect upon the core is zero, then the ratio of the currents will give inversely the ratio of turns. Provided the magnetising effect upon the core is exactly zero, there will be no reactive component, and the bridge can be balanced with purely resistive components. A difficulty arises if the turns do not have proportionate resistance values so that the volt drop due to resistance in the winding is equal to the voltage

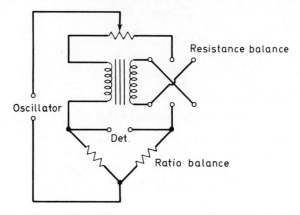

Fig. 8.11. Transformer turns ratio bridge

ratio in the transformer. This can be provided for by resistance equalisation in the arms of the bridge composed by the transformer windings. The circuit is shown in Fig. 8.11.

8.5.10. Transformers for A.C. Bridges

Earlier in this chapter it was shown that special care is necessary in the design of transformers for use with bridges, in order to throw no unknown impedances in parallel with any of the bridge arms. By the very nature of a bridge circuit, both the input and the output can neither have one side earthy nor be regarded as balanced. Either one or the other may be made to satisfy one or other of these conditions, for

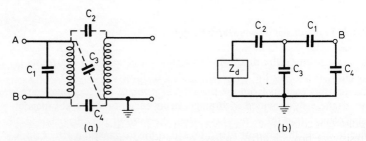

Fig. 8.12. Self-capacitances of unscreened transformer

the sake of stability, but the other must be completely isolated from any reference to earth potential if the bridge reading is to be true. Fig. 8.12 (*a*) shows a normal unscreened transformer, while (*b*) shows a theoretical equivalent. If *A* and *B* are the output terminals of a bridge, then the self-capacitance C_1 is in shunt with the detector arm, and does not affect the bridge measurement directly, but the capacitances C_2, C_3 and C_4 each contribute toward a complex impedance to earth, and so will appear in parallel with two of the bridge arms. If only one side had a direct capacitance to earth of known value, then this could be arranged to be in parallel with an arm of the bridge which already contains capacitance, and so form part of the calibrated capacitance.

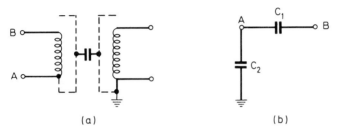

(a)   (b)

Fig. 8.13. Self-capacitances of screened transformer

Fig. 8.13 shows a method of doing this in a theoretical circuit. The self-capacitance C_1 between the input winding and its own screen forms part of the shunt capacitance across the detector while the capacitance C_2 between screens is associated with one side of the input winding so as to be a simple capacitance to earth from that side only. It is, of course, desirable that this latter capacitance should be as low as possible, and not subject to variations with temperature.

8.5.11. Thermal Comparator Method

This method is used for the measurement of the magnitudes of currents or voltages and utilises the null deflection in conjunction with a d.c. potentiometer. Very good accuracy is achieved up to at least 20 kHz. The instrument uses a special type of thermocouple known as a thermal converter. Two instruments used by the National Bureau of Standards in the U.S.A. are described below[1]

The model A voltmeter, Fig. 8.14 (*a*), consists of a 30-mA thermal converter connected with its heater in series with a commercial decade resistance box, modified to have two 1000-ohm-per-step decades, and a 100, a 10 and a 1-ohm-per-step decade, all in series. As shown in the

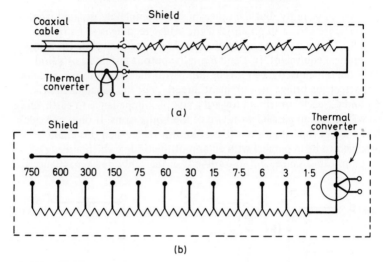

Fig. 8.14. N.B.S. voltmeter elements (a) Model A; (b) Model B

diagram, one end of the heater of the thermal converter is connected to the low-potential terminal of the case, with the shield of the case connected to the other end of the heater and to the screen of the coaxial cable connecting the instrument to the circuit. The centre lead of this cable is connected directly to the high-potential terminal of the case. Like the electrodynamic transfer standards used at lower frequencies, the series resistor is adjusted in use to give the same nominal current level for each measured voltage. This was chosen as 20 mA, resulting in a voltmeter having a constant 50 ohms-per-volt and an upper range of 400 V.

For the model B voltmeter, Fig. 8.14 (b), a built-in 7·5 mA thermal converter is used, with a fixed resistor having taps to give voltage ranges of 1·5, 3, 6, 7·5, 15, 30, 60, 75, 150, 300, 600, and 750 V. The resistances and thermal converter are mounted in a suitable shielded case with the shield connected to the low-potential terminal of the instrument, as shown in the diagram.

For both instruments the effects of capacitance currents and of the self-inductance of the resistors were carefully considered.

For an a.c. test of an ammeter, for example, the transfer thermo-element is connected to a reversible a.c./d.c. supply and its thermocouple to a d.c. potentiometer. The instrument under test is connected to the same a.c. supply, and a suitable four-terminal standard resistor is connected in series with the d.c. supply for use in measuring the d.c. current by means of another potentiometer. The a.c. is adjusted for the desired deflection of the test instrument, and the potentiometer is adjusted for an 'on-scale' deflection of the galvanometer. The standard instrument is then switched to d.c., which is adjusted to give the same galvanometer deflection and is then measured with the other potentiometer. The d.c. through the heater of the thermo-element is then reversed and the d.c. measurement repeated.

8.5.12. Admittance Bridges

Special types of bridge are available for measurement at very high frequencies, where stray capacitances render other types inaccurate. They employ wide-range screened transformers in a circuit as shown in Fig. 8.15. The input transformer may be regarded as a potential transformer, applying an equal potential to each of the impedances Z_s and $Z\mu$, while the output transformer is a current transformer, serving to balance the current in the two impedances. If the turns in each half of the primary of this transformer are equal, then there will be no potential drop across either (except that due to the small component of winding resistance) and zero signal will be passed to the detector.

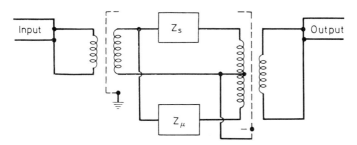

Fig. 8.15. V.H.F. admittance bridge

By utilising an output current transformer having unequal halves, the effect of ratio arms can be obtained, and it is also possible to use multiple tappings on the input voltage transformer for the same purpose.

If the impedance being measured is unbalanced, then the side of the transformer to which both the unknown and standard impedance are connected should be earthed. But if the impedance under test is balanced, then a centre tap on the input transformer winding should be earthed, so that the test potential is balanced.

By connecting the input transformer screen to earth any winding capacitance in this transformer will effectively appear across the input. The transformer is so designed that when using a balanced circuit the transformer is balanced with regard to capacitance as well as to turns.

The output transformer has its screen connected to the centre point, and the capacitance from each half winding to screen is such that capacitance leakage currents are in the same ratio as the main currents, and so form part of the detector impedance only.

Capacitance between secondary and screen is across either the whole or part of the input transformer winding, being from output transformer centre tap to earth when balance is obtained, since the whole of the output transformer secondary is then at earth potential. In the unbalanced connection, this capacitance is across the whole of the input transformer secondary, and hence does not interfere with the bridge measurement. In the balanced connection, this capacitance is balanced by the capacitance existing between the other side of the input winding and earth.

8.5.13. Further Applications of Null Methods

Two transformers can be compared by feeding their primaries from the same supply and connecting their secondaries so that they tend to send a current in opposite directions through a resistance. The current through the resistance — or the voltage across it — can be measured and if it is greater or less than certain values the transformer under test must be rejected due to its having incorrect ratio. Two standard applications of null methods are given below.

The ratio of instrument transformers must be known accurately. In the case of a current transformer the secondary has its normal load connected and the voltage across this load is compared with the voltage across a standard resistor in series with the primary. Since the value of the standard and the resistance of the secondary load are known, it is easy to calculate the ratio and phase shift from the potentiometer readings. In the case of potential transformers the primary standard resistor must, of course, be in parallel.

A.c. is used for measuring earth resistance to avoid electrolytic effects. Four stakes are employed, the two outer ones being used to pass a current and the potential being measured between the inner ones. The potential is compared with that across a resistance in series with the current supply. Thus in effect E and I are determined and R found from these. The current supply is in series with the potentiometer primary so that any variations will have no effect on the measurement. This method measures the resistance of the earth excluding the contact resistance. If the latter is required the potential between one of the 'current earth' plates and one potential plate is measured; one contact resistance is then included.

8.5.14. Transformer Ratio Arm Bridge

This is not to be confused with the transformer turns ratio bridge described earlier. The transformer ratio arm bridge has been used for many years for r.f. measurements and is being used more extensively at the present time for the general measurement of impedance. The general principles can be understood from the following worked example which concludes this chapter.

WORKED EXAMPLE

Question. Fig. 8.16 shows the circuit of a transformer ratio arm bridge. All three windings of the transformer have equal numbers of turns and the transformer may be assumed to be ideal.

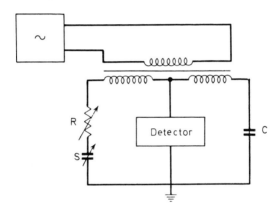

Fig. 8.16. Transformer ratio arm bridge

Balance is obtained at a frequency of 1000 Hz with $S = 0.01\ \mu\text{F}$ and $R = 50\ \Omega$. Calculate the capacitance and power factor of the capacitor C.

If the voltage output of the oscillator is 1 V r.m.s., calculate:

(*a*) the voltage across the capacitor C;

(*b*) the voltage across the detector when C differs from S by 1 per cent. The admittance of the detector may be neglected;

(*c*) the voltage across the detector when C differs from S by 1 per cent and the detector impedance is 1000 Ω resistance.

How would you modify the bridge in order to measure inductance?

(C. & G.)

Answer. In effect, the bridge has equal ratio arms. Hence, the capacitance of $C = S = \underline{0 \cdot 01}$ μF and the power factor, assuming a sinusoidal supply, is

$$\frac{1}{\sqrt{1 + \dfrac{1}{\omega^2 C^2 R^2}}} = \frac{1}{\sqrt{1 + \dfrac{1}{(2\pi \times 1000 \times 0 \cdot 01 \times 10^{-6} \times 50)^2}}}$$

$$\simeq \pi \times 10^{-3} = \underline{0 \cdot 00314} \text{ (see Fig. 8.17 } (a)).$$

(*a*) When the bridge is balanced the voltage across the capacitor C would be 1 V.

(*b*) Referring to Fig. 8.17 (*b*),

$$i \simeq \frac{2}{2 \cdot 01 Z} \text{ amperes (since } X_c \gg R)$$

Thus $\qquad V_{AB} \simeq 1 - Z \dfrac{2}{2 \cdot 01 Z} \simeq 1 - (1 - 0 \cdot 005) = \underline{0 \cdot 005 \text{ V}}$

(*c*) Referring to Fig. 8.17 (*c*),

$$1 = (1000 + Z) i_1 - 1000 \, i_2$$
$$1 = (1000 + 1 \cdot 01 Z) i_2 - 1000 \, i_1$$

from which $\quad (2000 + Z) i_1 = (2000 + 1 \cdot 01 Z) i_2$

$$\therefore \, i_2 = \frac{2000 + Z}{2000 + 1 \cdot 01 Z} \, i_1$$

Thus $1 = \left(1000 + Z - 1000 . \dfrac{2000 + Z}{2000 + 1 \cdot 01 Z} \right) i_1 = \left(\dfrac{2000 Z + 10 Z + 1 \cdot 01 Z^2}{2000 + 1 \cdot 01 Z} \right) i_1$

or, $\quad i_1 = \dfrac{2000 + 1 \cdot 01 Z}{Z(2010 + 1 \cdot 01 Z)}$

But $V_{AB} = 1000 \, (i_1 - i_2) = 1000 \left(1\% - \dfrac{2000 + Z}{2000 + 1 \cdot 01 Z} \right) i_1$

$$= 1000 \, \frac{0 \cdot 01 Z}{2000 + 1 \cdot 01 Z}$$

$$= 1000 \, \frac{0 \cdot 01}{2010 + 1 \cdot 01 Z}$$

But $\qquad Z = \dfrac{10^6}{2\pi \times 1000 \times 0 \cdot 01} \simeq 16{,}000 \text{ ohms.}$

Therefore $\qquad V_{AB} = \dfrac{10}{2010 + 16160} = \underline{0 \cdot 00055 \text{ V}}$

The modifications necessary in order that the bridge may measure inductance are shown in Fig. 8.17 (*d*).

It should be noted that the V.H.F. admittance bridge shown in Fig. 8.15 is one form of transformer ratio arm bridge.

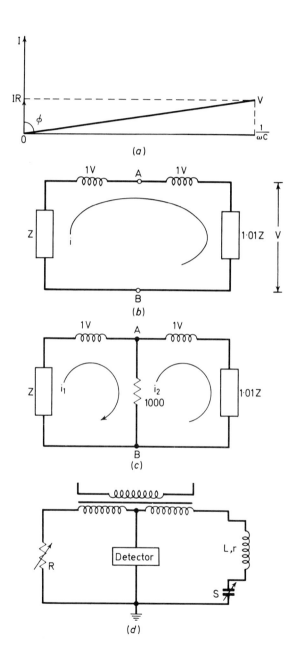

Fig. 8.17. Diagrams for worked example

EXERCISES

1. Describe the principle of operation of a.c. potentiometers of (a) polar, and (b) co-ordinate type. Outline briefly the reasons why a.c. potentiometers are instruments of less precision than d.c. potentiometers.   (Grad. I.E.E.)

2. Fig. 8.10 gives the connection of an Anderson's bridge for measuring the inductance L and resistance R of an unknown impedance between the points A and B. Find R and L if balance is obtained when $Q = S = 1,000\ \Omega$, $P = 500\ \Omega$, $r = 200\ \Omega$ and $c = 2\ \mu F$.
Draw a phasor diagram showing the voltage and current at every point of the network when the voltage across AC is $10\ V$ and the frequency is $100\ Hz$.

Answer. $R = 500\ \Omega$, $L = 1.4\ H$.   (B.Sc.)

3. The four arms of an a.c. bridge consist of the following screened components:

        AB: a capacitor C_1 in series with a resistor R_1;
        BC: a capacitor C_2 in parallel with a resistor R_2;
        CD: a resistor R_3;
        DA: a variable resistor R_4.

A variable-frequency sine-wave oscillator is connected between A and C and a detector between B and D.
Given that $C_1 = 0.2\ \mu F$, $C_2 = 0.05\ \mu F$, $R_1 = R_3 = 500\ \Omega$ and $R_2 = 2000\ \Omega$, determine the resistance R_4 and the corresponding frequency at which balance is obtained.

Show how the screens should be connected to minimise stray earth capacitances.

Explain the use of a Wagner earth and show how this device could be used with the given bridge. Suggest suitable values for the additional components that would be required.   (B.Sc. (Eng.) Part III, 1967)

Answer. $R_4 = 1262.5\ \Omega$, $f = 1591.5\ Hz$.

4. State the difficulties encountered in the measurement of impedances at very high frequencies. Describe a form of admittance bridge that overcomes these difficulties.

REFERENCE

1. HERMASH, F. L., *Thermal Converters as AC-DC Transfer Standards for Current and Voltage Measurements at Audio Frequencies. Journal of Research of the National Bureau of Standards*, 48, 2, Feb. 1952. (Research Paper 2296).

CHAPTER 9

Frequency Measurement

9.1. INTRODUCTION

Frequency is one of the few quantities in electronics that can and must be measured to a very high degree of accuracy. Ordinary radio transmitter frequencies have to be determined to an accuracy of the order of 1 part in 10^6; this is to ensure that there is minimum interference with the output of transmitters working on adjacent frequency channels.

For this reason frequency measurement should appeal to the electronic or radio engineer perhaps more than other types of measurement work, especially as it involves the use of oscillators and similar devices with which he should be thoroughly familiar.

9.2. FUNDAMENTAL UNIT

The unit of time is based upon the period of rotation of the earth. The principal observatories of the world make daily observations on the sun and set pendulum clocks to correspond with the earth's natural time. Atomic clocks and those using piezo-electric resonators are becoming widely used. Although this book is not concerned either with the astronomical observations or with the construction of the observatory clocks, it is interesting to remember that the frequency standards used in electronics work are based on these clocks.

The use of crystal oscillators in radio transmitters is well known. Such crystal oscillators can be used to control a multivibrator set to work on a sub-harmonic, e.g. a tenth, of the crystal frequency. This multivibrator can be used in turn to drive another sub-harmonic vibrator, and so on, until a frequency low enough to drive a synchronous clock is obtained. This clock can be compared with an observatory clock and so the crystal frequency may be found by simple multiplication. Any 'slip' in the multivibrators does not matter for they must slip back again so that there is no error over any reasonable period of time.

Fig. 9.1 shows how a stable 1 kHz oscillation may be obtained from a 100 kHz crystal oscillator. The output from the oscillator drives a

pulse generator, which produces steep-fronted pulses suitable for locking a chain of multivibrator frequency dividers; these reduce the
oscillation frequency in turn to 25 kHz, 5 kHz and 1 kHz. The greatest
frequency ratio in any one stage is limited to 5:1 to secure reliable
control, which is enhanced by the use of 'preferential locking'.

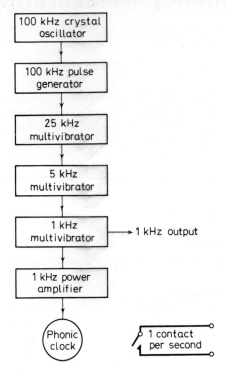

Fig. 9.1. Frequency divider system

Thus, when the division ratio is an even number the control pulses
are injected in the same phase to both valves of the multivibrator,
whereas for odd orders of division the control pulses are applied in
anti-phase to the two valves.

The 1 kHz signal may be used to check the frequency of the
100 kHz oscillator by means of time signals defining, say, a 24-hour
period. The 1 kHz oscillation is amplified and used to drive a phonic
motor clock, as shown in the diagram. Such a clock operates synchro-
nously and may have a contact which 'makes' nominally once per
second — actually once per 1000 alternations of motor current. Signals
from the clock contact may be compared with a time signal and again

with one 24 hours later, to obtain the time gain (or loss) of the clock. The gain (or loss) of the clock, expressed proportionately, is equal to the proportionate deviation of the 1 kHz signal from a precise 1 kHz; this, in turn, is equal to the mean frequency deviation of the 100 kHz from an exact 100 kHz during the period. Thus, suppose the clock to gain x seconds in 24 hours, then its proportionate error is $\dfrac{x}{86,400}$ and the mean value of the 100 kHz frequency is

$$100\left(1 + \frac{x}{86,400}\right)\text{kHz.}$$

This method is used for the absolute calibration of primary standards of frequency.

9.3. THE MULTIVIBRATOR

This circuit contains a pair of resistance-capacitance coupled valves or transistors, the output of each being fed to the input of the other so that approximately square-wave oscillations are produced. The frequency depends upon the time constant of the circuit but can be locked into step with a controlling frequency which can be an exact multiple or submultiple of the desired multivibrator frequency.

Fig. 9.2 shows the circuit of a transistor multivibrator and Fig. 9.3 shows an approximation to the waveforms to be expected. The action

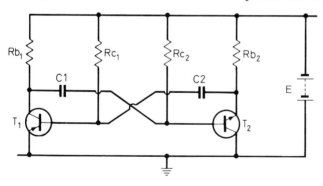

Fig. 9.2. Multivibrator circuit

of the circuit can be seen from these diagrams. Suppose that at the instant of switching on transistor T_1 conducts more readily than T_2. Then T_1 collector potential goes positive, communicating this change to T_2 base through capacitor C_1 and so cutting off T_2. Assuming that

Rb_1 and Rc_1 are so proportioned that T_1 bottoms (i.e. collector current saturated), the current builds up to almost E/Rc_1 and a voltage step of almost E is applied to the base of T_2.

During the transition, the charge on C_1 hardly changes, but thereafter it leaks away through Rb_2; the base voltage of T_2 falls exponentially from $+E$ towards $-E$ with time constant $C_1 Rb_2$. While this remains positive, T_2 is cut off, but when it goes negative, current begins to flow in T_2 and the reverse transition begins, i.e. when current flows in T_2 its collector potential rises, so cutting off T_1 (i.e. low collector current), and T_2 in turn becomes bottomed. The cut-off of T_1, and the consequent fall in T_1 collector potential, assists in the turn-on of T_2, the whole circuit constituting a regenerative loop. Thus the current in Rc_2 now builds up to almost E/Rc_2 and a voltage step of about E is applied to the base of T_1. Capacitor C_2 then begins to leak away through Rb_1 so that negative current starts to flow in T_1 and the cycle re-begins.

The frequency of operation is controlled by the discharge of C_1 through Rb_2 and C_2 through Rb_1, and is approximately equal to $0.77/CR$ when $C_1 = C_2 = C$ and $Rb_1 = Rb_2 = R$, as is usually the case in practice, the intervals t and T in Fig. 9.3 being then equal. Thus if $C = 5 \times 10^{-9}$ farads and $R = 27\ 000$ ohms the frequency of operation is about 5·7 kHz.

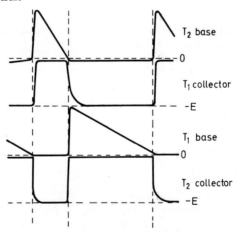

Fig. 9.3. Multivibrator waveforms

The multivibrator has two main functions in connection with measurement. One has already been mentioned, namely 'reducing' the frequency of a crystal oscillator so that the frequency of the latter may be compared with a standard clock. The other purpose is the opposite, i.e. the generation of harmonics of a crystal oscillator frequency in order to provide standards of comparison for high-frequency radio transmitters.

The waveform of a multivibrator is so rich in harmonics that even the 150th may be detected by the production of beats between it and an oscillation differing from it by an audible frequency.

Further details of the applications of multivibrators in measurement work, including the circuit of a valve multivibrator, will be found in the book *Principles of Electrical Measurements*[1] (Buckingham and Price), pp. 381–383.

9.4. OSCILLATORS

Oscillators are required for many purposes in measurement work, among which may be mentioned the driving of multivibrators as frequency standards, the alignment of radio receivers, and the operation of a.c. bridges. In the latter case ample output is required but a high degree of frequency stability is not normally necessary. However, on some a.c. bridges, for example the Hay bridge described in Chapter 8, frequency stability is very important since the balance equations include the term ω^2. Good waveform is desirable in the case of a.c. bridges and indeed in most cases since a poor waveform involves a doubt as to the exact frequency.

The causes of distortion in valve circuits have been studied for several decades. In transistor stages there are two main causes of distortion, namely, a non-linear relation between input and output voltage or current and non-linearity of input impedance.

There are many ways of generating sinusoidal oscillations and any of the well-known oscillator circuits can be used. It is assumed that the reader is familiar with these circuits, therefore this chapter will indicate only briefly some of the methods commonly used.

9.4.1. Buffer Stage

A stage is used to follow the oscillator in order to isolate it from the output circuit. For radio-frequency work the circuit should be so arranged that capacitive coupling through the stage itself shall be negligible.

9.4.2. Negative-resistance Oscillators

The timing circuit of a sinusoidal oscillator has to define a single frequency, and so is a resonant circuit or a number of coupled resonant circuits. A parallel (or anti-resonant) combination of inductance L and capacitance C presents a maximum impedance, and a series (or resonant) combination a minimum impedance, at the resonant frequency

$$f = 1/2 \pi \sqrt{LC}$$

the second order effect of losses in the components being ignored.

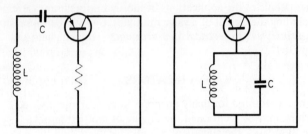

Fig. 9.4. Negative-resistance oscillators

Accordingly, negative-resistance oscillators use tuned circuits as shown in Fig. 9.4. These diagrams do not show the d.c. supplies, which must be arranged to locate the mean working point in the negative-resistance region. A load or output connection is conveniently placed in the collector lead, when its effect on frequency will be small provided the impedance is low.

The tunnel diode is also, of course, widely used in negative-resistance oscillator circuits.

9.4.3. Tuning-Fork Oscillator

Fig. 9.5 shows the basic circuit of a valve-maintained tuning-fork oscillator. The action of this circuit can be understood by assuming

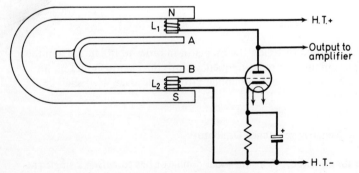

Fig. 9.5. Tuning fork oscillator

that oscillations are started by mechanical means: the prongs A and B vibrating in antiphase with respect to each other, i.e. while A is moving upwards B moves downwards and vice versa. In order that oscillations shall be maintained, the connections to the anode and grid coils must be such that when the grid voltage is made less negative the increase of anode current shall result in an induced voltage in the grid coil which causes a further anode-current increase.

The rate of change of flux through the two coils is the same owing to the symmetry of the magnetic circuit. Hence, if the polarity of the permanent magnet is as shown, the increase of flux through the anode coil (this occurs as A approaches L_1) is accompanied by an increase of flux through the grid coil, and the connections to this coil must be such that the grid voltage is increased in a positive direction. Conversely, when the anode current is reduced below its mean value the flux through both coils is reduced and the grid voltage must be consequently made more negative.

9.4.4. Feedback Oscillator

To obtain the best possible results automatic amplitude control can be used in oscillators. Besides preventing the oscillations from sweeping into the bends of the characteristic, it also ensures that the amplitude remains nearly the same for different frequency settings.

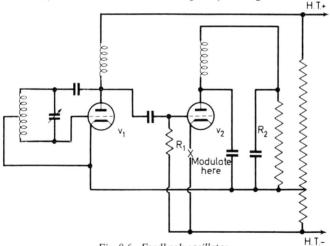

Fig. 9.6. Feedback oscillator

The automatic amplitude control principle can be satisfactorily applied to any ordinary feedback oscillator, for example a Hartley circuit, as shown in Fig. 9.6. The amplitude can be left small and therefore the waveform and frequency stability will be good. It is possible to obtain oscillations at higher frequencies in this way and the frequency is less dependent on valve characteristics.

The principle of the automatic amplitude control is that the oscillations produce a fall of potential across R_1 and so cause V_2, which is normally biased beyond cut-off, to pass current. The anode current then produces a potential across R_2 which is fed to the control grid of V_1, lowering its potential and therefore reducing the output. The circuit shown in Fig. 9.6 gives amplified control, and delay is provided by adjusting the bias of V_2.

9.4.5. Electron-Coupled Oscillators

The best-known use of this type of oscillator is in connection with superheterodyne receivers. In one common type the screen grid forms the anode of the oscillator while the valve anode provides a means of obtaining an output without direct connection to the oscillator circuit. The only coupling back from load to oscillator is by the stray capacitances in the 'pinch' of the valve. This is the chief value of this type of oscillator. With the screen-grid type there is a setting of the screen voltage for which the frequency is independent of small changes of operating voltages.

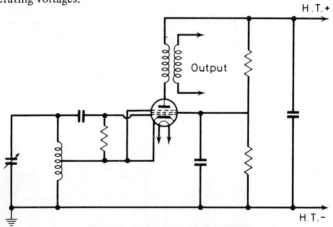

Fig. 9.7. Electron-coupled oscillator

The pentagrid, commonly used as a frequency-changer in battery superheterodyne receivers, does not give complete isolation of the oscillator from the output. In the language of the receiver designer, there is a certain amount of 'pulling'.

The resistance stabiliser of the automatic amplitude control can be applied to electron-coupled oscillators with the advantages mentioned above. If this type of oscillator is worked with a large grid bias, obtained by grid leak and capacitor, the waveform is very distorted. This is made use of in some heterodyne wavemeters by employing the harmonics to give additional ranges.

The circuit diagram of an electron-coupled oscillator is shown in Fig. 9.7. It should be noted that the screen-grid is earthed from an a.c. point of view; correct adjustment of the screen-grid voltage gives oscillations whose frequency is independent of anode voltage.

9.4.6. Crystal Oscillators

A quartz crystal of which the mechanical resonance is employed may be termed a 'resonator', and can be used to check a number of frequencies corresponding to its various modes of vibration, but the principal usefulness of crystals lies in their application to the frequency control of oscillations produced by a valve. The term 'quartz oscillator' or 'crystal oscillator' is to be interpreted as the combination of a quartz resonator and a valve circuit producing oscillations.

A large number of crystal oscillator circuits has been developed[1] Two of the oldest employ respectively the grid-cathode and grid-anode crystal connection, and are shown in Fig. 9.8 (a) and (b): the former is still one of the most commonly used. An alternative

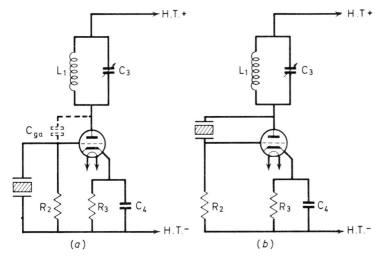

Fig. 9.8. Crystal oscillator circuits

biasing arrangement for use in these circuits consists in omitting R_3 and C_4, in which case R_2 serves as a grid leak and the capacitance of the crystal takes the place of the grid capacitor in a conventional circuit providing grid-current biasing.

Replacement of the crystal in the circuit of Fig. 9.8 (a), where the crystal oscillates at its parallel-resonant frequency, by its equivalent circuit shows that the entire circuit consists essentially of a tuned-anode tuned-grid oscillator in which the coupling element is the inter-electrode capacitance between anode and grid. The analysis of the circuit shows that the oscillation frequency is primarily dependent on the crystal constants and is only very slightly affected by other circuit parameters. A point of importance is that, in order to maintain oscillations the anode load must be slightly inductive, i.e. the anode circuit must be tuned to a frequency slightly above the resonant frequency of the crystal. This is because an inductive anode load causes a negative resistance to be reflected from the anode to the grid circuit; this negative resistance is necessary to neutralise the positive resistance of the crystal.

Either of the circuits shown in Fig. 9.8 may be modified by replacing the triode by a pentode; moreover, in modern circuits pentodes are preferred. In the former circuit this usually necessitates artificially increasing the grid-anode inter-electrode capacitance by connecting an additional coupling capacitor in parallel with it; the same addition may be required in a triode circuit intended to generate a low radio frequency.

The power output of a circuit employing a pentode may be made to exceed that obtainable with a triode owing to the higher power sensitivity of the former. The amplitude of the r.f. voltage that can safely exist across a crystal is limited by the risk of crystal fracture, whilst, in addition, the avoidance of crystal heating is also desirable. A pentode can be used to deliver the same output power as a triode, with the advantage of reduced crystal heating. The output of a crystal oscillator employing a beam tetrode may be as high as 15 W but, unless the number of valves in the equipment has to be severely restricted, it is preferable to operate the crystal stage at a much lower power level and to employ extra amplification in other stages.

In contrast to the circuit of Fig. 9.8 (a), that shown in Fig. 9.8 (b) oscillates only when the tuned circuit is adjusted to present a capacitive impedance, hence the resonant frequency of the anode circuit must be made lower than the crystal frequency. In this circuit the crystal oscillates at its series resonant frequency.

The crystal oscillator stage is normally followed by a buffer amplifier to isolate the oscillator stage from the rest of the circuit, and automatic amplitude control, of the amplified delayed type, is often used to ensure that any circuit changes do not have any appreciable effect on the crystal frequency. A common method of ensuring that the frequency is independent of temperature variations is to enclose the whole of the apparatus in an oven, while the crystal is in an inner oven. This topic is discussed further at the end of this chapter.

A tuning fork oscillator, described earlier, can be used as a frequency standard but it is giving place to the crystal type, mainly because the latter is more compact, more constant in frequency and requires less frequency multiplication.

9.4.7. The Wobbly Oscillator or Wobbulator

This arrangement is used in the measurement of frequency response rather than the measurement of a particular frequency, but it is convenient to consider it briefly here along with other oscillators. A radio-frequency oscillator is frequency modulated at, say, 50 Hz and the resultant 'wobbly' output is used for examining band-pass filters, in conjunction with a cathode-ray oscilloscope. This application was mentioned in Chapter 7 and will also be dealt with later when the testing of radio receivers will be described (Chapter 14).

In the circuit of Fig. 9.9, V_1 is a conventional tuned-anode oscillator whose frequency in the absence of V_2 would be very nearly equal to

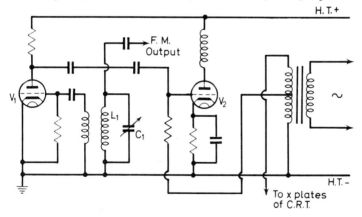

Fig. 9.9. Wobbulator

the natural frequency of the LC circuit. V_2 is termed a 'Miller valve' and its principle of operation is that the effective capacitance between the grid and cathode of an amplifier valve depends upon its stage-gain which in turn depends upon the grid-bias voltage, assuming the operating characteristic to be non-linear.

The grid voltage is varied at a low frequency; hence the input capacitance of V_2, which is effectively in parallel with the oscillator tuning capacitance, varies at the same frequency. The oscillations are consequently frequency-modulated. It is more usual in practice to use a saw-tooth voltage to feed the grid of V_2 and the X plates of the cathode-ray oscilloscope; with a well-designed circuit a linear variation of frequency with a negligible amount of amplitude modulation is produced.

9.4.8. R-C Sinusoidal Oscillator

A good waveform, suitable for bridge work, is provided by the simple two-stage R-C oscillator shown in Fig. 9.10. The frequency is about 2·5 kHz with fairly good temperature stability. Supply voltages from

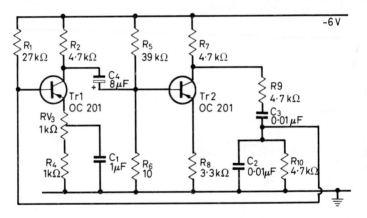

Fig. 9.10.   R-C sinusoidal oscillator

at least -3 V to -9 V can be used, providing RV_3 is suitably adjusted. RV_3 provides a convenient means of adjusting the waveform for amplitude and distortion, and for compensating for changes of temperature, say from one day to the next. The output is taken from R_7 or R_8.

When designing R-C phase shift oscillators for grounded emitter stages three considerations arise: (1) the R-C network is required to feed into a low impedance input; (2) the current gain of the transistor must be greater than the attenuation of the network; (3) the internal phase shift of the transistor must be added to that of the network. If the R-C oscillator is designed for a single transistor, it is found that three R-C sections are required to provide the external phase shift of about 180° (there being about 180° phase shift in the grounded emitter transistor) and the current gain must be at least 29 to allow for the attenuation of this network. By the time other features of the circuit are allowed for, it is found that a transistor such as the Mullard OC 201 would have to be selected for a high a'.

This circuit has therefore been designed to have sufficient gain in hand using two transistors. The frequency determining components form a Wien network C_3, R_9, C_2 and R_{10}. The Wien network has been chosen because it produces zero phase shift at the frequency of oscillation where the attenuation of $\frac{1}{3}$ compares favourably with that of other arrangements. The combined phase shift across the two transistors is of the order of 360°, and can be neglected. Oscillation therefore occurs at the frequency at which the Wien network gives zero phase shift.

9.4.9. Measurement of Interpolation

To adjust a local oscillator or radio transmitter to a standard frequency the two oscillations (i.e. from the transmitter and the standard oscillator) are directly heterodyned in the case of an unmodulated carrier.

The generator frequency is adjusted until the heterodyne beat frequency is reduced below the audible limit. At the centre of the silent band where, with unmodulated heterodyning frequencies, the beat frequency is inaudible, slow pulsations occur. This phenomenon is a periodic swelling, at the heterodyning frequency, of a 1000 Hz note which is heard due to rectification of what is, in effect, 1 kHz modulation of the harmonic frequency being selected and used. This beat can be made slow enough to count, i.e. the period may be reduced to several seconds. Hence the setting can be done to a very high accuracy. Now this method cannot be used directly on a *fixed* source, such as a distant transmitter. In this case a special stable oscillator is used to beat with the signal and the setting of zero beat found.

The received signal wave f is first heterodyned with the stable interpolation oscillator (shown at (*a*) in Fig. 9.11), both frequencies being received on the detector radio receiver. The oscillator must be set *exactly* to resonance with f and its scale reading noted. If the frequency being measured is modulated the exact position of resonance will be apparent by the lengthening period of the synchronisation beating or pulsations which are heard after the signals have been rectified in the receiver, which is set in a non-oscillating condition. For C.W. the process is similar but the usual beat oscillator of the receiver must be used.

Having found the scale reading corresponding to f, the aerial is switched off and the receiver coupled instead to the output from the

three multivibrators shown at (b) in Fig. 9.11. The outputs from the
three multivibrators are, for the purposes of this explanation, shown
in series and means are provided for varying the output of each from

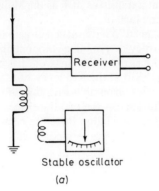

(a)

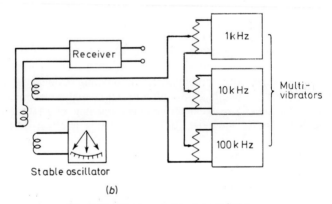

(b)

Fig. 9.11. Measurement by interpolation

zero. With the receiver in a non-oscillating condition, the stable
oscillator is then set to resonance with the nearest lower and higher
frequency harmonics, f_1, f_2, from the multivibrator. The scale positions of these embracing harmonic frequencies are engraved on the
oscillator scale to an accuracy of 1 part in 10^4 and their exact settings
on a degree scale are found by the slow synchronisation beating phenomenon previously described.

Simple arithmetical interpolation between these two scale readings
will give the value of f to an accuracy limited only by the scale reading
accuracy of the oscillator, its degree of linearity of frequency law and
its frequency stability throughout the duration of the measurement.

The stable interpolation oscillator referred to above could be a simple crystal oscillator circuit with thermal compensation. The scales on the capacitor are normally very elaborate and are provided with a magnifying vernier arrangement. The stray field from such an oscillator is sufficient coupling for the purpose described above.

The accurate measurement of frequency has been described in detail; less accurate determinations are correspondingly simpler. The 'transfer' to the crystal-controlled multivibrators is not required for any but the highest accuracy.

It will of course be appreciated that the power required from oscillator wavemeters is minute, whereas the signal generator used to supply radio receivers on test in a factory or for working bridges is relatively large, hence amplifiers are generally incorporated.

The old-fashioned absorption wavemeter is still used. An oscillatory circuit of good design is connected to an indicator such as a thermo-micro-ammeter to show resonance. The close coupling required makes great accuracy impossible.

A type of absorption wavemeter giving greater accuracy uses a buffer amplifier stage with the tuned circuit connected in its output; this results in the reduction of the coupling between the 'aerial' of the wavemeter and the tuned circuit to a minute value. The buffer stage output is also connected via a suitable capacitor to the input of a simple electronic voltmeter circuit. This arrangement avoids the necessity for a meter which will respond to radio-frequency currents. The wavemeter sensitivity can be controlled by a potential divider used to alter the bias of the buffer amplifier stage.

An important precaution to be observed in the use of such apparatus is the avoidance of overloading of the buffer amplifier due to an input signal which is too large; this will result in spurious responses to harmonics of the signal and these responses will be completely misleading unless the frequency to be measured is approximately known. It is always necessary to use the loosest coupling between wavemeter and oscillatory circuit consistent with a clear indication of resonance.

9.5. BRIDGE METHODS

It was mentioned in Chapter 8 that the Wien bridge could be used for measuring frequency in terms of L, C and R. This method is simple and quick and is often quite accurate enough for audio frequencies. The Wien bridge needs no inductors, which at audio frequencies present a difficulty since they must either be very large or iron-cored and therefore dependent upon the current carried.

Referring to Fig. 8.8 (c) of Chapter 8, the ratio of the resistance arms, P/Q, is made $1/2$. In addition C_x is made equal to C, and r_x equal to R; hence the condition for balance,

$$\omega^2 = \frac{1}{C_x C r_x R} \text{ becomes } f = \frac{1}{2\pi CR}.$$

R and r_x are ganged, and the dial is calibrated directly in frequency, the capacitors providing the frequency ratios. Each capacitor covers a frequency range of 10 to 1. As this ganging cannot be perfect, a resistor (like that marked R_c in Fig. 8.4 of Chapter 8) is connected between the arms P and Q, so that a fine balance may be obtained. The accuracy is not high (about 0·5%) chiefly because the bridge is naturally not balanced for harmonics of the supply frequency. These should be filtered out from the indicator.

A Wien bridge is used in the transistor oscillator shown in Fig. 9.10.

9.6. MODULATION OF OSCILLATORS

It has been indicated in Fig. 9.6 that modulation can be effected in series with the bias given by the automatic amplitude control. The operation of this system depends upon the fact that for equilibrium the bias on the oscillator valve will be constant. Hence, at any instant when the modulating voltage is negative a lower bias is required and hence a smaller amplitude to produce that bias.

9.7. LECHER WIRES

The reader familiar with ultra-short-wave technique will be aware that if an alternating potential is applied to a pair of parallel wires standing waves are set up. The proof of this fact is outside the scope of this book: briefly the idea is that a wave is propagated along the lines with a definite velocity and if the lines are short-circuited a distance of a half wavelength or a multiple of this the wave will be reflected in such a way as exactly to reinforce the next wave.

The shorting piece can be made to contain a current-indicating device to show when the correct position is obtained, which coincides with maximum current. In this way wavelength can be measured directly.

To determine the frequency it is assumed that the waves are propagated with the same velocity as in free space; hence

$$f = \frac{3 \times 10^8}{\lambda} \text{ Hz,}$$

when λ is measured in metres. The method is impracticable for any but very high frequencies due to the excessive length of the wires that would be needed.

9.8. TEMPERATURE CONTROL

Temperature control for oscillators would appear to be a simple matter with the aid of a thermostat, controlling some form of heating apparatus, so that the components requiring close temperature control can be enclosed in an 'oven' with the heating apparatus and maintained at constant temperature. However, there are several factors to consider before really close and precise temperature control can be achieved. All units have a certain thermal capacity, i.e. they absorb a certain amount of heat in changing their temperature. The heater reaches a higher temperature than it radiates, and continues radiating after the supply to it is reduced. The thermostatic control absorbs a certain amount of heat to register its controlling effect, so that, if the temperature is rising, the control will operate when the actual temperature is higher than that for which the thermostat is set. Added to this, the thermostat must have a positive control, to avoid chatter, so that the temperature at which the thermostat switches off the heater must be higher than that at which it switches it on again.

Fortunately, the fact that everything has thermal capacity can itself be made to solve the problem, by careful design. The usual method consists in allowing the thermostat a certain operational range of temperature, between that at which it switches on and off. The heater element will obviously vary over a greater range of temperature. The thermal capacity of the oven containing the components under control is made high compared to that of the controlling elements – the thermostat and heater. The position of the thermostat relative to the heater and the controlled oven is so chosen that, with its own thermal delay, it switches off when the temperature is rising just when the oven reaches the correct operating temperature, and switches on when the temperature is falling, also when the oven reaches the same operating temperature. In this way, although the heater and thermostat follow cyclic variations, the variations of temperature in the controlled oven will be very much smaller – almost infinitesimal.

The time constant of the switching on-and-off cycle will be very much smaller than that of the oven. It will be obvious that the controlled temperature must be hotter than the highest room temperature likely to be encountered by the equipment, or the control will fail. The oven should be so lagged that escape of heat follows the same path as the arriving heat from the heater, past the thermostat, and as little heat as possible can escape directly.

9.9. LISSAJOUS FIGURES

If two varying potentials are applied to a cathode-ray tube, one to each
pair of plates, the spot will execute a more or less complicated movement producing a design on the screen. The simplest case is when both
the deflecting potentials are sine waves. The shape of the figure will
then depend upon the phase difference.

Fig. 9.12 (*a*) shows how two sine waves in phase give rise to a
straight line, while Fig. 9.12 (*b*) shows that with a phase difference of

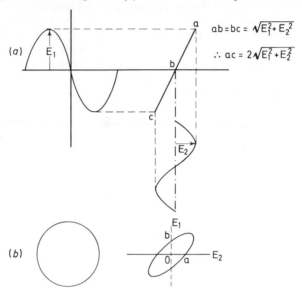

Fig. 9.12. Sine wave X and Y deflection

$90°$ a circle is produced. Intermediate phase values produce an ellipse.
The circle is of course only produced when both waves have equal
amplitudes.

The length of the trace is shown in Fig. 9.12 (*a*) to be given by
$2\sqrt{E_1{}^2 + E_2{}^2}$ where E_1 and E_2 are the amplitudes of the respective
components. In the case of a straight line, that ratio E_1/E_2 is obviously
equal to $\tan\theta$, where θ is the angle between the line and the horizontal.

When the trace is an ellipse the phase angle can be determined by
measuring the value of one component, say E_2, at the point where the
other $E_1 = 0$. This value is $E_2\sin\phi$, where ϕ is the phase angle. This
relationship is true whatever the relative amplitudes but the most
accurate results are obtained when they are nearly equal.

The phase relationship between a voltage and current can be measured using this method. The current is passed through a resistance and the resulting p.d. applied to one pair of plates, the voltage with which the current is to be compared being applied to the other pair. The method is particularly useful at radio frequencies where the methods of power factor measurement satisfactory for supply frequencies cannot be used.

As might be expected, if the two potentials applied to the deflecting plates are not of the same waveform the trace will be distorted from the ellipsoidal. If even harmonics are present the figure will not be symmetrical. The analysis of such figures is tedious and the advances in time base technique that have resulted from television and radar requirements have rendered the method out of date. It is, however, useful to be able to detect at a glance whether or not a particular waveform is reasonably pure. In the case of amplifier performance, the main concern is in minimising harmonic production rather than actually analysing the resultant wave. The distortion of the ellipse shows immediately when an amplifier is giving distortion and whether second or third harmonic is present.

9.10. FREQUENCY COMPARISON

When the two waves are not of the same fundamental frequency, very complicated figures are produced but if one is an exact multiple of the other the figure will be stationary, for every cycle of the lower frequency will be alike. This principle is used for comparing two frequencies, or adjusting one to an exact multiple of another.

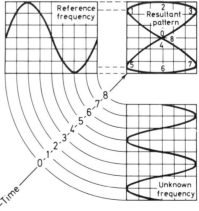

Fig. 9.13. Formation of Lissajous figure using 2:1 frequency ratio

The formation of a Lissajous figure using two sine waves of different frequencies (2:1 ratio) is shown in Fig. 9.13. The appearance of the

resultant Lissajous pattern may be determined by joining the intersections of projections from like-numbered points of the waveforms.
The ratio of the two frequencies can be determined by counting the
number of loops along the top (or bottom) edge of the pattern and the
number of loops down the right (or left) side of the pattern, and substituting the figures in the following formula:

$$\frac{\text{Frequency on horizontal axis}}{\text{Frequency on vertical axis}} = \frac{\text{Number of loops on side of pattern}}{\text{Number of loops on top of pattern}}$$

When the ratio is not an exact multiple the figure appears to rotate.
Assume the standard frequency is 100 Hz, the ratio nearly 5:1 and one
wave passes per second, then the error is 1 in 500, i.e. 499 or 501
according to which way the figure rotates. It is possible to detect much
slower drifts than this; thus an audio-frequency oscillator can be calibrated from a 50 Hz standard to an accuracy of the order of 0·001%.

Simpler patterns are produced by arranging for the trace to retrace
its path so that two 'ends' of the trace appear on the screen. In this
case, in applying the above rule, an end at one corner is counted as one
loop, while all the actual loops, being really two loops superimposed,
are counted as two. The method is evident from the various ratios
shown in Fig. 9.14. Further details of frequency measurement are given
in Ref. 2.

9.11. DIGITAL FREQUENCY METERS

These instruments are used to directly measure frequencies to a high
degree of accuracy. The following information is based on the Type
811R made by Racal Instruments Ltd., who make high quality
apparatus of this nature, and is reproduced with their kind permission.

The Type 811R measures frequency in the range 500 Hz to 150 MHz
with a choice of two gate times, i.e. 1 sec and 10 sec, with an accuracy
of ± 10 Hz ± timebase accuracy with the 1 sec gate and ± 1 Hz ± timebase accuracy with the 10 sec gate. The measured frequency is displayed
on eight in-line numerical indicator tubes with automatic decimal
point. Readout is stored while the subsequent measurement is accumulated so that the display changes only in response to differing inputs.
The internal frequency standard is a temperature-controlled crystal
oscillator which takes only three minutes to warm up.

The basic principles of operation of the instrument are briefly as
follows. The Type 811R measures frequencies by counting each tenth

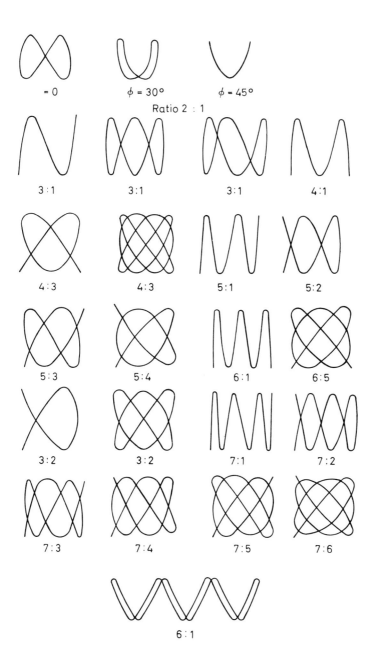

Fig. 9.14. Lissajous figures

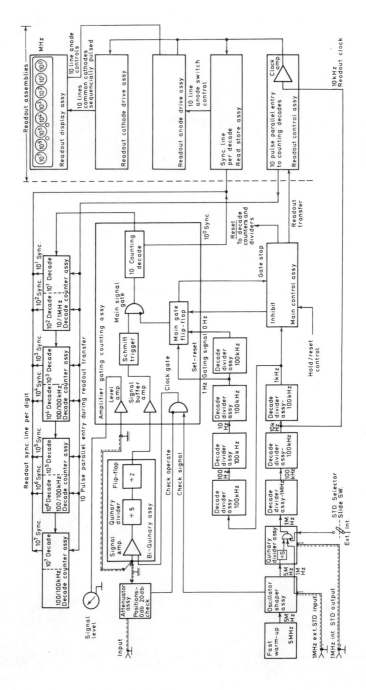

Fig. 9.15. Block diagram of Racal 811R v.h.f. digital frequency meter

cycle of an input signal for an accurately known period of time. The functional block diagram Fig. 9.15 illustrates the method.

The input signal, after passing through the attenuator assembly is divided by 10 in the bi-quinary scaler assembly. In the amplifier gate counting assembly the signal is shaped by means of a Schmitt trigger circuit and is then offered to the main signal gate. When the gate is opened, a pulse corresponding to each tenth cycle of the input signal is passed into the first decade of the counting chain. Subsequent decades of the counting chain are arranged in pairs on plug-in modules. The timing signals that control the opening and closing of the main signal gate are derived by digital division from the output of the fast warm-up oscillator. The output of this temperature-controlled crystal oscillator, at a frequency of 5 MHz, is shaped in the oscillator shaper assembly, divided to 1 MHz in the quinary divider assembly and subsequently in decades as shown (each of the decades is a separate plug-in module).

At the end of the gate period (a precise 1 or 10 seconds time interval) the count accumulated in the eight decades of the decade counter chain is transferred into the readout store assembly. All the counting decades and some of the time base divider decades are then reset to zero. This process occupies only 25 milliseconds, after which the instrument is released to begin its next cycle of measurement. Meanwhile, the readout store assembly, together with the other readout assemblies, maintains a constant display on the numerical indicator tubes until the next transfer signals are generated.

WORKED EXAMPLE

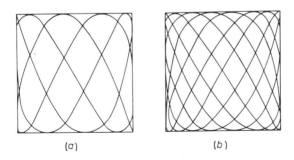

(a)   (b)

Fig. 9.16. Lissajous patterns for worked example

Question. Fig. 9.16 shows two Lissajous patterns. If the horizontal deflection signal is 50 Hz, find the possible frequency in the following cases:

(i) Stationary pattern as at Fig. 9.16 (*a*).

(ii) Stationary pattern as at Fig. 9.16 (*b*).

(iii) Moving pattern, such that exact replica of Fig. 9.16 (*a*) appears exactly once every second.

(iv) Moving pattern, such that exact replica of Fig. 9.16 (*b*) appears exactly once every second.

Suggest a method by means of which the ambiguity in answers (iii) and (iv) could be eliminated.

Answer.

(i) There are two loops and one end along a vertical side, and four loops and one end along the top or bottom. Thus the ratio of vertical deflecting frequency to horizontal deflecting frequency must be 9:5. If the horizontal frequency is 50 Hz, the vertical one must be:

$$\underline{90 \text{ Hz}} \; Answer \; (i)$$

(ii) Here there are five loops along the vertical sides, and eight loops along the top and bottom, so the vertical to horizontal frequency ratio must be 8:5, and if the horizontal frequency is 50 Hz, the vertical one must be:

$$\underline{80 \text{ Hz}} \;\; Answer \; (ii)$$

(iii) Careful thought will show that for an end, which represents an edge-on view of a loop, to come to the same corner, means that two consecutive wave crests in that direction of the vertical wave have changed places, compared with that particular wave in the horizontal direction. Normally, 9 cycles of vertical trace or 5 cycles of horizontal trace make up one complete pattern, and this takes, therefore, 1/10th of a second to be traced. During this time, 1/5th of a vertical cycle, or 1/9th of a horizontal cycle, would displace the pattern so that a similar one would appear. As this takes 1 second, or 10 traces, it is evident that the change of pattern represents the fact that either 90 plus 1/5th or 90 minus 1/5th of a cycle have corresponded with the 50 horizontal cycles, thus the frequency is either:

$$\underline{90 \cdot 2 \text{ or } 89 \cdot 8 \text{ Hz}} \;\; Answer \; (iii)$$

(iv) In this case the distance which a vertical loop must move is only half the distance between loops made by traces travelling in the same horizontal direction across the screen. A complete sequence of variations will include two different single ended patterns, having the ends in opposite pairs of corners, (that is the ends in one pattern occupy the corners where loops were in the other), and two identical symmetrical patterns of the continuous type, such as Fig. 9.16 (*b*). From this it can be deduced that the change in terms of cycles of either signal will only be half that of the previous case, i.e. 1/16th of a horizontal cycle or 1/10th of a vertical one. Thus the frequency in this case is either:

$$\underline{80\cdot1 \text{ or } 79\cdot9 \text{ Hz}} \quad Answer \text{ } (iv)$$

To eliminate the ambiguity from the results of answers (iii) and (iv), a simple method would be to introduce a small component of the horizontal frequency in series with the vertical deflection voltage, with a 90° advance or delay arrangement, so that the left to right of right to left traces would be slightly displaced vertically. The direction of rotation can then easily be distinguished, one direction indicating the upper and the other the lower frequency.

EXERCISES

1. Describe a method whereby a stable frequency of 1 kHz may be derived from a crystal-controlled source operating at 100 kHz.

How would you use the 1 kHz signal to check the frequency of the 100 kHz oscillator by means of time signals defining a 24-hour period?
                                              (C. & G. Radio III, 1948)

2. Give a circuit for a resistance-capacitance sine-wave oscillator (valve or transistor) suitable for audio frequencies and explain its operation. Derive an approximate expression for the operating frequency. Discuss the factors which affect the frequency stability of this type of oscillator.
                                              (L.U. B.Sc. (Eng.) Part III, 1967)

3. Describe an oscillating wavemeter suitable for use in measuring the frequencies of distant radio transmitters. Suggest a reason for any accuracy limitations and explain briefly what procedure can be adopted to correct for such possible errors and obtain readings as accurate as possible.

4. Explain how two radio frequencies can be compared by means of a cathode-ray oscilloscope and discuss what advantages, if any, this method has over the method of interpolation.

REFERENCES

1. BUCKINGHAM, H. AND PRICE, E. M., *Principles of Electrical Measurements*. E.U.P. (1955).
2. TERMAN, F. E., AND PETTIT, J. M., *Electronic Measurements*. McGraw-Hill, (1952).

CHAPTER 10

Resonance Methods of Measuring L, C, R, and Q

10.1. INTRODUCTION

Bridge methods of measuring circuit constants were fully dealt with in Chapter 8. It was pointed out that these methods are largely confined to audio frequencies, though radio-frequency bridges are built. These instruments are expensive and their accuracy is not always all that can be desired. The detector has to take the form of a receiver with a heterodyne oscillator, and this further complicates the measurement. When such a bridge is used it is advisable to use the substitution method mentioned in Chapter 8. This method ensures that the conditions of the bridge (i.e. stray capacitances, etc.) shall change as little as possible during the test.

Before dealing with the main subject of this chapter mention must be made of the meter often used to measure capacitance and inductance in radio service work. This consists of a rectifier instrument in series with a resistance, the apparatus under test and a supply derived from the a.c. mains. The terminals are short-circuited and a shunt across the moving coil instrument is set to give full-scale deflection. The 'short' is then removed and the apparatus under test connected. The deflection is then a measure of the impedance and, since the resistance is practically constant, as is the frequency, the scale can be marked directly in microfarads or millihenrys. The Model 7 AvoMeter contains this facility for measuring capacitance from $0.01 - 20\,\mu\text{F}$.

10.2. CAPACITANCE BY SUBSTITUTION METHOD

The advantage of a substitution method of measurement has been discussed previously and it was shown that it had many of the advantages of a null method, even if the circuit arrangement is not one that depends upon obtaining zero current. In applying the substitution method to a bridge circuit the capacitance of the capacitor under test is replaced by an increase in the capacitance of a standard variable capacitor. The accuracy of the measurement is then governed by the calibration of the standard and the discrimination of the balance indicator.

A similar procedure can be adopted when using a resonant circuit instead of a bridge. The unknown capacitor is used to tune an inductor and the resonant frequency found. The unknown is then changed for the calibrated variable capacitor which is adjusted until the same resonant frequency is obtained.

The resonant frequency can be detected by coupling the circuit to an oscillator, varying the oscillator tuning, and noting the frequency at which the oscillator anode current shows a sudden decrease. The oscillator frequency is then left at that value and the substitution made. The change in frequency due to drift in the oscillator will be negligible over such a short space of time. Another way of arriving at the same result is to include the capacitor under test in the oscillator circuit itself. The frequency generated is then found by one of the methods previously described, say by setting a sub-standard oscillator to give zero beat. Then with this standard oscillator untouched the variable capacitor is substituted and the first oscillator retuned for zero beat.

Either of these methods gives good results though perhaps the last is the more accurate. The coil used in the first method should have low resistance and the coupling should be loose, in order to obtain a sharp resonance peak.

10.3. INDUCTANCE OF TUNING COILS

It is possible to measure a reactance in terms of another reactance of either sign, thus it is possible to use a variable capacitor or a variable inductor for measuring capacitance and inductance. For general use, however, a variable capacitor is to be preferred as it can more easily be made with a negligible temperature coefficient and with small losses. For standards at special laboratories inductors are wound on marble and their values calculated, thus giving absolute standards, as described in Chapter 17.

The method of substitution can be used for measuring inductance, using a variable inductor in the same manner as described in the previous section for capacitance. It is more usual, however, to use a standard variable capacitor and a fixed inductor, in which case the coil under test is substituted for the known inductor in a resonant circuit and the circuit retuned to the original frequency.

So far it has been assumed that variable standards of inductance or capacitance are available. An alternative is to use a known frequency.

It was shown in Chapter 9 that frequency can be measured to a high degree of accuracy and moreover some means of generating or measuring known frequencies is essential in every electronics laboratory; hence this method is often convenient.

The method of substitution can be used, varying the frequency instead of the capacitance; thus an inductance can be found in terms of frequency and a standard capacitance. In this case a *fixed* standard capacitance or inductance only is required. A very useful quick method of measuring inductance at radio frequencies is the simple resonant circuit method indicated in Fig. 10.1. Either C or the oscillator

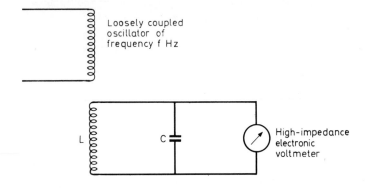

Fig. 10.1. Resonant circuit method of measuring L or C

frequency f (whichever is easier) is adjusted till resonance as indicated by maximum voltmeter reading is obtained. Then,

$$\omega = 2\pi f = \frac{1}{\sqrt{LC}}$$

whence L can be found if C and f are known.

If f is unknown but a standard variable capacitor and a fixed standard inductance L_1 are available then use the relation

$$\omega = 2\pi f = \frac{1}{\sqrt{L_1 C_1}} = \frac{1}{\sqrt{L_2 C_2}}$$

to calculate the unknown inductance L_2, where C_1 and C_2 are the capacitances to give resonance with the two inductors.

Now suppose that a capacitance is to be measured and that the set-up shown in Fig. 10.1 is again available. The oscillator is first loosely coupled to the circuit containing the standard capacitor C and any suitable inductance L; the oscillator is tuned to resonance and the frequency, say f_1, noted.

Then $$4\pi^2 f_1{}^2 LC = 1.$$

The capacitor C_x whose capacitance is to be measured is then connected in parallel with C, and the oscillator re-adjusted to resonance, the frequency then being, say, f_2.

$$4\pi^2 f_2^2 L(C + C_x) = 1.$$

$$\therefore C_x = \frac{1}{4\pi^2 f_2^2 L} - C$$

Substituting for L from the first equation, this becomes

$$C_x = \frac{f_1^2 C}{f_2^2} - C = C\left(\frac{f_1^2}{f_2^2} - 1\right)$$

10.4. DISTRIBUTED OR SELF-CAPACITANCE

In the previous section it was explained how the effective inductance could be found by balancing or comparing its reactance. It is clear, therefore, that the self-capacitance is included in the measurement. It is often desirable to measure this self-capacitance, or measure the inductance more accurately. The usual method is to tune the coil with a calibrated variable capacitor and measure the resonant frequency for a number of capacitor settings (or to find the capacitance required for resonance at a number of frequencies).

The reciprocal of the frequency squared is then plotted against capacitance. This gives a straight line, the slope of which is the true

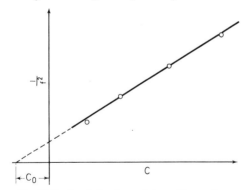

Fig. 10.2. Graph for determining self-capacitance

inductance, while the intercept, C_0, on the horizontal axis is the self-capacitance. The capacitance so found is the total capacitance of the circuit for zero setting of the variable capacitor, so allowance should be made for the minimum capacitance of the latter. Fig. 10.2 shows the kind of graph obtained. This method gives results quite accurate enough for ordinary requirements.

It should be noted at this point that the method of taking a number of readings and plotting the results is often a way of obtaining greater accuracy, since random errors of reading are averaged out. It is, of course, preferable to choose the variable for plotting so that a straight line results, but in cases where this is not practicable a larger number of readings should be taken, particularly if the slope of the graph changes rapidly.

If accuracy is of great importance, it is desirable to repeat the measurement using a different method and to average the results. For example, a coil and a standard capacitor can be used in an oscillator and the effective inductance obtained from the formula

$L_x = \dfrac{L_1 C_1}{C_2 - C_1}$. The experiment is then repeated, using different frequencies and $C_2 - C_1$ plotted against C_1. It will be seen that the slope of this curve gives the ratio L_1/L_x. The method described above of plotting $1/f^2$ against C can then be used and the results compared.

It is important to remember in all these measurements that the stray capacitance of the wiring is inevitably included. It is therefore difficult to measure the self-capacitance of a coil when this quantity is very small. The only way out of the difficulty is to measure this quantity by connecting two identical coils in parallel, measuring the total distributed capacitance as described above, and again with one of the coils disconnected. The value in the first case will be rather less than double that in the second. If C is the stray circuit capacitance and C_1 that of each coil the total stray and self-capacitance in the first case is $2C_1 + C$, and in the second $C_1 + C$. If the latter value is doubled and the former value subtracted from it, the value of C is obtained. This refinement, of course, is necessary only when the self-capacitance is required to be known to considerable accuracy.

10.5. MEASUREMENT OF SMALL CAPACITANCES

This determination calls for considerable ingenuity since a method must be found such that no allowance has to be made for stray capacitances. The best method is to measure the change in frequency of a negative resistance oscillator when the unknown capacitance is added to its tuning capacitance. First of all a standard variable capacitor is connected across the oscillator inductance coil (see Fig. 10.3) and the frequency measured at a number of capacitor settings. This capacitance can be reasonably large. The frequency produced is arranged to beat with a standard oscillator and the beat frequency measured. This can be done in several ways, but perhaps the best is to measure the frequency of the beat note by comparison with an audio-frequency oscillator. If the

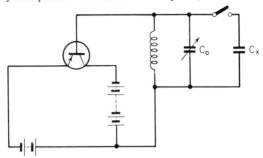

Fig. 10.3. Measurement of small capacitances

latter is well calibrated it is possible to adjust it to within one cycle of the beat tone, i.e., a change in the r.f. of one cycle per second can be detected.

In this way the changes in frequency of the r.f. oscillator produced by the addition of known capacitances are obtained and can be plotted. The result can be made to give a straight line by plotting $1/f^2$ against C, as before. The intercept on the horizontal axis gives the 'permanent capacitance' of the oscillator circuit, including stray capacitances and the residual capacitance of the capacitor C_0 in Fig. 10.3.

As the change in capacitance can be made large there is no difficulty in measuring the actual frequency generated. The values of the capacitor C_0 can be chosen so as to produce convenient frequencies for measurement.

The unknown capacitance is now connected and produces a change of frequency. This change will be small but can be measured very accurately; as stated above, a change of one cycle per second can be detected, and if the oscillator is operating at 1000 kHz, a change of 1 part in 10^6 can be observed.

Let C_s be the capacitance of the standard capacitor,

$\quad$ C_x the capacitance of the unknown capacitor,

$\quad$ f_1 the frequency with capacitance C_s only,

$\quad$ f_2 the frequency with capacitance $C_s + C_x$.

Then $4\pi^2 f_1{}^2 L C_s = 1$ and $4\pi^2 f_2{}^2 L (C_s + C_x) = 1$.

$$\therefore \frac{C_s + C_x}{C_s} = \frac{f_1{}^2}{f_2{}^2} \text{ whence } C_x = C_s \left(\frac{f_1{}^2}{f_2{}^2} - 1 \right)$$

$$= \frac{C_s (f_1{}^2 - f_2{}^2)}{f_2{}^2} = \frac{C_s (f_1 - f_2)(f_1 + f_2)}{f_2{}^2}$$

If C_x is very small compared with C_s, f_1 is very nearly equal to f_2;

$$\therefore\ C_x = \frac{C_s\,(f_1 - f_2)..\,2f_2}{f_2{}^2}\,(\text{very nearly}) = \frac{2C_s\,(f_1 - f_2)}{f_2}$$

In Fig. 10.4 is shown the schematic arrangement. The audio-frequency note is arranged to beat with one produced by an a.f.

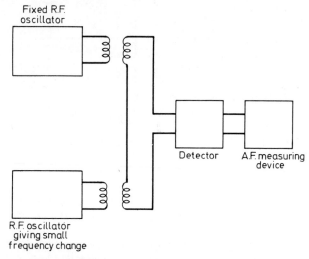

Fig. 10.4. Method of measuring small frequency changes

oscillator the exact frequency of which need not be known. The change in beat tone is then easily obtained by counting the beats.

If preferred, these radio frequencies can be compared by the cathode-ray tube method. This really amounts to the same thing, for the difference between the frequencies is counted by watching the progression of the Lissajous figure. The objection to this method is that the two oscillators must work at very nearly the same frequency and consequently unless their outputs are kept well separated there is risk of 'pulling'.

The 'fixed' oscillator should, of course, be adjustable and calibrated, since the actual value of f_1 is required. A capacitance as small as $10^{-5}\mu\mu$F has been measured in this way, using a frequency of 10 MHz.

10.6. HIGH FREQUENCY RESISTANCE

In high-frequency a.c. circuits the power loss is often greater than that which would occur if a d.c. current of the same value were flowing. This is due to such factors as dielectric losses, eddy current losses, skin effect losses, and losses due to the so-called proximity effect. The effective a.c. resistance is given by P/I^2, where I is the current and P the power absorbed in the circuit. In a resistive circuit, the main loss is due to skin effect.

10.6.1. Skin Effect

At high frequencies the current carried by a conductor is not uniformly distributed over its cross-section as in the case of d.c., but tends to flow near the surface. This is due to the production of eddy currents by the change in magnetic flux which encircles part, but not all, of the conductor. The lines of force form concentric circles and some flux exists inside the conductor as well as outside it. The flux inside links with the current near the centre whilst not linking with the current near the surface. The result is that the centre portion has the greater inductance because of the greater number of flux linkages.

At radio frequencies the reactance of this centre region is sufficient to cause considerable reduction in the proportion of the total current flowing in it. The centre therefore carries less than its share of the total current and the effective cross-sectional area of the conductor is reduced.

Thus, when skin effect is present, the current is distributed over the cross-section of the conductor in such a way as to make most of the current flow where it is encircled by the smallest number of flux lines. This tendency of alternating currents to flow in the outer parts or 'skin' of a conductor is called skin effect. It increases with frequency, since the higher the frequency the greater is the rate of change of flux.

Skin effect can be reduced by the use of tubular conductors and by the use of stranded wire. However, the skin effect in the individual strands is still pronounced at relatively high frequencies.

From the foregoing it is evident that it is desirable to measure the effective resistance of circuits at a frequency somewhere near to that at which they are intended to work. Most methods measure the total losses, in effect, and the dielectric losses are separated by comparing a coil (or other apparatus) having similar dimensions and conductors, and differing only in the insulating material and method of support.

10.6.2. Resistance-Variation Method

This resembles a method sometimes used in d.c. work where approximate results suffice, for example, the measuring of galvanometer resistance. The change in current produced in a circuit by the addition of a known resistance is observed, the voltage being kept constant. If the current is I_0 when the circuit resistance is R_x, and the current is I_1 when the *added* resistance is R_s, then

$$R_x = R_s \frac{I_1}{I_0 - I_1} .$$

In the case of a radio-frequency circuit it is necessary to tune to the frequency of the supply, then its impedance is a pure resistance and is given by R_x in the above equation.

Fig. 10.5 shows the method. It will be seen that a voltage is induced in the circuit and the current is measured by a thermo-couple milliammeter. The experiment is repeated with several values of R_s and the

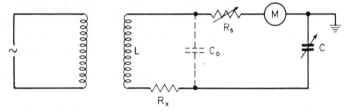

Fig. 10.5. Resistance-variation method of measuring h.f. resistance

results can be plotted, as in finding the self-capacitance of a coil. This gives an added check because if the points obtained when $1/I$ is plotted against R_s do not lie on a straight line, something is wrong.

There are several precautions necessary for accurate results. The varying load must not cause any change in 'primary' current for this implies a change in induced voltage. The voltage is assumed to be all induced in series, i.e. the only coupling must be inductive, hence screening and loose coupling are desirable. R_s must, of course, be non-reactive and its resistance at radio frequencies accurately known. The resistance of the meter should be included. A straight thin wire can be used, in which case the r.f. resistance will be practically the same as the d.c. resistance. The capacitance C should be large compared with the self-capacitance of the coil since the milliammeter does not measure the component of current through the latter, shown dotted in Fig. 10.5. Alternatively, this can be separately measured and allowed for.

The true value of resistance R_x', is given by

$$R_x' = R_x \left(\frac{C}{C_0 + C} \right)^2$$

This measurement is clearly no more accurate than the thermo-milliammeter method. It cannot compare, therefore, with the Wheatstone bridge method. Nevertheless, it gives results good enough for many purposes.

10.6.3. Capacitance-Variation Method

The circuit arrangement is practically the same as that shown in Fig. 10.5, except that R_S is not required. The current, say I_0, is measured at resonance; the capacitor is then increased to a value C_2 giving a current I_1 and then decreased to a value C_1 below that giving resonance such that the current is again I_1. Then the following equations apply:

$$E = I_0 R \tag{i}$$

$$E = I_1 \sqrt{R^2 + \left(\omega L - \frac{1}{\omega C_1}\right)^2} \tag{ii}$$

$$E = I_1 \sqrt{R^2 + \left(\omega L - \frac{1}{\omega C_2}\right)^2} \tag{iii}$$

Now clearly $\omega L - \dfrac{1}{\omega C_1}$ and $\omega L - \dfrac{1}{\omega C_2}$ must be equal but of opposite sign.

$$\therefore \omega L - \frac{1}{\omega C_1} = -\omega L + \frac{1}{\omega C_2} \text{ whence } 2\omega L = \frac{1}{\omega C_2} + \frac{1}{\omega C_1}$$

$$\therefore \omega L - \frac{1}{\omega C_1} = \frac{1}{2}\left(\frac{1}{\omega C_2} + \frac{1}{\omega C_1}\right) - \frac{1}{\omega C_1} = \frac{1}{2}\left(\frac{1}{\omega C_2} - \frac{1}{\omega C_1}\right)$$

Substituting in equation (ii) gives:-

$$E = I_1 \sqrt{R^2 + \frac{1}{4}\left(\frac{1}{\omega C_2} - \frac{1}{\omega C_1}\right)^2}$$

Substituting for E from equation (i) gives:-

$$I_0 R = I_1 \sqrt{R^2 + \frac{1}{4}\left(\frac{1}{\omega C_2} - \frac{1}{\omega C_1}\right)^2}$$

$$\therefore I_0^2 R^2 = I_1^2 R^2 + \frac{I_1^2}{4}\left(\frac{1}{\omega C_2} - \frac{1}{\omega C_1}\right)^2$$

$$\therefore R^2 = \frac{I_1^2\left(\frac{1}{\omega C_2} - \frac{1}{\omega C_1}\right)^2}{4(I_0^2 - I_1^2)} \quad \therefore R = \frac{I_1\left(\frac{1}{C_2} - \frac{1}{C_1}\right)}{2\omega\sqrt{I_0^2 - I_1^2}} = \frac{I_1(C_1 - C_2)}{2\omega C_1 C_2 \sqrt{I_0^2 - I_1^2}}.$$

As in the previous method corrections are required for self-capacitance and for the milliammeter resistance.

It may happen that a suitable thermo-couple meter is not available while a valve voltmeter is. In this case the change in voltage across the

capacitor can be measured instead of the current; the resistance is then
given by:-

$$R = \frac{C_2 - C_1}{2\omega C_1 C_2} \sqrt{\left(\frac{C_2 + C_1}{2C_1}\right)^2 E_0{}^2 - E_1{}^2}.$$

At very high frequencies a correction must be made for the capacitance of the valve voltmeter if the highest possible accuracy is required.

10.6.4. Frequency-Variation Method

This method is the same in principle as the previous one. The current
through (or voltage across) the capacitor is noted for the resonant
frequency f_0, then the oscillator frequency is decreased to f_1 and the
current again noted; the frequency is then increased to f_2 so that the
current is the same as at f_1.

Again instead of measuring the current directly, the voltage across
the capacitor can be measured by means of a valve voltmeter. The
method assumes that the current in the 'primary', i.e. the coil connected
to the oscillator, remains constant. As a check on this, it is a good plan
to provide some sort of output measuring device on the oscillator.

The results are given by the equations

$$R = 2\pi L \, (f_2 - f_1) \sqrt{\frac{E_1{}^2}{\frac{f_0{}^2}{f_1{}^2} E_0{}^2 - E_1{}^2}} \quad \text{or} \quad R = 2\pi L (f_2 - f_1) \sqrt{\frac{I_1{}^2}{I_0{}^2 - I_1{}^2}}$$

The proof of these equations is as follows.

Let I_0 = current at resonant angular frequency ω_0,

I_1 = current at some other angular frequency ω.

Then $I_1{}^2 = \dfrac{E^2}{R^2}$

and

$$I_1{}^2 = \frac{E^2}{R^2 + \left(\omega L - \dfrac{1}{\omega C}\right)^2} = \frac{E^2}{R^2\left\{1 + \dfrac{1}{R^2}\left(\omega L - \dfrac{1}{\omega C}\right)^2\right\}}$$

$$= \frac{E^2}{R^2\left\{1 + \dfrac{1}{R^2}\left(\omega L - \dfrac{\omega_0{}^2 L}{\omega}\right)^2\right\}}$$

$$\left(\text{since at resonance, } \omega_0 L = \frac{1}{\omega_0 C}, \; \therefore \; \omega_0{}^2 L = \frac{1}{C} \text{ and} \frac{\omega_0{}^2 L}{\omega} = \frac{1}{\omega C}\right)$$

$$= \frac{E^2}{\left\{R^2 \; 1 + \dfrac{L^2}{R^2}\left(\omega - \dfrac{\omega_0{}^2}{\omega}\right)^2\right\}}$$

$$\therefore \frac{I_0{}^2}{I_1{}^2} - 1 = \frac{L^2}{R^2}\left(\omega - \frac{\omega_0{}^2}{\omega}\right)^2$$

$$\therefore \sqrt{\frac{I_0{}^2 - I_1{}^2}{I^2}} = \frac{L}{R}\left(\omega - \frac{\omega_0{}^2}{\omega}\right) = y \text{ (say)}$$

$$\therefore \omega y = \frac{\omega^2 L}{R} - \frac{\omega_0{}^2 L}{R}$$

whence
$$\omega^2 - \frac{Ry}{L}\omega - \omega_0{}^2 = 0$$

The solutions of this equation are ω_1 and ω_2 respectively, where

$$\omega_1 = \frac{-\dfrac{Ry}{L} \pm \sqrt{\dfrac{R^2 y^2}{L^2} + 4\omega_0{}^2}}{2} \quad \text{and} \quad \omega_2 = \frac{\dfrac{Ry}{L} \pm \sqrt{\dfrac{R^2 y^2}{L^2} + 4\omega_0{}^2}}{2}$$

Since both ω_1 and ω_2 must be positive, only the positive values of the surd are admissible.

$$\therefore \omega_2 - \omega_1 = \frac{Ry}{L} \text{ whence } R = \frac{L}{y}(\omega_2 - \omega_1) = 2\pi(f_2 - f_1) L \sqrt{\frac{I_1{}^2}{I_0{}^2 - I_1{}^2}}.$$

If I is made equal to $\dfrac{I_0}{\sqrt{2}}$ the term under the root becomes equal to unity, this simplifying the calculation. Substituting $I_0 = E_0 \omega_0 C$ and $I_1 = E_1 \omega_1 C$ in the above equation gives

$$R = 2\pi(f_2 - f_1) L \sqrt{\frac{E_1{}^2 \omega_1{}^2 C^2}{E_0{}^2 \omega_0{}^2 C^2 - E_1{}^2 \omega_1{}^2 C^2}}$$

$$= 2\pi(f_2 - f_1) L \sqrt{\frac{E_1{}^2}{\dfrac{\omega_0{}^2}{\omega_1{}^2} E_0{}^2 - E_1{}^2}}$$

$$= 2\pi(f_2 - f_1) L \sqrt{\frac{E_1{}^2}{\dfrac{f_0{}^2}{f_1{}^2} E_0{}^2 - E_1{}^2}}.$$

It should be noted that in this method the total capacitance is not altered during the measurement and also, in the valve voltmeter modification, the self-capacitance does not form a separate short circuit. This point is made clear by Fig. 10.6.

In Fig. 10.6 (a), I is not the current in the *coil* nor is E directly proportional to the current in the coil. In Fig. 10.6 (b), which relates to the frequency variation method, E is directly proportional to the coil current since the self-capacitance C_0 and C are virtually one capacitance. This method does not require correction for coil capacitance.

The accuracy clearly depends upon the accuracy with which the frequency difference and the currents or voltages can be measured. As explained earlier, the frequency difference can be determined very accurately. At very high frequencies the valve voltmeter input resistance

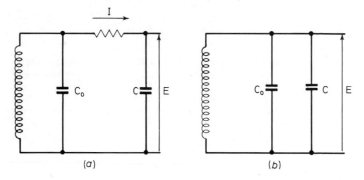

Fig. 10.6. Circuits relating to measurement of h.f. resistance

has to be allowed for. This effect, however, can be made smaller by using for C a small and large capacitor in series and connecting the voltmeter across the latter; thus the voltmeter is loosely coupled. This method is perhaps the best, especially at ultra high frequencies, though it is not the quickest.

The reader will appreciate that the methods described up till now in this chapter are somewhat finical, since the coupling between the oscillator and the circuit under test must be loose enough to ensure that the applied signal is of only one particular frequency yet sufficiently tight to obtain a usable signal. Moreover, in practice, an electrostatic screen should be fitted between oscillator and tuned circuit to prevent mutual coupling of capacitances, and stray fields are likely to affect the measurement. For this reason Q meters, also known as magnification meters, as described in section 10.7, are often used in modern practice for r.f. measurements on passive components. Although the instrument is used mainly for measuring the Q of inductors, the inductance value is easily calculated from the frequency and capacitance calibration, and the scale can therefore be calibrated in terms of inductance as well as Q or a conversion chart can be supplied with the instrument. Capacitance can also be measured, by slideback method for small capacitors, or by resonance method, for larger capacitors, against a previously measured inductor. Resonance methods have been included in this book because it is important that the principles should be known and that they still form the subject matter of examination questions.

Constructional details of instruments for the r.f. measurement of capacitors and inductors are given in the book *Basic Electronic Test Instruments*[1].

10.7. Q MEASUREMENTS

Before proceeding to a consideration of methods of measuring Q, a brief survey of the factors upon which Q depends will assist in appreciating the precautions necessary in making measurements and interpreting the results. Q may be defined as the 'magnification factor' or 'quality factor' of a coil, being the ratio of reactance to effective resistance at the operating frequency.

At low operating frequencies, i.e. in the audio range, an air-cored coil may be regarded as simply its d.c. resistance combined with an inductance only. This means that, initially, Q is proportional to frequency. There are two ways in which the limit to this effect appears, namely, self-capacitance and h.f. resistance.

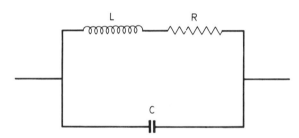

Fig. 10.7. Equivalent circuit of inductor at high frequencies

Assuming for convenience that the self-capacitance is lumped, and neglecting the effect of h.f. resistance or any other loss than d.c. resistance, the impedance of a coil consisting of L, R and C (Fig. 10.7) can be written:

$$\frac{\dfrac{1}{j\omega C}(R + j\omega L)}{R + j\omega L + \dfrac{1}{j\omega C}} \quad \text{which rationalises to} \quad \frac{R + j\omega L\left(1 - \dfrac{CR^2}{L} - \omega^2 LC\right)}{(1 - \omega^2 LC)^2 + \omega^2 C^2 R^2}$$

In general, for any resonant circuit, the denominator of this expression will be less than unity, so that R will increase in effective value as the real part of the expression. The imaginary part, which represents the inductance value, decreases in value as resonance is approached so that the net effect is a decrease of Q. Since Q is given as the ratio X/R it may be written:

$$Q = \omega\left(\frac{L}{R} - CR\right) - \frac{\omega^3 L^2 C}{R}$$

The first term $\omega L/R$ is the normal value for Q in an inductance and resistance combination. The second term $-\omega CR$ represents a depreciation in Q proportional to frequency, and so could be considered as a fixed proportionate reduction in the effective value of the first term. The third term represents a depreciation in Q which is proportional to the third power of frequency. Thus it is seen that the Q of an inductor rapidly diminishes as it approaches its natural frequency.

The effect of h.f. resistance upon a simple conductor is to introduce an additional term into its effective resistance, proportional to frequency squared, due to the reduction in useful cross-sectional area of the conductor. When the conductor is arranged in the form of a coil, adjacent turns have an additional restricting influence on the effective cross-sectional area of the conductor, so that its h.f. resistance is further increased according to a more complex law. The effect can be reduced by the use of either tubular conductors or stranded and insulated conductors.

Screening cans are another possible way in which the Q of a coil may be reduced, since effectively they loosely couple a short-circuited turn to the coil, which has the effect of reducing the inductance and increasing the resistance of the coil. This again has the effect of decreasing the Q by a fixed proportion at the lower frequencies, but at the higher frequencies introduces a negative term proportional to the frequency cubed.

10.7.1. Core Losses

Various types of core material may be used to improve the Q-value over certain frequency ranges. This is achieved by increasing the magnetic field produced by the magnetising current in the coil. However, with the improved value of inductance thus obtained, certain losses are also introduced due to effects in the core. If the increased loss is as great as the increased value of inductance, then no advantage accrues from the use of such a core, and either air-cored types must be used, or a better core material must be sought.

The losses in core materials are of two kinds. For a given maximum flux density, one group of losses, of which the chief form is hysteresis, is proportional to frequency, and approximately proportional to the square of the flux density. Since for a specified applied voltage, or back e.m.f., the maximum flux density is inversely proportional to frequency, this means that this group of losses is approximately inversely proportional to frequency for a constant applied voltage. The other group of losses, of which the chief form is eddy current loss, is proportional to frequency squared for constant flux density, and proportional to flux density squared at constant frequency, so for constant applied voltage this group of losses is practically constant.

The first group of core losses may be regarded as a shunt resistance approximately proportional to frequency, so that the effect on Q due to this form of loss does not vary greatly with frequency, since the reactance is also approximately proportional to frequency. The second group of core losses may be regarded as a constant shunt resistance. The effect of this on the Q value of the coil will be to introduce a degradation component which is proportional to frequency.

10.7.2. Dielectric Losses

There is another source of loss due to electric forces in either the coil insulation or the core material. These may be regarded as equivalent to the losses in a capacitor connected across a coil, caused by a small series resistance in series with it. This situation produces a shunt resistance whose value eventually varies approximately as the reciprocal of frequency squared. As this is in shunt with the inductance which is varying approximately direct as frequency, the degrading effect as frequency rises will be approximately proportional to frequency cubed.

10.7.3. Q Meters

From the foregoing, it will be seen how complex the nature of Q, and the precise value of L, can become at very high frequencies. At frequencies which are below an optimum value, Q will tend to rise in proportion to frequency, flattening off as the other forms of loss become considerable in the optimum region, and finally falling off at a rate that may represent any power of frequency up to the third, and even, by combination of effects due to the fact that L itself is changing, perhaps up to the fourth power.

At radio frequencies, especially with coupled circuits, it is very important to be able to determine Q values in design work, and also to be able to test Q values in production to ascertain that production coils are within specific tolerances. Thus Q meters fall into two types, namely, those giving results to some standard of accuracy in absolute measure, and those enabling a check to be made by comparison with another of the same type, giving a 'plus and minus' indication with reference to a 'production standard'.

Fig. 10.8 shows the basic circuit of a *Q* meter of the first type. It includes a built-in radio-frequency oscillator which covers the frequency range from, say, 50 kHz to 75 MHz in several ranges, within a calibration accuracy of the order of ± 2%. From this generator a small, accurately known voltage is delivered into a circuit consisting of the coil under test and calibrated low-loss capacitors built into the instrument. The voltage developed across these internal capacitors is then indicated by an electronic voltmeter of very high input impedance, calibrated directly in *Q* values. The accuracy of these instruments is of the order of ± 5% for all ordinary coils up to a frequency of about 15 MHz, above which the accuracy falls somewhat. A typical normal range of the main tuning capacitor will be 50 to 500 pF on a 300° scale, this capacitor being shunted by a vernier capacitor of range about

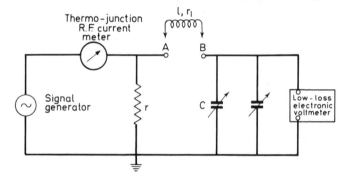

Fig. 10.8. Basic circuit of Q meter

± 3 pF. For frequencies above 1·5 MHz it is important that the standard resistor *r* in Fig. 10.8 should have negligible effective self-inductance. This can be achieved by special construction as shown in Fig. 10.9.

By including other components in the circuit, as well as an inductor whose inductance and *Q* are already measured at the working frequency,

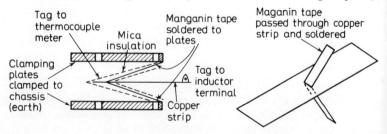

Fig. 10.9. Construction of standard resistor

such components may be evaluated by the substitution method already described in Chapter 8. In this way an instrument of this type can be used for measurements on capacitors, resistors, transmission lines, and the like, if more directly suitable instruments are not available. It should be noted that the accuracy of such additional measurements falls off in time, due to the fact that any errors which the circuit produces are added to its previous errors in measuring the inductance used in the circuit.

In Q comparators used as routine checkers of production coils, a standard inductor is connected to the instrument and controls are adjusted so that a meter reading representing 100% Q value is attained and a vernier tuning capacitor, which is the only control used in actual routine testing, is at the zero position. When other coils are connected, the capacitor setting is varied to find resonance and the meter scale reads the difference in tuning capacitance. Variations in coil inductance corresponding to these differences in capacitance are marked on the meter scale, so that it can be seen at once whether or not the coil under test is within the required tolerance as regards its inductance value.

WORKED EXAMPLE

Question. Fig. 10.8 shows the circuit of a Q-meter. State the characteristic required for the voltmeter, and describe a suitable instrument.

If the resistor r has a resistance of 0·1 ohm and a self-inductance of 0·01 μH calculate the correction required to the Q-factor reading when measuring a coil of 20 μH and Q = 200 at 1·6 MHz.

How would you construct the resistor r so as to minimise its effective self-inductance?   (C. & G. Radio IV, 1955 (Modified)

Answer. The descriptive part of the answer to this question is given in the the text. Referring to Fig. 10.10, at a frequency of 2 MHz,

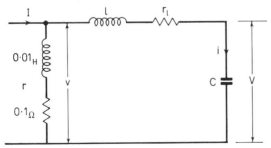

Fig. 10.10. Equivalent circuit for Fig. 10.8.

$$\omega l = \frac{1}{\omega C} = 2\pi \times 1 \cdot 6 \times 10^6 \times 20 \times 10^{-6} \simeq 200.$$

$$\text{Now } Q = \frac{\omega L}{r_l} \quad \therefore \quad r_l = \frac{\omega L}{Q} = 1 \text{ ohm.}$$

The current flowing through the capacitor at resonance is

$$i = \frac{0 \cdot 1 + j(2\pi \times 1 \cdot 6 \times 10^6 \times 0 \cdot 01 \times 10^{-6})}{1 + 0 \cdot 1 + j0 \cdot 1} I \quad \therefore \quad |i| = \frac{0 \cdot 1414}{1 \cdot 103} I = 0 \cdot 128 I$$

$$\therefore \text{ Measured } Q = \frac{V}{v} = \frac{0 \cdot 128 \, I \times 200}{0 \cdot 1 \, I} = 256.$$

$$\therefore \text{ Correction required} = \frac{200}{256} = \underline{0 \cdot 782} \quad Answer.$$

EXERCISES

1. A circuit consisting of a coil, a variable capacitor and a thermo-couple is lightly coupled to a variable-frequency power oscillator. A galvanometer is connected to the couple. The circuit is in resonance when the oscillator is adjusted to 1000 metres. When the oscillator is adjusted to 1005 metres, the galvanometer deflection is halved. If the capacitor setting is $0 \cdot 0015 \, \mu F$, what is the resistance of the coil?

Answer. $\underline{2 \, \Omega.}$ (C. and G.)

2. How would you determine the natural wavelength of a coil? An oscillatory circuit containing a thermo-milliammeter is weakly coupled to a power oscillator and tuned to resonance when the reading of the thermo-milliammeter is 20 mA. A resistance of 5 Ω is then added in series with the resonant circuit and the current becomes 4 mA. What is the resistance of the coil?   (C. and G.)

Answer. $\underline{1 \cdot 25 \, \Omega,}$ including the meter resistance.

3. Describe how you would proceed to determine experimentally the inductance, resistance, and self-capacitance of a coil at a frequency of about 100 kHz.   (C. and G. Final Grade).

REFERENCE

1. TURNER, RUFUS P., *Basic Electronic Test Instruments (Revised Edition).* Holt, Rinehart and Winston, Inc. (1963).

CHAPTER 11

Measurements on Transistors and Integrated Circuits

11.1. INTRODUCTION

The development of the point-contact transistor was announced in 1948 and that of the junction transistor and diode in the following year. Since then, the transistor and similar semiconductor devices have revolutionised the whole art of electronics.

The various characteristics of transistors can be determined by direct measurement, or by bridge methods. Transistor circuits are normally divided into three basic classes or configurations, namely common-base, common-emitter and common-collector, where the quoted electrode is in each case common to both the input and output circuits. Most of the measurements described in this chapter apply to a *p-n-p* transistor operating in the common-emitter configuration, but they are equally applicable to the *n-p-n* transistor and the other basic circuit configurations, provided that the polarities of the batteries are changed accordingly.

This chapter is mainly concerned with the plotting of the I_c/V_{ce} and the I_b/V_{be} characteristics (see below for symbol definitions) and the determination of the current gain a', the leakage current I'_{co}, the cut-off frequency f'_c and the hybrid or h parameters. Most commercial transistor testers will only test the current gain and the leakage current, since the measurement of these two parameters is normally sufficient to determine the serviceability of a given transistor, the other parameters being more applicable to circuit design. However, it will be shown that only three fundamental test circuits are required to perform the first five measurements.

11.2. TRANSISTOR CHARACTERISTICS

Fig. 11.1 shows the common-emitter circuit and the four basic electrical quantities associated with it, all of which are relatively easy to measure, namely,

(1) the voltage between base and emitter V_{be},
(2) the voltage between collector and emitter V_{ce},

(3) the transistor base current I_b,
(4) the transistor collector current I_c.

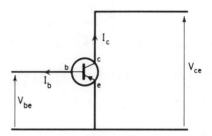

Fig. 11.1. Common-emitter circuit

From the mutual relationships between these voltages and currents the various characteristics of the transistor may be derived and presented in the form of characteristic curves.

11.2.1. The I_c/V_{ce} Characteristic

By means of the circuit shown in Fig. 11.2 the relationship between I_c and V_{ce} for different values of I_b can be determined. M_1 and M_2 are milli-ammeters, but for some transistors M_1 may have to be a microammeter.

Switch S_1 is first closed and the base current adjusted to the required value by means of potentiometer P_1. Switch S_2 is then closed and the

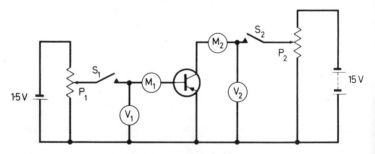

Fig. 11.2. Basic test circuit

collector voltage set to a suitable value by means of potentiometer P_2. The corresponding collector voltages and currents are recorded at intervals as the voltage as set by P_2 is increased in suitable steps. It is important that the base current does not change during the measurements; if it does, P_1 must be re-adjusted accordingly.

The measurements are then repeated using other values of base current and the results plotted to form a family of characteristic curves as shown in Fig. 11.3. These curves will now be analysed.

At the left-hand end there is a steeply-sloping region where a very small increase in collector voltage produces a considerable increase in collector current. This region exists below a V_{ce} of about 200 mV for most transistors, and is of considerable importance in the design and operation of transistor switching circuits. For this reason, and since the region is rather cramped on the overall curves, this part of the characteristic is usually plotted separately to a larger scale in published transistor data.

On the nearly horizontal portion of the curves a large increase in collector voltage produces very little change in collector current. This is the so-called linear range of the transistor, and represents the limits within which normal amplifier circuits are designed, as in the case of a pentode valve.

The upward curving region (shown dotted) at the right-hand end is where an increase in collector voltage results in a large rise in collector current due to breakdown of the *p-n* junction, and no transistor must ever be operated in this region. The maximum collector voltage is always specified in manufacturer's data and must never be exceeded.

11.2.2. Current Gain a'

The current amplification of a transistor in the common emitter mode of operation is symbolised by a' and is defined as the ratio between the change in collector current for a given change in base current, the collector voltage remaining constant, or

$$a' = \left(\frac{\delta I_c}{\delta I_b}\right)_{V_{ce} \text{ const.}}$$

Note that a dash ($'$) attached to a symbol always denotes the common emitter configuration.

If the I_c/V_{ce} characteristic curves have been plotted as shown in Fig. 11.3, then a' can be plotted from them by drawing a vertical line on the graph to represent a given constant collector voltage. Two adjacent intersections on this line then represent a given change in base current, against which can be read off the corresponding change in collector current; these values are then substituted in the above formula for a'. The smaller the change in base current, the more accurately will a' be determined.

Transistor data usually quote the value of a' for a specified value of collector voltage and base current. The test circuit of Fig. 11.2 can be

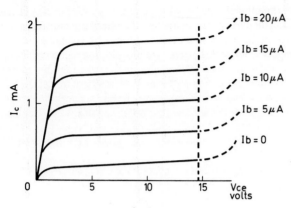

Fig. 11.3. I_c/V_{ce} characteristics

used to check this figure without drawing the I_c/V_{ce} curves. Potentiometers P_1 and P_2 are first set to give the specified conditions. P_1 is then adjusted until the base current is, say, 10 μA above the published value. The base current, I_{b1} say, and the corresponding collector current I_{c1} are recorded. P_1 is then readjusted until the base current is 10 μA below the published value, this base current and the corresponding collector current being recorded as I_{b2} and I_{c2} respectively. Then

$$a' = \frac{I_{c1} - I_{c2}}{I_{b1} - I_{b2}}.$$

In general, the smaller the variation in base current for this test, the more accurate will be the measured value of a' at the specified operating point.

11.2.3. The I_b/V_{be} Characteristic

This is sometimes referred to as the input characteristic, being a measure of the input conductance of the transistor, and can be determined using the basic test circuit of Fig. 11.2 as follows. First, switch S_2 is closed and the collector voltage set to zero by adjusting P_2. Switch S_1 is now closed and the base voltage gradually increased by adjustment of P_1, the corresponding values of voltage V_{be} and current I_b being recorded at intervals.

The measurements are then repeated for different values of collector voltage as set by P_2. The collector voltage must remain constant during each set of measurements; if it varies, P_2 must be adjusted accordingly.

The experimental results are plotted in the form of curves as shown in Fig. 11.4. The part of the characteristic where the emitter is negative with respect to the base can be plotted if desired by reversing the polarity of the voltage V_1. When the curves are plotted, they show a strong resem-

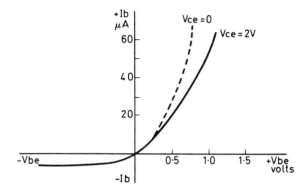

Fig. 11.4. I_b/V_{be} characteristics

blance to those of a crystal diode, and it will be seen that when V_{be} is more negative than -1 V the collector voltage V_{ce} has little or no effect on the base current I_b.

11.2.4. Leakage Current I'_{co}

The leakage current of a transistor is very sensitive to changes in temperature, and the maximum value is always quoted for a particular value of collector voltage and specific temperature, usually $25°$C.

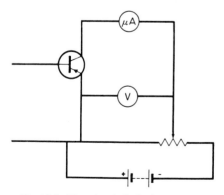

Fig. 11.5. Test circuit for leakage current

A suitable circuit for measuring the leakage current is shown in Fig. 11.5. The collector voltage V_{ce} is adjusted to the required value using the potentiometer, the base circuit being left open-circuited. The leakage current is then read off the microammeter.

If the transistor is held tightly between the fingers for a few seconds the leakage current will show a large increase; thus a transistor should never be held in the hand when making test measurements.

11.2.5. Cut-off Frequency f_c'

The cut-off frequency of a transistor is defined as the frequency at which the current gain a' drops 3 dB relative to that at 1000 Hz. An approximate determination of f_c' can be obtained using the circuit of Fig. 11.6.

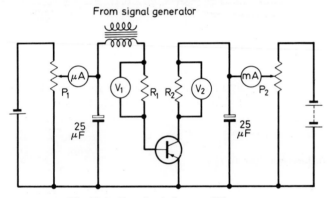

Fig. 11.6. Test circuit for cut-off frequency

The potentiometers P_1 and P_2 are first adjusted to establish the specified d.c. working point, and a 1000 Hz voltage from the signal generator is then fed into the base circuit via the transformer. The current amplification a' is now given by the ratio of the a.c. collector current to the a.c. base current. The alternating voltages across R_1 and R_2 are measured by suitable a.c. meters and if $R_1 = R_2 = 100\ \Omega$, say, then

$$a' = \frac{V_2}{V_1}$$

The signal frequency is now gradually increasing keeping V_1 constant and after a certain frequency has been reached it is found that V_2 begins to fall. The frequency at which V_2 drops to 0·7 (3 dB down) of its value at 1000 Hz is the cut-off frequency.

11.2.6. Resistance Tests

Quick checks on a transistor for open or short circuits can be made with an ohmmeter provided that the instrument operates with a current less than 2 mA and a terminal voltage not greater than 3 V. If a multimeter set to the OHMS range is used for these tests it is essential to check the actual polarity of the terminals marked positive and negative on the instrument as in most cases their polarity with respect to the battery contained in the instrument is reversed. Fig. 11.7 is the relative resistance

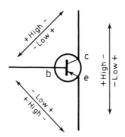

Fig. 11.7. Resistance tests

diagram and refers to the true polarity of the test leads applied.

The relative resistance measurements are based on the fact that the transistor can be considered as two junction diodes connected in series opposition. For an *n-p-n* type transistor the relative resistance readings are completely reversed.

11.2.7. Use of the Cathode-ray Tube

Dynamic transistor characteristics can be traced by applying a 50 Hz voltage to the base of the transistor in series with the appropriate bias and also to one pair of c.r.t. deflector plates. The other pair of plates are fed from the voltage developed across the collector load resistance. In this way the output volts/base volts curve is plotted automatically.

Two more basic circuits are shown in Fig. 11.8. The circuit at (*a*) is for base voltage/collector current characteristics, with the d.c. collector voltage altered in steps for successive positive excursions of the a.c. base voltage. Circuit (*b*) produces collector voltage/collector current curves, with the base voltage being altered in steps between successive positive excursions of the collector voltage.

A further refinement includes arrangements for switching in positions for tracing out the vertical and horizontal axes, the switching being

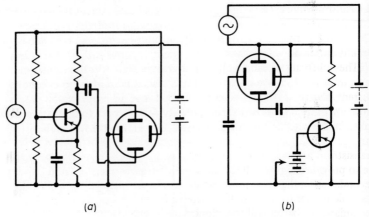

Fig. 11.8. Transistor curve tracer circuits

performed electrically by multivibrator circuits (see Chapter 9). This method is a useful one for testing transistors of any given type, giving simultaneous indications of all its basic parameters in visual form. The same method can of course be used for obtaining the characteristics of complete amplifiers.

Thus, it is seen that this method traces the curve instantly, as no other method does, and is accurate enough for most purposes. Moreover the transistor is less liable to damage by positive base voltages since the operating conditions do not have to be maintained steady for an appreciable time so as to take a meter reading.

11.2.8. Characteristics of Various c.r.t. Methods

Suppose the base is supplied with a potential given by

$$e_b = E_0 + E_1 \sin \omega t,$$

where E_0 is the base-bias potential.

The collector current consists also of a steady and an alternating component. The emitter and base can be connected to the deflector plates and the collector current passed through coils arranged for magnetic deflection. The deflection of the spot will then be directly proportional to the instantaneous base voltage and collector current, thus tracing out a transistor characteristic.

There are several difficulties of this method in practice. One of these is the need to provide for magnetic deflection as well as the electrostatic usually provided for in commercial oscilloscopes. Another is that the deflections will only be large enough in the case of transistors of considerable power. A representative value for c.r.t. sensitivity is 0·5 mm/V. Therefore to obtain a grid base of 80 mm a base swing of 160 V peak-to-peak is required.

These difficulties can be overcome easily if no attempt is made to reproduce the base voltage or the steady component of the collector current directly on the c.r.t. screen. In this case the input can be derived from a voltage divider across the secondary of a transformer and tappings taken to the X plates and to the transistor base. Clearly it is easy to arrange for the former to be many times as great as the latter, or, if the transistor is a power type, the reverse can be done. An alternative would be to provide the two voltages by separate transformers or from different secondaries on the same transformer. As the frequency is only 50 Hz it is a simple matter to measure the ratio of the voltages of these two secondaries or better still to calibrate the arrangement as a whole by observing the amount of deflection of the c.r.t. beam for known voltages on the base transformer secondary. As both of these secondaries are very lightly loaded, even when the transistor takes base current, there should be no appreciable difference in phase.

The vertical deflection can be obtained in a similar way with a transformer in the collector circuit. To obtain the true collector current-base voltage curve this transformer should have small impedance compared with that of the transistor; this again is easily calibrated.

11.3. HYBRID OR h PARAMETERS

The simplified basic equations for a transistor are as follows:

$$V_{be} = h_{11} I_b + h_{12} V_{ce} \qquad (11.1)$$
$$I_c = h_{21} I_b + h_{22} V_{ce} \qquad (11.2)$$

where the h terms are the hybrid parameters. These are determined by partial differentiation of the above equations, keeping either I_b or V_{ce} constant in each case. Then,

Input resistance = $h_{11} = \dfrac{\partial V_{be}}{\partial I_b} = h_{ie}$ for common emitter

Return or reverse voltage ratio = $h_{12} = \dfrac{\partial V_{be}}{\partial V_{ce}} = h_{re}$ for common emitter

Forward transfer current ratio = $h_{21} = \dfrac{\partial I_c}{\partial I_b} = h_{fe}$ for common emitter

Output admittance = $h_{22} = \dfrac{\partial I_c}{\partial V_{ce}} = h_{oe}$ for common emitter

A circuit for the determination of h_{fe}, also known as the current gain, by a dynamic method is shown in Fig. 11.9. By convention, such measurements are made at a frequency of 1 kHz. When switch S_1 is in position 1 a current from the audio oscillator passes through R_3 and develops a voltage across R_4. This voltage is inversely proportional to R_3 since R_3 is much greater than R_4.

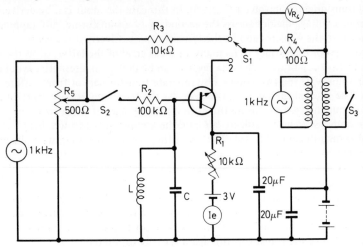

Fig. 11.9. Dynamic method of measuring current gain

When switch S_1 is in position 2, the emitter current of the transistor can be set by R_1. Then if R_2 is much larger than the input impedance of the transistor the current which is passed from the oscillator is inversely proportional to R_2 and so the voltage developed across R_4 is proportional to h_{fe}/R_2. The tuned circuit LC is to provide a high impedance so that the input impedance of the transistor is not shunted. At the same time, due to the low d.c. resistance of L, it permits the transistor to be biased into conduction by a resistance path much lower than that through R_2. The tuned circuit LC is, of course, tuned to 1 kHz. S_3 is kept closed for h_{fe} measurements. A numerical worked example on the use of this circuit is included at the end of this chapter.

The value of h_{fe} can be read at a number of emitter currents by adjustment of R_1. If H_{fe} is greater than 100, R_2 can be increased to 1 MΩ. Thus a graph can be plotted relating h_{fe} to the emitter current of the transistor.

The other h parameters of the transistor can be determined in a similar fashion. Thus to measure h_{ie}, switch S_1 is set to position 1, S_2 opened and S_3 closed. I_e is then set to the required value and V_{be} (i.e. the voltage across C) measured with an electronic voltmeter.

To measure h_{oe}, S_1 is set to position 2 and S_2 and S_3 opened. Then h_{oe} is given by the ratio of I_c ($= V_{R_4}/R_4$) to V_{ce} (measured by electronic voltmeter between collector and emitter).

The parameter h_{re} is measured by setting S_1 to position 1 and opening S_2 and S_3. Then h_{re} is given by the ratio of V_{be} (measured across C) to V_{ce} measured from collector to emitter (or earth since so far as a.c. is concerned the emitter is at earth potential due to the 20 μF capacitor).

11.4. BRIDGE MEASUREMENTS

The bridge method of measuring transistor properties gives fair accuracy with simple equipment, and its application to all the linear parameters at low frequencies will be described. Direct measurements of gain, as mentioned earlier, are often useful in a specific circuit, especially at higher frequencies.

As stated in the previous section, low-frequency parameter measurements are usually made at 1 kHz. Although some parameters are substantially real at this frequency, it should be remembered that the common-emitter current gain a' of a normal low-frequency junction transistor can have a significant phase shift. It may not be necessary to measure a quadrature component, but in bridge measurements one must usually balance it out in order to obtain an accurate value for the real component or the modulus: the circuits given here have provision for this. The bridge source should be a 1 kHz oscillator with adjustable output level; the detector should be a tuned amplifier with a differential input stage and a meter or oscilloscope as indicator.

A bridge for measurement of $(1 + a)$ and hence a and a' is shown in Fig. 11.10. The arms R_1 and R_2 are of large and equal resistance, so that equal alternating currents flow into the emitter and into R_3. By-pass capacitors C_1 and C_3 are fitted. The current in the base, hence through R_4, is a fraction $(1 + a)$ of I_e, thus at balance

$$(1 + a) = R_3/R_4 \qquad (11.3)$$

Phase balance is obtained by adjustment of C_2. The value obtained from equation (11.3) is, strictly, the real part of $(1 + a)$. The phase shift ϕ is given approximately by

$$\tan \phi = \omega C_2 R_1 \qquad (11.4)$$

Fig. 11.11 shows a bridge for measuring input impedance Z. This is a simple Wheatstone bridge; at balance

$$Z = R_3 \qquad (11.5)$$

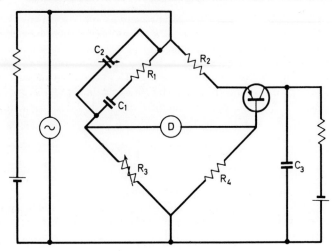

Fig. 11.10. Bridge measurement of (1 + a)

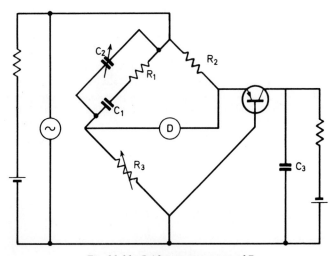

Fig. 11.11. Bridge measurement of Z

Strictly, this is the real part of Z: the phase angle is the same as in equation (11.4).

The bridge circuit shown in Fig. 11.12 is used to measure the output admittance Y. This is also a simple Wheatstone bridge, giving the real part of Y as

$$Y = \frac{R_3}{R_1 R_4} \tag{11.6}$$

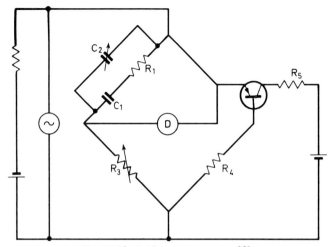

Fig. 11.12. *Bridge measurement of Y*

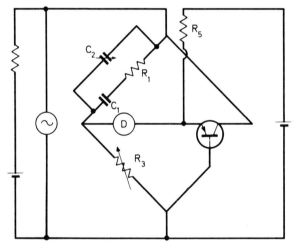

Fig. 11.13. *Bridge measurement of β*

It is necessary for R_5 to be much larger than the input impedance of the transistor, to simulate an open-circuit: in practice 100 kΩ is sufficient.

Measurement of the voltage feedback factor $β$ is made using the bridge shown in Fig. 11.13. This is effectively a Wheatstone bridge balancing r_c and r_b against R_1 and R_2. At balance,

$$β = \frac{R_3}{R_1 + R_3} \simeq \frac{R_3}{R_1} \tag{11.7}$$

Most of the common-emitter parameters are simply related to the common-base parameters; the exception is the feedback factor β', which it is convenient to measure directly. The arrangement is shown in Fig. 11.14; it is very similar to Fig. 11.13 except for the changes imposed

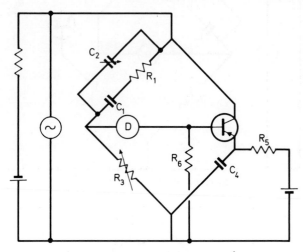

Fig. 11.14. Bridge measurement of β^1

on the d.c. supply circuits by the common-emitter configuration. C_4 is a by-pass capacitor, and R_6 is a large resistance (100 kΩ is suitable). At balance,

$$= \frac{R_3}{R_1 + R_3} \simeq \frac{R_3}{R_1} \tag{11.8}$$

A more direct measurement of current gain, especially in common emitter configurations, is sometimes wanted. The method shown in Fig. 11.9, and discussed in the previous section, can be used.

A general precaution in all the measurements described in this section is to ensure that signal levels are low enough for distortion to be insignificant. If an oscilloscope is used as the detector, a ready check is available. Otherwise, it is best to compare measurements at two signal levels differing by, for example, about 2:1 and to halve the level again if a discrepancy occurs.

11.5. HIGH-FREQUENCY PARAMETERS

Some of the information needed to assess high-frequency properties can be found by straightforward bridge measurements of impedances, either under some standard condition of open or short-circuit (as when measuring Y and Z) or with the terminations occurring in some working circuit. The main requirement is a good admittance bridge, covering a wide range of conductance and susceptance, and suitable for the required frequency range (see Chapter 8).

11.6. INTEGRATED CIRCUITS

The technology of integrated circuits represents a complete departure from conventional equipment design and manufacturing techniques. The conventional building blocks of electronics, as described throughout the rest of this book, virtually disappear as separate entities. Their specific functions are accomplished by microscopically small depositions or growths of material layers, or films, which may be individually unrecognisable and inseparable from a complete circuit.

11.6.1. Classification

Integrated circuits can be divided into three classifications: thin film, semiconductor (or monolithic) and hybrid circuits. The first two classifications are generic, using entirely different design and manufacturing principles. The third classification represents a combination of the two generic systems.

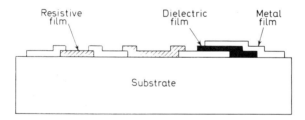

Fig. 11.15. Cross-section of thin film integrated circuit

The thin-film circuit (Fig. 11.15) consists of a passive substrate, such as glass or ceramic, on which passive parts are deposited in the form of thin-patterned films of conductive or nonconductive materials. Suitable techniques for the deposition of active elements are in the advanced stages of development.

The semiconductor (monolithic) circuit (Fig. 11.16) consists of a semiconductor substrate into which all the circuit parts are fabricated by diffusion and epitaxial processes that have been thoroughly developed

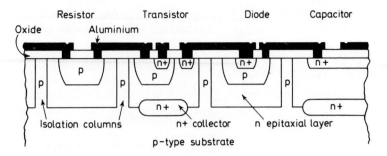

Fig. 11.16. Cross-section of semiconductor integrated circuit

for transistor manufacture. Interconnections are made by a process using vacuum evaporation of a suitable material over the surface of the wafer and etching the metal to form the desired interconnecting patterns.

Different techniques can be used in the manufacture of hybrid circuits, and each technique can be considered as a separate classification. To avoid the introduction of excessive terminology at this point, however, a hybrid circuit will be considered as one in which the passive components are made by thin-film techniques and the active components by semiconductor techniques. The active components may be individually packaged or unpackaged, the latter being called *chips*. The necessary interconnections are accomplished by a suitable method.

At present, the chief disadvantage of thin-film circuits lies in the fact that only passive components are readily made by this technique. The main advantage of semiconductor integrated circuitry is that the active components become an integral part of the circuit itself. A disadvantage in semiconductor circuits has resulted from the close proximity of elements in the wafer and the coupling capacitance between regions which limit the isolation capability. Recently developed techniques, however, largely eliminate these isolation difficulties. Semiconductor resistors and capacitors also have considerably different properties as a function of temperature and bias from those typically found for conventional components. Thus new circuits must be developed on a semi-empirical basis requiring considerable time and effort before a satisfactory result is achieved.

The various aspects of manufacture of integrated circuits, which include photolithographic masks, thin-film technology, semiconductor technology and packaging techniques are beyond the scope of this book. The reader who requires more information on these aspects is recommended to study a book devoted exclusively to integrated circuit technology[4].

11.6.2. Reliability

Reliability is one of the principal advantages of integrated circuitry. In some cases, such as manned aero-space equipment, it is the main consideration. There are three major problems: (1) component reliability, (2) component misapplication, (3) unreliable connections. Regarding (1), an electronic equipment can be no more reliable than the cumulative reliability of its components. Since some reliability factors are directly dependent upon the number of basic elements in an equipment, equipment reliability is improved by the use of integrated circuits merely by reducing the total number of functional elements. Regarding (2), because integrated circuits are designed around specified parameters and will not function unless used under these conditions, the application will closely duplicate the design criteria and optimum conditions for which the circuit was manufactured and tested. Reliability problems due to misapplications will, therefore, be reduced. With regard to (3), the majority of the connections are internal to the integrated circuit package, thus their integrity can be assured by the integrated-circuit manufacturer. The increased reliability of integrated circuits will no doubt lead to their increased use in electronic test equipment.

11.6.3. Measurements on Integral Circuits

The special nature of integrated circuits makes it difficult to test them by conventional techniques. Only a functional test can be applied to the circuit, as described in Chapters 13 and 15. The individual components are, of course, inaccessible and if one of these is faulty the whole circuit block must be scrapped. For example, if the integrated circuit to be tested is a sinusoidal oscillator, then the measurements to be made will be the output frequency (Chapter 9), power (Chapter 12) and distortion (Chapter 15).

Integrated circuits are usually manufactured by automatic processes, and are tested during and immediately after production by automatic testing techniques. Usually, the equipment can test the circuits during and after manufacture and also apply quality control and other special tests. The computer associated with the tester enables statistical analyses to be made of results for a large number of tested circuits.

These automatic testing techniques have been developed by individual manufacturers for application to their own specific products, and are, therefore, too numerous to mention individually. However, the following description of the automatic testing equipment developed by the French Division of IBM is typical of modern testing equipment.

The IBM system is composed of three principal parts, namely, a computer for controlling the system and recording the test results, a converter which transforms the binary data from the computer into analogue data which are used as the test signals to the circuit and also transforms the circuit output signals back into digital form for computer processing, and mechanical units for manipulating the individual circuits to be tested.

Three types of integrated circuits can be tested by the system: these are (a) thin film circuits with no connecting wires, (b) thin film circuits with connecting wires, and (c) monolithic circuits. They are tested as follows:

(a) A large number of circuits are arranged in the form of a matrix on a flat table capable of horizontal movement in two orthogonal directions. Thus each circuit is passed in turn under the test probes by a type of 'scanning' method.

(b) An ingenious method is used whereby a large number of circuits are placed in a vibrating 'bowl' having grooves into which the circuits are shaken and aligned so that the connecting wires make contact with the test pins.

(c) A similar arrangement to that for (b) positions each monolithic circuit in a test housing where it is clamped by a controlled shutter and automatically ejected after test.

The only task of a human operator during the test procedure is to ensure that the actual test devices or 'manipulators' are kept amply loaded with circuit blocks.

The chain of operations is as follows:

(i) The operator selects the type of manipulator to be used, that is, either (a), (b) or (c) above, and programmes the computer to test the appropriate type of circuit by means of a punched card;

(ii) The computer detects the punched card information and arranges for the required test;

(iii) When the circuit is in the correct testing position, the automatic manipulator signals the computer accordingly, and the latter supplies the appropriate test instructions;
(Operations (i), (ii) and (iii) take two to four minutes.)

(iv) After each test, the results are recorded on magnetic tape at a rate of 11 μs for each character;

(v) When the test sequence on each circuit is terminated, the manipulator is instructed to deal with the next microcircuit in the sequence;

(vi) When all the circuits have been tested, the information on the magnetic tape is processed by the computer, which may be programmed to yield such information as the mean variations and the dispersion of the circuit parameters, the correlation between parameters, the variation of these parameters as a function of the

location of each component on the film or substrate, and the
physical origin of certain electrical faults.

Standardisation of the tester is accomplished with the aid of precision
passive components or with known active elements. If the circuits under
test contain only passive components, a very rapid test can be made
using a special computer programme and direct voltages and currents.
The range of test voltages is 1, 10 and 100 V with a precision of 0·1%
and the precision of measurement is 0·1% for voltages and 0·5% for
currents.

11.6.4. Testing Integrated Circuits

The high reliability levels expected of modern complex electronic equipment require high-reliability integrated circuits, but it is impractical to
determine integrated-circuit reliability by testing under operational conditions due to the time and economic factors involved. Accelerated
testing techniques must be used, providing a time compression and a
reduction in the number of samples required for the test.

The essential requirement of any accelerated reliability test programme
is that the stresses applied to the devices must accelerate the same failure
mechanisms which will reduce reliability under normal operating conditions. If an accelerated stress introduces a new failure mechanism, it is no
longer valid for predicting reliability at lower stress levels. A thorough
knowledge of integrated-circuit failure mechanisms, therefore, is essential
if reliability test results are to be valid.

A typical integrated circuit reliability evaluation programme consists
of tests under actual conditions designed to stress the in-use failure
mechanisms, including high-temperature non-operating life, high-temperature and room temperature operating life, mechanical stress, environ-
mental stress, and special conditions such as step stress.

All reliability testing and recording are usually carried out on a
circuit-by-circuit basis. As stated earlier, if any part of the circuit fails
because it either becomes inoperative or drifts out of specification, the
entire circuit is considered to have failed.

Accelerated-stress tests have been conducted on circuits with a wide
range of complexities, including many different functional parameters.
It is difficult and perhaps misleading to group the results of such a
variety of test programmes in an attempt to draw general conclusions,
thus each type of circuit must be considered individually. For example,
samples of a circuit might be subjected to the following stress tests:
non-operating life at 175°C for 1000 hours, temperature step stress,
static life at 125°C for 1000 hours, and switching life at 125°C for
1000 hours. The input-output characteristics of all the circuits should be

measured initially and periodically during the test to determine circuit
stability, because this characteristic is dependent upon all elements of
the circuits.

The term 'step stress' used above should be defined. This is a method
of reliability testing in which a sample of the device or circuit under
evaluation is subjected to successively increasing stress levels. After each
level, the parameters are measured and the number of rejects determined.
This process is continued until nearly all the devices included in the test
have failed. Temperature stress is the most commonly used for analysis
of the reliability of semiconductor devices. This technique is valid for
integrated circuits because they are low-level (low-voltage and low-current
semiconductor devices, and temperature is one of the most significant
stresses encountered in application.

WORKED EXAMPLE

Question. In the circuit of Fig. 11.9, I_e is set to 1 mA and R_5 adjusted
so that with switch S_1 in position 1 a signal of 10 mV is developed across
R_4. Switch S_1 is then set to position 2 and switch S_2 closed, and the
voltage across R_4 is read. If this is 40 mV, what is h_{fe}?

Answer. If 10 mV are inversely proportional to 10 kΩ (R_3) the output
voltage is proportional to $h_{fe}/10^5$ (h_{fe}/R_2). Thus since the output voltage
is 40 mV,

$$\frac{40}{10} = \frac{kh_{fe}}{100} \frac{10}{k}$$

where k is the constant of proportionality. Therefore h_{fe} = 40.

EXERCISES

(These refer to a transistor operating in the common-emitter configuration.)

1. Draw a circuit suitable for obtaining the I_c/V_{ce} characteristic curve
of a transistor and show how the value of the current gain for a given
collector voltage can be obtained from these curves.

2. Describe with the help of a circuit diagram how the leakage current
of a transistor can be measured. How can the effect of temperature on the
the leakage current be easily demonstrated?

3. Show with the aid of a suitable circuit diagram how the cut-off
frequency of a transistor can be measured. Describe how an ohmmeter
can be used to make quick checks on a transistor for open or short circuit

REFERENCES

1. CATTERMOLE, K. W. *Transistor Circuits.* Heywood (1964).
2. DOSSE, J. *The Transistor.* D. Van Nostrand Co. (1964).
3. CHISTYAKOV, N. I. *Transistor Electronics in Instrument Technology.* Pergamon Press (1964).
4. DOYLE, J. M. *Thin-Film and Semiconductor Integrated Circuitry.* McGraw-Hill Book Co. (1966).

CHAPTER 12

Measurement of Power

12.1. INTRODUCTION

The simplest case of power measurement is, of course, in d.c. circuits, where the current and voltage are measured by separate meters and the product of the readings calculated. This is sometimes called the voltmeter-ammeter method.

In cases where the resistance of the circuit is known, or can be easily measured, it is sufficient to measure the current, since power is always given by I^2R. There are, however, a great many cases where this is not possible, e.g. that of the power delivered to a motor. In this instance the *effective* resistance is not the resistance measurable by ordinary means, thus the two-meter method is adopted. When the power lost in heating a winding is required, however, the I^2R method is the easiest to apply.

12.2. A.C. POWER

In the case of a.c. the power is not, in general, given by EI, but it is always I^2R. Therefore this method is still applicable in a great many cases provided that it is remembered that the r.m.s. value of current is involved.

It is shown later that the most common method of measuring audio-frequency current is by this method, since for test purposes an 'artificial load' of known resistance is usually employed.

12.2.1. Dynamometer Wattmeters

For supply frequencies a wattmeter is normally used. This is a dynamometer instrument, as described in Chapter 4, in which the magnetic field of one coil is proportional to the voltage because the coil is in series with a high resistance and connected across the supply. The torque equation for instruments of this type (which are today normally called 'electrodynamometers') may be derived as follows.

If the magnetic flux Φ passing through a coil varies, the induced e.m.f. is

$$E = \frac{-d\Phi}{dt}.$$

If the coil is carrying a current I, the power at any instant is the product EI, and the work done $= \int EI\, dt = \int I \frac{d\Phi}{dt}\, dt = \int I\, d\Phi$. If I is constant the work done by it will be $I \int d\Phi = I\Phi$, and this must be equal to the work done on the coil by the field or the potential V of the coil. If the coil has N turns, the e.m.f. will be N times as great, and $V = IN\Phi$.

Now if the coil moves so as to alter the flux passing through it, then $dV = F\, ds$ or $F = \frac{dV}{ds}$ where F is the mechanical force and ds is the element of distance moved.

If I is constant therefore $F = \frac{dV}{ds} = NI\frac{d\Phi}{ds}$.

and by similar reasoning the torque $T = \frac{dV}{d\theta}$ or $NI\frac{d\Phi}{d\theta}$ where θ is the angular displacement.

In the case of dynamometer instruments let I_1 be the current in the first coil and I_2 that in the second, then the number of linkages $N\Phi$ in the first coil are equal to MI_2, so that

$$\frac{d\Phi}{ds} = I_2 \frac{dM}{ds} \text{ and } F = I_1 I_2 \frac{dM}{ds}$$

$$\text{or } T = I_1 I_2 \frac{dM}{d\theta} \tag{12.1}$$

In the simplest constructional arrangement for a deflectional watt-meter the centre of the scale corresponds to the position of minimum mutual inductance between the fixed and moving coils. However, $\frac{dM}{ds}$ is then zero and from the torque equation (12.1) the torque is also zero. But a reasonable initial torque is required to overcome the inertia and friction of the meter movement, thus some advantage may be gained by departing from this simple arrangement.

When the instrument is connected as a wattmeter the force on the moving coil is proportional to

$$E_m \sin \omega t \times I_m \sin (\omega t - \theta)$$
$$= E_m I_m \sin \omega t \, (\sin \omega t . \cos \theta - \cos \omega t . \sin \theta)$$
$$= E_m I_m \, (\sin^2 \omega t . \cos \theta - \tfrac{1}{2} \sin 2\omega t . \cos \theta)$$

The average value of this over a complete cycle is

$$\frac{E_m I_m}{2} \cos \theta$$

or, writing r.m.s. values, the deflecting force is proportional to the power:

$$EI \cos \theta$$

These instruments can be used to measure reactive volt-amperes by modifying the current circuit so that the current in the moving coil leads the voltage by nearly 90°. The original scale calibration is retained except that the divisions represent reactive volt-amperes instead of watts.

Phase differences can be measured by first connecting the instrument normally, so that it indicates the power of the circuit. A capacitor is then added in series with the voltage circuit of the wattmeter and from the ratio of the two readings the phase angle can be calculated if the constants of the voltage circuit are known.

These instruments suffer from the usual disadvantages of dynamometer meters, i.e. they are sensitive to external fields, the operating forces are small, and there is a frequency error due to the inductance of the voltage coil. However, wattmeters are made with Precision Grade accuracy for use up to at least 100 Hz. A detailed description of the design of several different versions of this type of instrument is given in a book by Drysdale and Jolley[1]

12.2.2. Induction Meters

In addition to the dynamometer type there are also induction and electro static wattmeters. The latter was mentioned in Chapter 4 when dealing with electrostatic meters in general. Fig. 12.1 shows the principle of the induction wattmeter. There are two electromagnets with laminated cores one being energised by a coil in series with the supply and known as the current coil and the other by a pressure coil across the supply. A copper ring (the 'shade ring') is fixed around the poles of the pressure coil magnet to cause the resultant flux to lag by 90° on the applied voltage. To achieve the same object the pressure coil is made as inductive as possible. The interaction of these two fluxes sets up eddy currents in the aluminium disc in such a manner that it tends to rotate. A spring control is employed. The deflection is proportional to $EI \cos \theta$, i.e. to the power

In practice the deflection is not quite independent of frequency. These meters have the advantages of a long scale, large torque and relative freedom from the influence of outside fields. Dynamometer meters are more accurate and can be used on d.c. The latter is a point of great importance when a 'transfer' instrument is required.

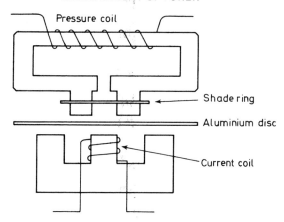

Fig. 12.1. Induction wattmeter

Instrument transformers can be used with wattmeters just as with ammeters and voltmeters, the method being used for currents over 100 A. There are ways of measuring power by means of three voltmeters or three ammeters though they are not often used.

12.2.3. Three-Ammeter Method

Fig. 12.2 shows the circuit employed for three-ammeter power measurement. The principle is that the current, I_1, measured by A_1 is the vector sum of the load current I_3 and the current I_2 taken by the non-inductive resistance.

Hence

$$I_1^2 = I_2^2 + I_3^2 + 2 I_2 I_3 \cos \theta$$

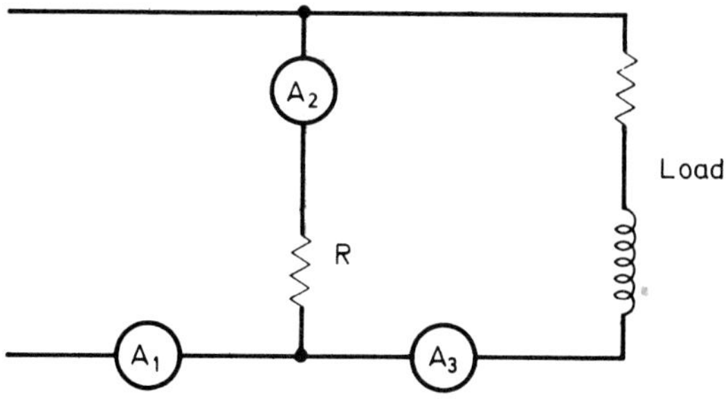

Fig. 12.2. Three-ammeter method of measuring power

But $I_2 = \dfrac{E}{R}$

Hence the power is given by

$$EI_3 \cos \theta = \frac{(I_1^2 - I_2^2 - I_3^2)R}{2} \tag{12.2}$$

12.2.4. Three-Phase Power

To measure power in a three-phase system it might at first seem that three wattmeters will be required, one for each phase; however, this is not so. Two wattmeters can be used, having their current coils in lines 1 and 3, say, and their pressure coils respectively between 1 and 2 and between 2 and 3. Fig. 12.3 shows the arrangement.

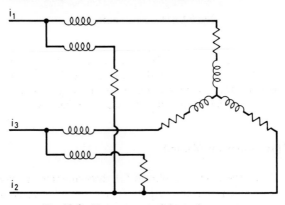

Fig. 12.3. *Measurement of three-phase power*

The total power is obviously

$$e_1 i_1 + e_2 i_2 + e_3 i_3 \tag{12.3}$$

where e_1, e_2 and e_3 are instantaneous phase voltages.
  Now in any three-phase system,

$$i_1 + i_2 + i_3 = 0$$

Therefore the total power is

$$e_1 i_1 + e_2(-i_3 - i_1) + e_3 i_3 = i_1(e_1 - e_2) + i_3(e_3 - e_2) \tag{12.4}$$

The terms are the instantaneous powers measured by the two watt-meters. Hence the sum of the two wattmeter readings gives the total average power.

Under normal conditions the line voltages are all equal and each $\sqrt{3}$ times the phase voltage E. The wattmeter readings can then be expressed as

$$W_1 = I_1\sqrt{3}\,E \cos a \quad \text{and} \quad W_2 = I_3\sqrt{3}\,E \cos \beta$$

where a and β are the angles by which the currents I_2 and I_3 lag the line voltages supplied to the same meter.

Thus
$$a = 30° + \phi \quad \text{and} \quad \beta = 30° - \phi$$

Then, if all the line currents are equal, sum of wattmeter readings

$$\begin{aligned} W_1 + W_2 &= \sqrt{3}\,EI\left[\cos(30° + \phi) + \cos(30° - \phi)\right] \\ &= 3\,EI \cos \phi \end{aligned} \tag{12.5}$$

It is interesting to note that if a or β exceeds $90°$ one of the meters will read backwards; one of its coils must then be reversed and the *difference* of the readings taken. Then

$$\begin{aligned} W_1 - W_2 &= \sqrt{3}\,EI\left[\cos(30° + \phi) - \cos(30° - \phi)\right] \\ &= -\sqrt{3}\,EI \sin \phi \end{aligned} \tag{12.6}$$

Hence
$$\tan \phi = \frac{\sqrt{3}(W_2 - W_1)}{W_1 + W_2} \tag{12.7}$$

It is thus seen that the power factor can also be found from these readings.

It will be observed that the two-wattmeter method gives the true power even when the system is not balanced, for equation (12.4) makes no assumptions about balance.

Polyphase wattmeters are also available. These are, in effect, two wattmeters having their moving coils mounted on a common spindle so that the addition in the two-wattmeter method takes place in the instrument itself.

12.3. A.F. AND H.F. POWER

12.3.1. Valve Wattmeters

Two valve voltmeters of the square-law type (see Chapter 5) can be combined so as to measure power. Fig. 12.4 shows a suitable circuit.

The voltage E_1 is that between the lines supplying power to the load while the equal voltages $E_2 + jE_3$ developed across the series resistances are proportional to the current, E_2 being proportional to the component of current in phase with E_1, and E_3 to the quadrature component.

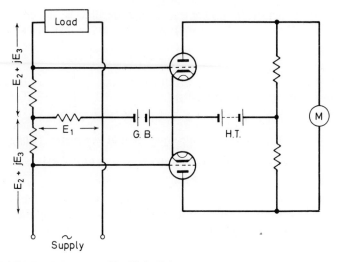

Fig. 12.4. Valve wattmeter

The meter M reads the difference between the changes of anode current of the two valves, and the anode current of each valve is proportional to the square of its grid voltage. Hence the meter deflection, D, is given by

$$D = k\,[(E_1 + E_2)^2 + E_3^2 - \{(E_1 - E_2)^2 + E_3^2\}]$$
$$= k_1 E_1 E_2$$
$$= k_2 E_1 I \cos \theta, \tag{12.8}$$

since E_2 is proportional to the in-phase current.

The two valve voltmeters must have identical characteristics and this is not always easy to maintain. The chief advantage of the method is that it is largely free from frequency error and the meter consumes only minute power.

12.3.2. Three-ammeter Method for H.F.

The three-ammeter method already described is not much used for supply frequencies but it can be turned to good account for radio frequencies where most other methods present considerable difficulties. The arrangement is shown in Fig. 12.5.

It is convenient to replace the resistance R by a capacitor whose value can be varied to adjust the reading of A_2 to a suitable value for different h.f. voltages. The equation giving the power can be easily obtained from

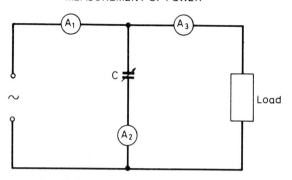

Fig. 12.5. *Three-ammeter method for h.f.*

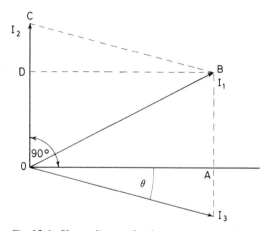

Fig. 12.6. *Phasor diagram for three-ammeter method*

the phasor diagram given in Fig. 12.6. E is the voltage across the load; I_1, I_2 and I_3 are the currents read by the meters A_1, A_2 and A_3 respectively. The power developed in the load is given by the product of the voltage E and the in-phase component, OA, of the current, where $OA = I_3 \cos \theta$. Now $OA = DB$ (opposite sides of a rectangle) and

$$DB = \frac{2 \times \text{area of triangle } OCB}{OC}$$

But by a well-known trigonometrical formula the area of OCB is given by

$$\triangle OCB = \sqrt{S(S - OC)(S - CB)(S - OB)}$$

where S is half the perimeter.

Thus $\quad OA = DB = \dfrac{2}{I_2} \sqrt{S(S - I_2)(S - I_3)(S - I_1)}$

where $\quad S = \dfrac{I_1 + I_2 + I_2}{2}$

Now $\quad E = \dfrac{I_2}{\omega C}$

Therefore the power,

$$W = \sqrt{\dfrac{2}{\omega C}} S(S - I_1)(S - I_2)(S - I_3) \qquad (12.9)$$

If this equation is studied on the lines suggested in Chapter 1, it will be found that the greatest accuracy is to be expected when $I_1 = I_2 = I_3$ and the capacitor is made variable in order to obtain approximately this condition as far as the last pair is concerned. This condition can be obtained only for a phase angle of $30°$. The loss of accuracy with smaller angles is not serious, but the accuracy becomes poor for large angles; for large leading angles I_1 becomes large and hence $(S - I_1)$ becomes small and an error in I_1 makes a large difference to the product, and for large lagging angles I_1 becomes small and consequently $(S - I_2)$ approaches $\dfrac{I_3 - I_2}{2}$ which if I_2 is nearly equal to I_3 is nearly zero (as also is $(S - I_3)$), hence again slight errors in meter readings greatly affect the result.

This method is used for measuring the power carried by radio-frequency feeders, which in practice is the same thing as the power output from a radio transmitter to its aerial.

12.3.3. Power Output and Power Level

In audio-frequency work, it is frequently necessary to know how much power can be delivered by a particular piece of apparatus. For example, it is not normally required to measure the power being delivered by an amplifier while it is operating (it would be a very difficult measurement to carry out accurately in any case) but it must be tested under artificial conditions, either before it is put into service or to check it for results. In this case, a pure resistance load of appropriate value must be provided and the r.m.s. value of current measured. Alternatively the p.d. across the load can be measured.

For this purpose a thermal meter is to be preferred because it reads r.m.s. values, with good accuracy at all frequencies. This last factor is of special importance at radio frequencies. A thermo-couple meter can be used in this way for any circuit whose resistance is known or is measurable; for example, the behaviour of a Class C power amplifier can be studied by first measuring the resistance of the tank circuit by one of the methods described in an earlier chapter, then supplying the amplifier in the ordinary way and measuring the tank circuit current. A suitable circuit is shown simplified in Fig. 12.7.

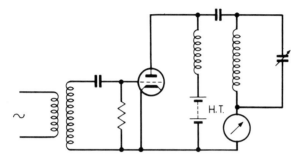

Fig. 12.7. *Class C power amplifier measurement*

Output meters for use on audio frequencies normally use a rectifier meter and a series resistance. The circuit is, of course, identical whether a rectifier or thermal meter is used but the former is often preferred as, while being accurate enough, it is much more robust. The Marconi Instruments 10-watt A.F. Power Meter TF 893A is of this type.

By applying a suitable shunt (Fig. 12.8) the effective resistance of a standard rectifier voltmeter can be reduced to match the secondary of, say, a loudspeaker transformer, and the meter dial can be calibrated in

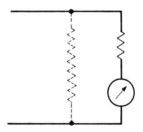

Fig. 12.8. *Output meter shunting*

milliwatts if desired. For many test purposes, however, such meters are calibrated in decibels, with the centre of the scale marked "0" and the actual zero of the instrument marked, say, −6 dB. The reason for this practice is considered later in this chapter.

The reader will observe that an output meter is a very simple device and may wonder why it is given a special name as if there were some new principle involved. The reason is simply that its resistance is specially chosen to provide the correct load for the type of apparatus to be tested.

An obvious objection to rectifier meters is that they do not read r.m.s. values. In testing most electronic apparatus, however, it is usual to supply a pure sine wave and to operate it under practically distortionless conditions, hence any waveform error is quite negligible. For special laboratory tests where non-sinusoidal waveforms are encountered, a thermal meter sould be used.

A transformer with a number of tappings can be provided as part of an output meter to make it applicable to any amplifier, as shown in Fig. 12.9.

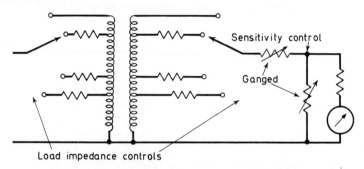

Fig. 12.9. *Impedance matching of output amplifier*

A valve voltmeter can be used as an output meter by connecting it across the lines. The load into which a transmission line operates is necessarily constant; hence a measure of the voltage between the conductors gives an indication of the power being transmitted. Sensitive galvanometers are often used, in conjunction with bridge rectifiers, so that negligible power is drawn by the indicator. The galvanometer is often heavily damped so as to show only average speech power.

A valve voltmeter, again, can be used as a power level monitor. An inductor of about 30 H is connected in series with the anode galvanometer and a capacitor of $2 \mu F$ connected between anode and cathode, in order to prolong the time interval over which the reading remains steady.

Incandescent lamps can be used as output meters for radio frequencies. The lamps are wired to form the load of the radio transmitter under test and the illumination measured by a photometer. The lamps are then calibrated by supplying them with d.c. the value of

which is adjusted to give the same illumination. The power is then equal
to the square of the d.c. required to give the same illumination multiplied by the resistance of the lamps at the temperature attained during
the measurement.

12.4. PEAK POWER

Electronic voltmeters for measuring peak values were described in
Chapter 5, but these do not meet the requirements of measuring the
transient part of a wave, which may show extreme peaks only
occasionally and is often required to be measured.

Some method of 'storing' the peak long enough for it to be
measured must be devised. This can be done by charging a capacitor

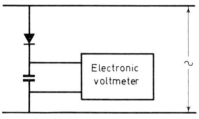

Fig. 12.10. Peak power meter

through a rectifier and measuring the voltage across the capacitor
with an electronic voltmeter. The capacitor is charged to the peak
voltage and its charge, once received, can leak away only slowly
since the time-constant of the discharge circuit is made high. The
basic circuit is shown in Fig. 12.10.

12.5. BOLOMETRIC AND CALORIMETRIC METHODS

A bolometer is a device which changes its resistance when radiant
energy falls on it. A lamp used in a bridge circuit, as described in
Chapter 18 for example, is sometimes incorrectly referred to as a bolometer. The bolometer method of measuring small microwave power
levels is described in Chapter 16.

Fig. 12.11 shows a calorimetric power meter made by Hewlett-
Packard Ltd. It is an automatic-nulling bridge-type instrument that
operates from d.c. to 12.4 GHz, and will measure power in the range
from 10 mW to 10 W with an accuracy of at least 5%. Power
attenuators may be employed to extend the range of the instrument
above 10 W.

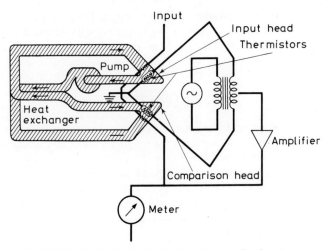

Fig. 12.11. Hewlett Packard calorimetric power head meter

The instrument consists of two power-conversion heads. The input signal dissipates power in the load resistor of the input head. Heat is transferred from the load to a circulating oil bath. The increase in temperature of the oil bath in the head alters the resistance of the temperature-sensitive resistor (thermistor). This tends to unbalance the electrical bridge and an a.c. off-null signal is delivered to the amplifier. The amplified signal is used to heat the load in the comparison head. This raises the temperature of the oil bath in this head, which alters the resistance of the thermistor in the comparison head. The bridge is, therefore, self-balancing.

Note that although the oil flow is in a series circuit the temperature of the oil that enters each head is the same. This is accomplished by means of the heat exchanger.

12.6. USE OF CATHODE-RAY TUBE

Chapter 7 describes the use of an elliptical trace on a c.r.t. to measure phase relationships. Another interesting application of the elliptical trace is to the measurement of power. The p.d. which is proportional to the current (or the p.d. applied to the circuit, whichever is more convenient) is given a 90° phase shift, as shown in Fig. 12.12. A straight line trace will then represent quadrature and a circle unity power factor. The area of the ellipse which is given by πab, where a and b are the semi-axes of the ellipse, is proportional to the power in the circuit per cycle.

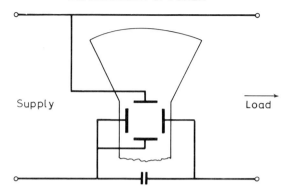

Fig. 12.12. C.R.T. method of measuring power

This method is applicable to radio frequencies, and the only error in the method is that due to the losses in the capacitor used to obtain the 90° phase shift. In cases where the figure is not an ellipse the measurement of area may be laborious.

WORKED EXAMPLE

Question. Describe the two-wattmeter method of measuring power in a three-phase circuit. If the readings of the wattmeters are 3 kW and 1 kW respectively, the latter being obtained after reversing the connections to the current coil of one wattmeter, calculate the power and power factor. Prove the formulae employed. (B.Sc.)

Answer. The two-wattmeter method is fully described in the text, eqn. (12.3) is deduced from Fig. 12.3, and eqns (12.4), (12.5) and (12.7) are derived.

Calculation. The power is the algebraic sum of the wattmeter readings.

$$\therefore \text{ Power} = W_2 + W_1 = 3 + (-1) = \underline{2 \text{ kW.}} \qquad Answer \ (i)$$

$$\tan \phi = \frac{\sqrt{3}(W_2 - W_1)}{W_1 + W_2} = \frac{\sqrt{3} \times 4}{2} = 2\sqrt{3}$$

$$\therefore \ \phi = \tan^{-1} 2\sqrt{3} = \tan^{-1} 3.4642 = 73° 54'$$

$$\therefore \ \cos \phi = \underline{0.277} \qquad\qquad Answer \ (ii)$$

EXERCISES

1. Describe the dynamometer wattmeter and show that the deflecting force on the moving coil is proportional to the power being measured.

2. Describe a method of measuring the power output of a radio transmitter.

3. Explain with the aid of a circuit diagram how two square-law valve voltmeters can be combined so as to measure power.

4. Show with the help of suitable circuit diagrams how rectifier meter are used in power output meters, and how galvanometers are employed as power level meters.

5. Give an account of how an electric voltmeter can be used to measure peak power.

6. Develop the torque equation of the electro-dynamometer and show how this instrument can be adapted to measure

(*a*) power

(*b*) reactive volt-amperes

(*c*) phase differences.

Explain, using a torque equation, why, in deflectional wattmeters, some advantage may be gained by departing from the simple arrangement whereby the centre of the scale corresponds to the position of zero mutual inductance between fixed and moving coils.

(I.E.E. Part III, 1966)

REFERENCE

1. DRYSDALE, C. V. and JOLLEY, A. C. *Electrical Measuring Instruments.* (pt. 1). Chapman & Hall (1952).

CHAPTER 13

Signal Generators

13.1. INTRODUCTION

A signal generator consists basically of an oscillator stage of one of the types described in Chapter 9, an amplifier, and an attenuator as described at the end of this chapter, for providing a known fraction of the signal generator output voltage.

An oscillator having a very high frequency stability is termed a 'primary frequency standard'. This is naturally an expensive piece of equipment but when used to control a radio transmitter innumerable 'secondary frequency standards' may be checked from it. Primary frequency standards are checked against the time signals from observatories.

Most frequency measurements made in the laboratory employ secondary frequency standards. The accuracy of such standards depends upon their design and is governed by the purpose they are intended to serve. It would obviously be an absurd waste of equipment to use a 'standard signal generator' costing several hundreds of pounds for work which could be done equally well with a test oscillator. The salient features in the design of various types of r.f. signal generators are dealt with in the following sections.

13.2. TEST OSCILLATORS

The majority of test oscillators operate on frequencies between about 100 kHz and 30 MHz; sometimes a higher frequency range utilising harmonics is included. When required, the output may be modulated to a depth of about 30 per cent at any approximate frequency of 400 Hz. Provision is sometimes made for modulation by means of an external circuit. The amplitude of the output voltage is controllable in steps by means of a ladder attenuator and intermediate values of signal strength are obtained by a potential divider. The output is fed via a screened lead and a dummy aerial.

As indicated above, the accuracy of the frequency calibration, although sufficient for broadcast receiver servicing, is not of a high order, and the readings of the attenuator dials cannot be taken as a reliable indication of the output voltage. For comparative tests, however, such instruments may supply all the information required.

Fig. 13.1 shows the basic circuit of a test oscillator employing an electron-coupled r.f. oscillator and a Hartley a.f. oscillator. For simplicity only two-wave-range switching is shown. It is convenient to use a two-gang tuning capacitor with the sections paralleled for C_1.

13.3. STANDARD SIGNAL GENERATORS

A detailed discussion of the design and construction of standard signal generators is outside the scope of this book and attention is confined to a few important features.

The essential differences between a standard signal generator and a test oscillator may be summarised thus:

  (i) more thorough screening is employed to minimise stray fields and to ensure that the output voltage closely approximates the indicated voltage;

 (ii) in the interests of frequency stability the modulation voltage is applied to an amplifier fed from the r.f. oscillator and not to the oscillator itself;

(iii) the output voltage is adjusted to its nominal value by references to the indication of an electronic voltmeter or thermocouple meter;

(iv) the modulation depth is controllable and measurable.

Elaborate screening is necessary between the oscillator and the output lead and between the oscillator and the attenuator; the different sections of the attenuator must also be screened from each other. As the frequency is raised these requirements present problems of increasing difficulty and their solution adds greatly to the cost of the instrument. The general principles of screening are very thoroughly discussed by Hartshorn[1] and their application to signal generators and attenuators by Terman[2].

The circuit of Fig. 13.2 is one arrangement by means of which the output voltage and its modulation depth may be measured. With no input voltage the 'set zero' control is used to bring the microammeter reading to zero. An unmodulated voltage is then applied and the r.f. gain control adjusted so that the pointer of the meter coincides with a certain mark, which usually corresponds to 1 V input. With a suitably designed electronic voltmeter circuit, the relationship between greater input voltages and meter deflection is square law. Thus when the input voltage is modulated the modulation depth can be determined since the r.m.s. of

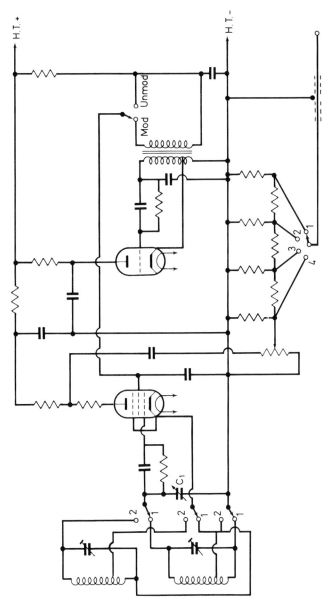

Fig. 13.1. Test oscillator

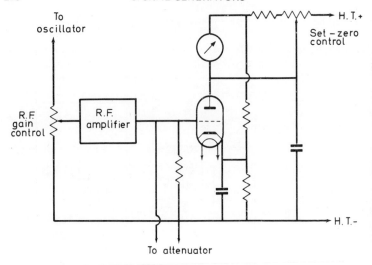

Fig. 13.2. Measurement of output voltage and modulation depth

a modulated wave is $\hat{V}_c \sqrt{\frac{1}{2} + \frac{k^2}{4}}$, where $\hat{V}_c$ is the peak value of the carrier voltage. The meter can therefore be calibrated in terms of the modulation depth, k.

13.4. V.H.F. SIGNAL GENERATORS

At the higher radio frequencies, certain special aspects of design have to be taken into account. The basic circuit diagram of a v.h.f. (30 to 300 MHz) signal generator is shown in Fig. 13.3; it comprises a triode oscillator V_1 using a Colpitts' circuit. The latter is particularly suited to operation at relatively high frequencies, provided that the valve itself is suitably designed, i.e. has short anode, grid and cathode leads, together with the reduced separation between the anode and grid necessary to minimise transit-time effects.

The range 30 to 300 MHz would be covered in a number of bands, e.g. 30 to 70 MHz, 60 to 150 MHz and 130 to 300 MHz, by switching inductors. For the two highest frequency ranges the inductors L might consist of silver-plated copper bars, the lower frequency inductor being a coil of a few turns. The tuning capacitor C is of the split-stator type, the rotor being earthed for radio frequencies.

The output is required to be variable and accurately known, perhaps covering the range 0 to +100 dB relative to one microvolt. This wide range can be covered by a piston attenuator; Fig. 13.3 shows an attenuator in which two loops (L_1 and L_2) are enclosed in a brass tube and can be moved axially in order to vary the coupling. The attenuation in decibels varies almost linearly with the separation of the loops.

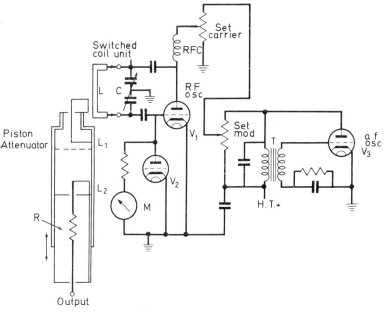

Fig. 13.3. V.H.F. signal generator

A resistor R of 75 Ω in series with the output loop enables the impedance to be matched approximately to the output cable. Provision is made for:

(a) monitoring the output voltage by the diode rectifier V_2 and meter M,

(b) adjusting the carrier level, and

(c) adjusting the modulation depth of the carrier.

An audio-frequency oscillator (V_3 and T) is provided for the generation of 400 Hz or 1000 Hz tone for modulating the carrier; the facility (not shown) for using V_3 as an amplifier for an external source of modulation is often included. The modulation depth may be determined from the increase of the reading on the meter when modulation is applied.

The features that are essential in order to avoid inaccuracies in the output voltage are:

(a) effective screening, usually obtained by double-screening the oscillator,

(b) thorough radio-frequency decoupling of all supply leads and other leads entering the oscillator compartment,

(c) the use of a reliable and stable means for monitoring the output voltage, and an accurate initial calibration of this monitoring device,

(d) the avoidance of stray fields due to circulating currents (the double-screening referred to above is helpful in this respect; it is also desirable to insert insulating gaps in controls such as variable capacitor spindles passing through the front panel),

(e) the use of an accurately calibrated and reliable attenuator.

13.4.1. Use of Signal Generators

The principles of measuring r.f. gain are the same as those described in Chapter 15 for the measurement of a.f. gain. In the case of r.f. amplifiers used for radio reception there are always associated with them a detector and an a.f. amplifier, and it is convenient to use these in the test. A signal is applied to the input of the stage under test and the input attenuator set to give a convenient deflection of the output meter of the a.f. amplifier. The signal source is then applied to the input of the next stage and the attenuator reset. The ratio of these settings gives the voltage amplification directly.

Obviously the same procedure is followed in obtaining the gain of a complete amplifier. If the r.f. circuit includes a superheterodyne system this in no way affects the procedure, for the total gain will then include the conversion gain of the frequency-changer.

It is even more important in r.f. work than in a.f. work that tests should be made with all other stages in operation. This is because feed-back effects (either positive or negative) may be considerable and the only useful measurement is one that includes these effects.

Fig. 13.4 shows the essential parts of a superheterodyne receiver; the points where a test signal may be applied are lettered (a) to (e). When the first stage of the receiver is included in the test, the signal is fed through a circuit containing inductance and capacitance to simulate the aerial. In general, the values of these will be made to correspond with the aerial for which the set is intended but for broadcast receivers a conventional standard of artificial aerial has been agreed upon, viz. $200 \mu\mu F$, $20 \mu H$ and 25Ω, all in series. The standard test signal is modulated by a 400 Hz tone to a depth of 30%, and adjusted to give an output of 50 milliwatts of audio-frequency power. For telegraph receivers an output of one milliwatt is often used.

The gain of a radio-frequency stage in a transmitter could be measured in a similar way but in most cases this serves no useful purpose

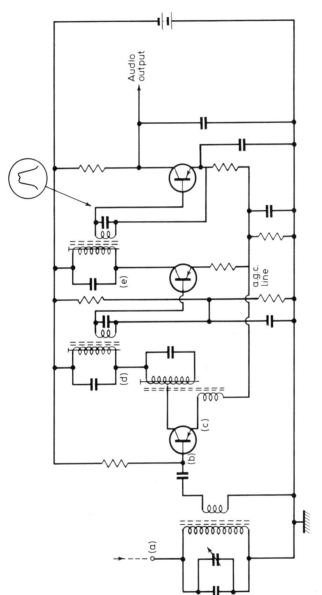

Fig. 13.4. Superhet receiver

In a transmitter, efficiency is a very important factor as is also harmonic production; consequently the behaviour of a transmitter is better studied by a more detailed method, in particular by using an oscilloscope.

13.4.2. Measurement of Conversion Conductance

For direct measurement of conversion conductance a signal frequency is chosen at approximately the centre of the desired range of tuning frequencies (Fig. 13.5). Suitable values are 700 kHz for medium and long

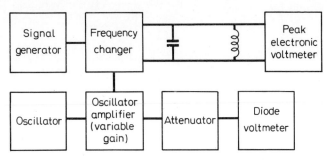

Fig. 13.5. Arrangement for measuring conversion conductance

wavebands and 10 MHz for the short waveband. The signal voltage for transistor frequency changers must be much less than 0·1 V and not greater than about 10 mV because the maximum oscillator voltage rarely exceeds about 100 mV. The oscillator voltage is obtained from an oscillator followed by an amplifier, the gain of which is changed by bias variation.

The output of the amplifier includes a tuned circuit, which rejects oscillator harmonics. This is essential for harmonic-response measurement. Large oscillator voltages are obtained by capacitance-resistance coupling from this tuned circuit to the appropriate oscillator electrode in the frequency changer stage. Peak voltages not exceeding about 15 V are obtained from a pick-up coil wound on the earthed end of the tuned circuit. A diode voltmeter may be used for measuring the oscillator voltage across the pick-up coil, and since this voltage is directly related to that across the tuned circuit to which the pick-up coil is coupled, its readings may be calibrated in terms of the oscillator peak voltage across the tuned circuit.

The diode voltmeter is not satisfactory for directly measuring the oscillator voltage required by transistors, and a low impedance attenuator must be inserted between the diode voltmeter across the pick-up coil and the transistor injection point. The d.c. resistance of the attenuator must be low if a direct coupling is used to the transistor. The output circuit of the frequency changer consists of a tuned circuit resonant at the i.f., and a peak voltmeter is used to measure the output voltage.

To calculate conversion conductance the resonance or dynamic resistance of the tuned output circuit must be measured as follows. The input signal is adjusted to give a certain output voltage, such as 1 V peak (a low value is chosen to prevent the possibility of non-linearity between input and output voltages). The tuned circuit is then paralleled by a known non-inductive resistance and the input signal increased to give the same output voltage. If E and E' are the input peak signal voltages with and without the non-inductive resistance R, then

$$E_o = 1 = gER_d = gE' \frac{R_d R}{R_d + R}$$

where E_o = the output peak voltage,

g = conversion conductance,

R_d = the dynamic resistance of the tuned circuit.

whence $R_d = R\left[\dfrac{E'}{E} - 1\right].$

Now provided the collector of the transistor frequency changer is tapped into the tuned circuit at a point where the effective tuned circuit impedance is much less than the transistor output resistance, or alternatively the dynamic impedance of the tuned circuit is reduced to fulfil this condition by using a low value of inductance and adding damping, then it can be assumed that the output resistance is much greater than R_d and the conversion conductance is given by

$$g = \frac{E_o}{ER_d}.$$

13.4.3. Measurement of Oscillator Harmonic Response

Interference whistles from interaction between undesired signals and harmonics of the oscillator are normally more serious than undesired signal harmonic interference, and the ratio of conversion conductance for the second and third oscillator harmonics to that for the fundamental is a good indication of the interference capability of the frequency changer.

The apparatus is the same as that shown in Fig. 13.5, but the signal frequency is adjusted to give the i.f. by interaction with the particular oscillator harmonic under consideration. For example, if desired signal and i.f. frequencies are 1000 and 465 kHz respectively, the signal frequencies for measuring second and third harmonic responses are 2465 (2 × 1465 − 465) and 3930 (3 × 1465 − 465) kHz. It is essential that the oscillator voltage source be free from harmonics, and this may be checked with oscillator amplifier at full gain by placing a potentiometer across the output and reducing the oscillator voltage applied to the frequency changer to about one-fifth of its optimum value. The oscillator harmonic response under these conditions should not be greater than 1% of the fundamental. Typical curves of percentage

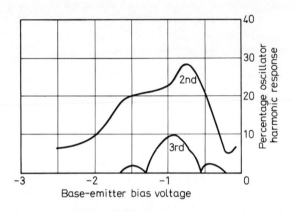

Fig. 13.6. Typical oscillator harmonic response curves

oscillator harmonic response against base-emitter bias are plotted in Fig. 13.6, the percentage oscillator harmonic response being given by

$$\left(\frac{g \text{ harmonic}}{g \text{ fundamental}} \times 100\%\right).$$

These curves are only of some significance in selecting the optimum bias point because a.g.c. is rarely used in transistor receivers in practice.

13.4.4. Measurements on Detectors

The technique involved in detector measurements is much the same as previously described. A carrier, modulated to a known degree by a sinusoidal audio-frequency signal, is applied to the input circuit and the audio-frequency voltage resulting at the input of the first a.f. stage is measured. This voltage can be measured directly with an electronic volt-meter or by a method of substitution. In the latter case the reading on the output meter of the complete a.f. amplifier is noted and then a separate a.f. oscillator is substituted for the detector output, the attenuation being set to give the same amplifier output.

The detector gain is then given by

$$\frac{\text{A.F. output voltage}}{\text{modulation factor} \times \text{carrier amplitude}}.$$

Frequency distortion can easily be determined by repeating the process for a number of modulation frequencies. The c.r.t. response curve method is, of course, as applicable as for a.f. amplifiers but in this case the output of the beat-frequency oscillator, one of whose components is used to control the horizontal deflection, is used also to modulate the input carrier.

Non-linear distortion, which is far more important, is also determined in the same way as for an amplifier. In this case, however, there are more possible variables, for the distortion should be measured not only for different carrier voltages but for different depths of modulation.

A term frequently used is 'detector efficiency'. It is the ratio of the actual a.f. voltage obtained to that which would be obtained from a perfect detector. In the case of a diode, this is obviously equal to the detector gain, as defined above.

This efficiency can be measured by carrying out the test already described and then replacing the modulated carrier by an a.f. oscillator and adjusting this to give the same a.f. voltage at the output (i.e. the input of the next stage). To obtain the correct result it is required, however, that the detector be biased by a battery to the same value as the rectifying action produces. In the case of the detector shown in Fig. 13.4 the a.f. test signal should be superimposed on a carrier voltage of required amplitude. It should be noted that this means the two voltages are applied in series, which gives a resultant voltage waveform quite different from a modulated waveform.

The frequency-changer of a superheterodyne is tested in a similar way. A signal is applied and its value adjusted to give a convenient reading on the receiver output meter. The signal generator is then tuned to the i.f., applied to the input of the first i.f. stage, and its amplitude adjusted to give the same output as before.

It should be carefully noted that all these measurements are made under actual working conditions as far as possible. It would be of much less value to set up an isolated detector and measure its behaviour for there would be no means of knowing how the results would be modified by the following a.f. amplifier. Again, in the case of frequency changers, the test is carried out with the local oscillator working normally.

13.5. FACTORY TESTING OF RADIO RECEIVERS

To illustrate how a complete equipment is tested at the production stage, a domestic radio receiver has been chosen, as it is one of the most well-known pieces of electronic equipment, and contains both r.f. and a.f. amplifiers.

Factory testing can be divided into two sections: detailed examination of special receivers or of new types, and routine testing of mass-produced sets. All the methods of testing previously described can be employed in the detailed examination of a new design but, in general, at least for broadcast receivers, the three main tests are sensitivity, selectivity and fidelity.

The first test is in practice a measurement of gain, for the input voltage required to produce the standard 50-milliwatt output is determined. Fig. 13.7 shows a block diagram of the test equipment and the left-hand side of Fig. 13.8 shows a typical receiver sensitivity curve.

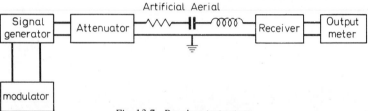

Fig. 13.7. Receiver test set-up

Selectivity is sometimes measured by setting the receiver to a particular frequency and repeating the sensitivity test with the input oscillator deliberately mistuned. It is then a simple matter to plot a selectivity curve. (Right-hand side of Fig. 13.8.) The objection to this

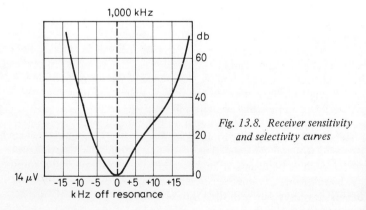

Fig. 13.8. Receiver sensitivity and selectivity curves

method is that in practice it is required to know the ability of the set to reject signals in the presence of a wanted signal. A linear detector has a demodulating effect, i.e. the strong wanted carrier suppresses the modulation of a weak unwanted signal. Besides this effect there is the action of automatic gain control which makes the gain of the receiver dependent on the total rectified voltage.

To overcome this difficulty a 'wanted' signal is applied to the set, but when the set is tuned and the signal strength adjusted to a convenient value the modulation is switched off. An 'unwanted' signal modulated 30% at 400 Hz is then introduced and the value adjusted to give 50 mW output. The strength of the interfering signal is then plotted against frequency difference from the 'wanted' signal.

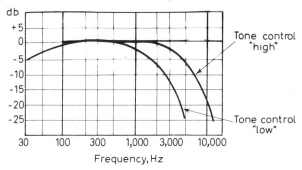

Fig. 13.9. Fidelity curves of radio receiver

Fidelity measurement is simply obtaining the response curve previously described, no notice being taken of non-linear distortion (Fig. 13.9).

In designing and constructing an experimental receiver it is desirable to test every stage for gain and the i.f. stage for selectivity. The method of determining i.f. selectivity is to take the resonance curve while actually 'lining up' the stage, and will be given later.

The frequency-changer can be simply tested by making the oscillator section inoperative, applying the correct i.f. frequency to the frequency-changer input (point (*b*) in Fig. 13.4) and measuring the gain, for it should behave as a good i.f. amplifier. Since the gain of the i.f. stages is already known they would be included in the test, thus checking the whole set from the frequency-changer onwards.

Next, the local oscillator is reconnected and tuned to give maximum output with a signal supplied to the input of frequency-changer stage. Thus the conversion gain can be measured. Should this not reach the desired figure the fault is usually an unsuitable oscillator voltage.

The oscillator voltage can be measured by an electronic voltmeter connected across the appropriate electrodes of the frequency-changer

(c) (Fig. 13.4). The check should be made over all the frequencies for which the oscillator is designed.

The oscillator frequency can be checked with an absorption wavemeter; this is quite accurate enough if loosely coupled.

13.5.1. Routine Tests

A chassis comes down the factory conveyor belt, and each worker solders in one or more components until the chassis reaches the inspector, who fixes the dial and dial lamps and examines the chassis generally to ensure that all the components are present and correctly and firmly joined.

He then passes the chassis to the i.f. tester, who connects up the power supply and his test board with its loudspeaker and output meter and then applies the signal to the primary of the last i.f. transformer (Fig. 13.4). If it is a very simple set with two i.f. transformers only (as is normally the case with domestic receivers), he adjusts the trimmers on the last i.f. transformer for the maximum sound and switches over to the meter to check the gain. This is done, it will be remembered, by setting the attenuator at the standard position and noting whether the meter reads zero or a plus value.

If a final touch on the trimmer will not give the required result the label attached to the chassis is marked accordingly and passed on the 'trouble shooter'.

If the set has band-pass i.f. tuning, as in the majority of sets, the cathode-ray oscilloscope is connected across the diode load resistance, and a frequency-modulated oscillation from the tester's board is applied to the base of the transistor preceding the i.f. transformer being aligned. It is then only necessary to adjust the trimmers until the familiar double-humped curve appears on the c.r.t. screen. The input is then moved back to the input of the frequency-changer stage (b) and the first i.f. transformer brought into line. The whole i.f. part of the set should show one double-humped curve, as in Fig. 13.1 at (f). The gain is then checked by switching on the output meter.

This is thought by some manufacturers to be the most satisfactory way of lining up i.f. transformers as it takes only a few minutes at the most. One i.f. tester can keep four chassis testers supplied with work. The frequency-modulated supply, as explained earlier, is specially generated and pass over transmission lines to the respective test boards and to the accompanying oscilloscopes.

When the chassis has been finally passed by the i.f. tester and labelled accordingly it is passed to another worker who is sometimes known as the 'chassis tester'. His job is to carry out the alignment of the

input tuned circuits, and the procedure of course varies with the type
and manufacture of the set under consideration. Manufacturers provide
'service sheets' to appointed agents: these sheets give details of the
alignment procedure for the particular receiver to which they apply.
Adjustment of the sectors of the end vanes of the tuning capacitor
sections for correct matching is sometimes carried out by a separate
tester.

The set is then passed to the assembly room for fixing in the cabinet
with its own loudspeaker, after which it is given its final check.

Commercial receivers are naturally tested much more thoroughly, gain
and selectivity being carefully measured and plotted. The procedure is
less straightforward because cost is not so vital a factor.

13.6. ATTENUATORS

The advantages of making measurements in terms of resistance values,
in preference to direct pointer readings, cannot be too highly stressed.
Bridges and potentiometers are not much used at high frequencies but
the basic principle of comparing two quantities in terms of the ratio of
two resistance values is of the greatest importance. Many examples of the
method are given in this book.

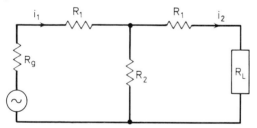

Fig. 13.10. Symmetrical T-section attenuator

A simple case in d.c. work is the calibration of a voltmeter by means
of a known voltage and a potentiometer. The value of one voltage is
known because that of another voltage is known, the ratio being that of
two resistances. This method is unfortunately not always applicable
because it throws a different load on to the circuits at every setting of
the potentiometer.

An attenuator, in the case under consideration, is a resistance network that, while offering a constant impedance to the external circuit,
provides known ratios of voltage or power. Another way of regarding it
is that an attenuator is a 'volume control' that does not upset the matching between the load and the source of power.

One of the best-known practical forms is the symmetrical T-section attenuator shown in Fig. 13.10. The usual requirement in supplying power to any load in electronics work is that the load impedance shall equal the generator impedance, which of course is the condition for delivery of maximum power. Examples of this are: the connection of a signal generator to a radio receiver, of an audio amplifier to a loud-speaker or dummy load, and most particularly the connection of a power source to a feeder for if the latter is not correctly matched reflec-tions will occur. (It should be noted, however, that in general the 'optimum load' of an output valve is not equal to its a.c. resistance because the question of distortion as well as power output has to be considered.) The insertion of the T-section must leave this matching unchanged, i.e. its impedance when loaded looking into the input end must equal that of the load. Since it is symmetrical its impedance as seen from the other end must also be equal to the load. From Fig. 13.10 the condition for this matching is seen to be

$$R_g = R_1 + \frac{R_2(R_1 + R_L)}{R_1 + R_2 + R_L} \qquad (13.1)$$

The currents i_1 and i_2 are obviously related by

$$i_2 = i_1 \frac{R_2}{R_1 + R_2 + R_L} \qquad (13.2)$$

The voltage E_L delivered to the load is $i_2 R_L$, while the input voltage E_i (which equals that which would be applied to the load in the absence of the T-section) is $i_1 R_g = i_1 R_L$. (Since $R_g = R_L$ for correct matching.)

Hence $\dfrac{E_i}{E_L} = \dfrac{i_1 R_L}{i_2 R_L} = \dfrac{R_1 + R_2 + R_L}{R_2}$ from eqn. (13.2)   (13.3)

and since $R_L = R_g$ this ratio can be expressed in decibels:—

$$\text{Attenuation} = 20 \log_{10} \frac{E_i}{E_L} = 20 \log_{10}\left(\frac{R_1 + R_2 + R_L}{R_2}\right) \quad (13.4)$$

From equations (13.1) and (13.4) a symmetrical T-section attenuator can be designed for any particular requirement.

It must again be emphasised that attentuation in decibels *cannot* be simply obtained from the voltage ratio *unless the impedances are equal.*

Such a section gives a certain fixed attenuation but it is a simple matter to arrange for R_1 and R_2 to be variable and operated together so as to maintain the input resistance constant while varying the attenua-tion. There is a practical limit to this process, however, when R_2 become inconveniently small in relation to R_1, in which case the accuracy of the calibration becomes poor. It is generally considered that 40 dB is the greatest attenuation that should be attempted with one section.

From equation (13.1), putting $R_g = R_L$,

$$R_L = R_1 + \frac{R_2(R_1 + R_L)}{R_1 + R_2 + R_L} = R_1 + \frac{R_1 + R_L}{\left(\dfrac{R_1 + R_2 + R_L}{R_2}\right)}$$

and writing $\dfrac{E_i}{E_L} = A$, this gives $R_L = R_1 + \dfrac{R_1 + R_L}{A}$

$$\therefore R_1 = R_L\left(\frac{A-1}{A+1}\right) \tag{13.5}$$

Also, from equation (13.3),

$$A . R_2 = R_1 + R_2 + R_L$$

$$\therefore R_2 = \frac{R_1 + R_L}{A - 1} = \frac{R_L\left(\dfrac{A-1}{A+1}\right) + R_L}{A - 1} = R_L\frac{2A}{A^2 - 1} \tag{13.6}$$

For high attenuation this approximates to

$$R_2 = R_L\frac{2}{A} \tag{13.6a}$$

If the attenuation is 40 dB, then from equation (13.4)

$$40 = 20 \log_{10}\frac{E_i}{E_L}$$

i.e.
$$\frac{E_i}{E_L} = \text{antilog } 2 = 100$$

Hence, from equation (13.6a),

$$R_2 = 0.02\, R_L$$

and from equation (13.5),

$$R_1 = 0.98\, R_L.$$

Thus for the case where R_L is 600 Ω, R_2 is 12 Ω and R_1 is 588 Ω.

When a higher degree of attenuation is required a number of T-sections are switched in, as shown in Fig. 13.11. By this method any amount of attenuation can be obtained by means of units of convenient size, and the control can be made fine by making one of the sections continuously variable. Each section is, of course, designed to present the same resistance. This is the 'iterative' impedance and is equal to the resistance offered by an infinite chain of sections.

An attenuator of this type can be made up and calibrated in decibels. The fine dial could give from 1 to 10 dB, the next 9 would each add

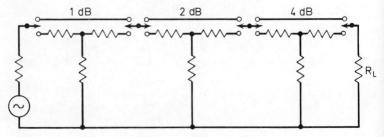

Fig. 13.11. Variable attenuator

10 dB, and then more sections adding 100 dB could be used if required. Alternatively it can be constructed so as to read voltage ratios, the fine dial reading up to 10, the next sections to 100, and so on. The latter method is preferable when it is required to know what fraction of a known voltage is being applied to an equipment on test.

It is sometimes desirable that an attenuator shall be balanced, i.e. both lines have the same characteristics. Two T-sections are then joined back to back producing an H-section, as shown in Fig. 13.12.

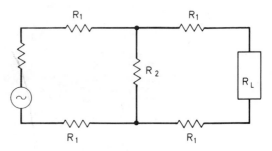

Fig. 13.12. Balanced T or H-section attenuator

A T- or H-section attenuator is not normally required to work between different impedances but some mis-matching may occur accidentally. An example of this arises in radio work when the load is a loudspeaker, whose resistance varies with frequency and so cannot be matched during the whole of a test. In this case the attenuation is increased by an added amount given by

$$10 \log \frac{(1 + r)^2}{4r}$$

where r is the ratio of the resistance of the load actually employed to that required for matching. The added loss is called a 'reflection loss'. It should be noted that a very considerable amount of mis-matching is

permissible without causing any serious change in the attenuating properties of the network. For example, if the load is double what it should be,
then

$$\text{reflection loss} = 10 \log \frac{9}{8} = 0\cdot5 \text{ dB (approx.)}.$$

This is quite small, for 1 dB is about the smallest change in volume
detectable by the human ear if the change is made suddenly.

It is sometimes necessary for an attenuator to match both generator
and load. It is then possible to build a rather simpler device from
L-sections, as shown in Fig. 13.13. In this case the condition of matching
is

$$R_g = R_1 + \frac{R_2 R_L}{R_2 + R_L}$$

since the load R_L is in parallel with R_2.

For the case where $R_L = R_g$, substituting $R_1 = 0$ in equation (13.4),

$$\text{voltage attenuation} = 20 \log_{10} \frac{R_2 + R_L}{R_2}.$$

Clearly the values of R_1 and R_2 can be set to obtain matching for
any value of R_g.

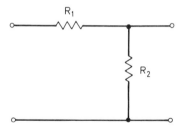

Fig. 13.13. L-section attenuator

A number of L-sections can be connected up and arranged to be
switched, just as in the case of T-sections. Such an attenuator can be
used when the load is a pure resistance whose sole purpose is to load
the apparatus under test. For example, the load may be an output meter,
in which case the output mis-matching is quite unimportant if the actual
attenuation at each setting is known.

A very simple attenuator can be constructed when absolute matching
on either side is essential; this is the continuously variable 'ladder'
attenuator shown in Fig. 13.14. In this case exact matching can be
obtained at the points where the shunt resistances are connected. The

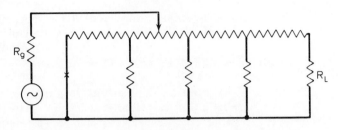

Fig. 13.14. Continuously variable ladder attenuator

main virtue of this device is its cheapness and ease of construction, one moving contact only being required; moreover the variation in resistance is not great on either side of the tapping points.

13.6.1. Some Applications of Attenuators

The output from a signal generator is sometimes applied to a ladder-type attenuator whose output resistance is of the order of 10 Ω. The output then matches the standard artificial aerial used in receiver testing and the voltage is known from the attenuator setting and the current flowing in the input side.

In measuring the attenuation of a filter, or other device, it is replaced by a T-type attenuator whose impedance is equal to that of the filter surge impedance. In this case it is convenient to design the sections so that each setting of the switch shows the attenuation in dB. If the input and output impedances are equal the voltage attenuation will double the power attenuation. In the previous case, it is more convenient to employ a decimal attenuator, i.e. one having switched sections giving ratios 1:100, 1:1000, and so on, and another variable section giving ratios from 0 to 100. This of course can be re-labelled in dB by marking 1:100 '40 dB', 1:1000 '60 dB', and so on, but the scale is an awkward one to use, since people naturally think in tens.

If tests are being made on a cable under working conditions it is advisable to use an H-type attenuator so that stray capacitances to earth shall be equal on both sides. One calibrated in dB is obviously the most convenient.

It is common practice in broadcast receiver factories for a large signal generator to distribute r.f. to perhaps several dozen testing points. At each of these points an attenuator is provided for supplying a receiver under test. Each attenuator cannot then be required to match the generator, for at one time all the testers may have receivers on their benches while at another time only two or three may be actually taking a signal. In this case L-section attenuators could be used, but some form of ladder network is preferable, for the generator load will then be more nearly constant and the mis-matching of the artificial aerials will be less than that caused in everyday use by the fact that domestic aerials are widely dissimilar.

These few notes on the use of attenuators are not intended to be complete but merely to enable the reader to see that each particular case has to be considered on its merits and a common-sense balance struck between accuracy, cost and ease of operation.

13.6.2. Miscellaneous Types of Attenuator

Ultra-high-frequency generators are sometimes provided with capacitance attenuators of the type shown in Fig. 13.15. These have some advantages in that small capacitors are more easily made than resistors having small self-capacitance and skin effect. They can be made very compact. The accuracy is not high but no measurement at these ultra-high frequencies can be made very accurately.

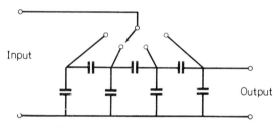

Fig. 13.15. Capacitance attenuator

A special type of ladder attenuator can be made by closing it at one end by a resistance equal to the iterative impedance of the sections, at the point X in Fig. 13.14. This ensures that for all positions of the switch the input resistance is constant. The output resistance, however, varies because the generator resistance is shunted between points at different distances from the output.

The correct values for the components are given by

$$R_1 = R_L(A - 1)$$

$$R_2 = R_L\left(\frac{A}{A - 1}\right).$$

These relationships can be obtained in the same way as those for the T-section.

WORKED EXAMPLES

Question 1. An attenuator of T type is required to produce a loss of 10 dB in a 600 Ω transmission line. Compute the values of the shunt and series resistances.   (C. & G. Final Grade).

Answer 1. The T-type attenuator is shown in Fig. 13.10. The loss required here is certainly a power loss, hence the design equations are

$$R_g = R_1 + \frac{R_2(R_1 + R_L)}{R_2 + R_1 + R_L} \tag{1}$$

$$\text{Attenuation} = 20 \log_{10} \frac{R_1 + R_2 + R_L}{R_2} \tag{2}$$

Substituting the given values, and noting that $R_g = R_L = 600 \ \Omega$, then

$$600 = R_1 + \frac{R_2(R_1 + 600)}{R_1 + R_2 + 600} \tag{3}$$

$$10 = 20 \log_{10} \frac{R_1 + R_2 + 600}{R_2} \tag{4}$$

From equation (4),

$$\frac{R_1 + R_2 + 600}{R_2} = \sqrt{10} = 3 \cdot 162$$

whence $R_1 = 2 \cdot 162 \, R_2 - 600$

Substituting for R_1 in equation (3):

$$600 = 2 \cdot 162 \, R_2 - 600 + \frac{R_2 \times 2 \cdot 162 \, R_2}{3 \cdot 162 \, R_2}$$

Therefore $R_2 = \dfrac{1 \cdot 200}{2 \cdot 846} = \underline{421 \cdot 7 \ \Omega}$ *Answer (ii)*

and $R_1 = (2 \cdot 162 \times 421 \cdot 7) - 600 = \underline{311 \cdot 8 \ \Omega}$ *Answer (i)*

Question 2. What is the difference between a ladder attenuator and a balanced symmetrical attenuator? Explain why the former type is sometimes preferred to the latter. Find from first principles the attenuation in dB obtained when the attenuator of Question 1 is used with a source of power to which it is correctly matched but with a load of 1200 Ω.

Answer 2. A symmetrical attenuator is a network that presents a constant impedance to both source and load for all settings. A balanced attenuator has equal properties in both lines. The combination of these properties is best illustrated by the H-section attenuator.

A ladder attenuator is usually constructed with its series elements in one line only and does not present a constant impedance either side, though it may be designed so that the variations are not serious. The only reason it is sometimes preferred is that it is cheaper to construct and is equally good when exact matching is not required.

Using the same notation as in Fig. 13.10, the current in the load

$$i_2 = i_1 \frac{R_2}{R_1 + R_2 + R_L}$$

But $i_1 = E_i/R_0$, where E_i is the voltage generated by the source of power, and R_0 is the total resistance of the circuit given by

$$R_0 = R_g + R_1 + \frac{R_2(R_1 + R_L)}{R_1 + R_2 + R_L} \qquad (1)$$

Hence $i_2 = \frac{E}{R_0} \cdot \frac{R_2}{R_1 + R_2 + R_L}$

Power developed in the load, $P_2 = i_2^2 R_L$

If the attenuator were removed the current in the load would be i_0, i.e.

$$\frac{E}{R_g + R_L}$$

Thus $P_1 = i_0^2 R_L$

The attenuation produced by the attenuator is therefore

$$\frac{P_1}{P_2} = \frac{i_0^2 R_L}{i_2^2 R_L} = \left[\frac{R_0(R_1 + R_2 + R_L)}{R_2(R_g + R_L)} \right]^2$$

Substituting for R_0 from equation (1), this becomes

$$\frac{P_1}{P_2} = \left[\frac{(R_g + R_1)(R_1 + R_2 + R_L) + R_2(R_1 + R_L)}{R_2(R_g + R_L)} \right]^2$$

Since $R_g = 600, R_L = 1200, R_1 = 311 \cdot 8, R_2 = 421 \cdot 7$,

$$\frac{P_1}{P_2} = \frac{(600 + 311 \cdot 8)(311 \cdot 8 + 421 \cdot 7 + 1200) + 421 \cdot 7(311 \cdot 8 + 1200)}{421 \cdot 7(1200 + 600)}$$

$$= 3 \cdot 162^2$$

Therefore attenuation $= 10 \log_{10} 3 \cdot 162^2 = 20 \log_{10} 3 \cdot 162$

$$= \underline{10 \cdot 0 \text{ dB.}} \qquad \textit{Answer}$$

EXERCISES

1. Give the circuit diagram and describe with sketches the main constructional features of a standard signal generator for use at V.H.F. (30–300 MHz), indicating particularly those features that are essential in order to avoid inaccuracies in the output voltage.

(C. & G. Radio IV, 1954)

2. Give details of the tests carried out to obtain sensitivity, selectivity and fidelity characteristics of a broadcast receiver. What values of inductance, etc., would you use for a standard aerial for these tests?

3. Show how a cathode-ray oscilloscope may be used to check overloading in the intermediate-frequency amplifier of a superheterodyne receiver.

4. A three-gang capacitor assembly as used for broadcast receivers is provided with trimming capacitors and end-vane adjustment. Describe the method that you would adopt and the apparatus necessary to adjust the three elements so that they matched accurately at four points in the range.

REFERENCES

1. HARTSHORN, L., *Radio Frequency Measurements by Bridge and Resonance Methods,* Chapman and Hall Ltd.
2. TERMAN, F. E., *Radio Engineer's Handbook,* McGraw-Hill Book Co., Inc.

CHAPTER 14

Magnetic and Dielectric Measurements

14.1. INTRODUCTION

Magnetic and dielectric materials are widely used in electronics. This chapter gives the basic principles of measurements on these materials and of magnetic fields, and begins by showing how the magnetic moment and hence the pole strength of a bar magnet can be measured. The reader who has done elementary laboratory work in magnetism will be familiar with the neutral point method,[1] and it is assumed that he is familiar with the formulae for the field due to a bar magnet in Gauss's Tangent A and Tangent B positions, which are respectively:

$$H = \frac{2Md}{4\pi\mu_0(d^2 - l^2)^2} \simeq \frac{2M}{4\pi\mu_0 d^3} \text{ when } d \text{ is large compared with } l/2,$$

and

$$H = \frac{M}{4\pi\mu_0(d^2 + l^2)^{\frac{3}{2}}} \simeq \frac{M}{4\pi\mu_0 d^3} \text{ when } d \text{ is large compared with } l,$$

where H = field strength,
 d = distance between centre of magnet and point where H is measured,
 l = distance between magnet poles (the pole location can be found with a plotting compass),
 $M = 2ml$ = magnetic moment of magnet, where
 m = pole strength of magnet.

14.2. MEASURING THE MAGNETIC MOMENT

14.2.1. Use of Deflection Magnetometer

A practical method of determining the magnetic moment and hence the pole strength of a bar magnet is to use a deflection magnetometer. This consists of a long pointer suspended so as to rotate about its centre, the angle of rotation being measured by a circular scale calibrated in degrees. At the centre of the pointer is a small bar magnet fixed at right angles to the pointer axis. A scale is usually provided so that the distance between the pointer/magnet centre and the magnet under test can be fairly accurately measured.

One method of use is to place the magnetometer with its scale arms lying East and West so that the Earth's field H_0 (assumed known) is orthogonal to the field F of the magnet under test, as shown in Fig. 14.1(a). Then,

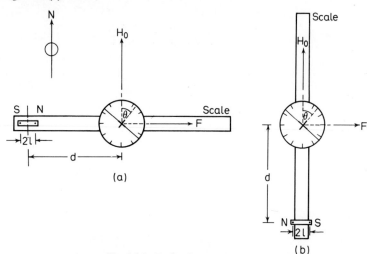

Fig. 14.1. Deflection magnetometer
(a) Gauss "A" position; (b) Gauss "B" position

$$\frac{F}{H_0} = \tan\theta \text{ or } F = H_0 \tan\theta = \frac{2Md}{4\pi\mu_0(d^2 - l^2)^2}$$

$$\text{whence } M = \frac{4\pi\mu_0(d^2 - 1^2)^2}{2d} H_0 \tan\theta \qquad (14.1)$$

For each value of d one should:

(a) read both ends of the magnetometer needle,

(b) reverse the magnet end for end and repeat (a),

(c) place the magnet at the same distance away on the other arm and repeat readings (a) and (b).

θ is then taken as the average of the eight readings.

Alternatively, the above procedure can be carried out with the magnetometer and the magnet in the 'Gauss B' or 'broadside-on' position as shown in Fig. 14.1(b). In this case,

$$M = 4\pi\mu_0 H_0(d^2 + l^2)^{\frac{3}{2}} \tan\theta.$$

14.2.2. Vibration Magnetometer

Yet another method of determining magnet moment is to use a vibration magnetometer, the construction of which is shown in Fig. 14.2(*a*). The procedure is as follows:

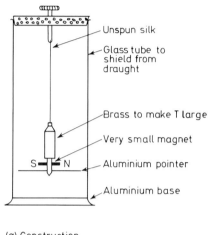

Unspun silk

Glass tube to shield from draught

Brass to make T large

Very small magnet

Aluminium pointer

Aluminium base

(*a*) Construction

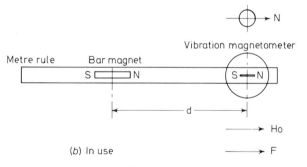

N

Vibration magnetometer

Metre rule   Bar magnet

S [   ] N   S —■— N

d

Ho

F

(*b*) In use

Fig. 14.2. Vibration magnetometer

(1) With the aid of a compass needle, a metre rule is placed on the laboratory bench along the magnetic meridian; the bar magnet to be tested being placed a safe distance away.

(2) The vibration magnetometer is placed on the north end of the rule with its small magnetic needle above the 10 cm mark, and the suspension fibre is twisted until the magnetometer needle lies along the magnetic meridian (i.e. in the direction of the rule).

(3) The magnetometer needle is then set into oscillations of small amplitude in the Earth's field H_0 alone by bringing a magnet near to it, and
the time for 20 oscillations determined.

(4) The bar magnet is then placed on the rule with its N pole pointing
North and its mid point d cm due south of the vibration magnetometer.
The field acting on the needle is then $(F + H_0)$ where F is the field due
to the bar magnet alone. The time for 20 oscillations is again determined,
(Fig. 14.2(b)).

(5) The above process is repeated for various values of distance d.

The theory of this method is as follows.

In general, for a vibrating magnet

$$T = 2\pi \sqrt{\frac{P}{MH_0}} \qquad (14.2)$$

where P = moment of inertia. Therefore

$$H_0 = \left(\frac{4\pi^2 P}{M}\right)\frac{1}{T^2} = \frac{4\pi^2 P}{M} n^2$$

where T = periodic time in seconds and $n = \frac{1}{T}$ = number of vibrations per
second.

Now since $\left(\frac{4\pi^2 P}{M}\right)$ is constant for the vibration magnetometer, then

$H_0 \propto n^2$ or $H_0 = Kn^2$ where K is a constant.

Now supposing that in the Earth's field alone the needle makes n_0
vibrations per second, then $H_0 = Kn_0^2$. And supposing that in field
$(F + H_0)$ due to magnet and Earth the needle makes n_1 vibrations per
second, then $F + H_0 = Kn_1^2$.

Whence $\qquad \dfrac{F + H_0}{H_0} = \dfrac{n_1^2}{n_0^2}$ so that $F = H_0\left(\dfrac{n_1^2 - n_0^2}{n_0^2}\right).$

Thus if H_0 is known, F can be determined, and thus the magnetic
moment M of the bar magnet can be calculated since for a *short* magnet,

$$F = \frac{2M}{4\pi\mu_o d^3} \text{ so that} \qquad M = 2\pi\mu_o F d^3$$

For the final calculation a value of d should be chosen which is
about ten times the magnetic length of the magnet.

14.2.3. Determination of H_0

In considering the application of the deflection and vibration magneto-
meters, it was assumed that the value of the horizontal component H_0

of the Earth's field was accurately known. Conversely, if a bar magnet of known magnetic moment M and moment of inertia P is available, H_0 can be determined to a good degree of accuracy.

From equation (14.2) above,

$$MH_0 = \frac{4\pi^2 P}{T^2} \qquad (14.3)$$

Now P, the moment of inertia of the magnet, is given by

$$P = \text{Mass} \times \frac{a^2 + b^2}{3} \ ,$$

where $2a$ = depth, and $2b$ = length, of magnet.

P can therefore be determined by measurement and weighing.

If the magnet is suspended at its centre and set swinging, the time for one oscillation = T.

Now dividing equation (14.3) by equation (14.1),

$$H_0^2 = \frac{2d}{4\pi\mu_0 (d^2 - 1^2)^2 \tan\theta} \cdot \frac{4\pi^2 P}{T^2} \ \text{ whence } \ H_0 = \frac{1}{T(d^2 - 1^2)}\sqrt{\frac{2dP\pi}{\tan\theta \cdot \mu_0}}$$

14.2.4. Relation Between Magnetising Force and Intensity of Magnetisation

The relation between magnetising force H and intensity of magnetisation J for ferromagnetic material can be found as follows. It is assumed that the specimen is in the form of a long thin bar.

It is first necessary to demagnetise the specimen, using the arrangement shown in Fig. 14.3(a). The variable output mains transformer (such as the commercial Variac type) is set to say 100 V, the specimen inserted, and the voltage from the Variac reduced gradually to zero. The demagnetised specimen is then slowly withdrawn from the coil.

To find the relationship between H and J, the magnetometer arrangement shown in Fig. 14.3(b) is used. This consists of a vertical solenoid wound with a main magnetising coil and a neutralising coil to eliminate the vertical component of the Earth's field, a compensating coil and a deflection magnetometer. The main magnetising coil is connected in series with the compensating coil. The neutralising coil is in series with a resistance calculated to give just the right current which, flowing in the coil, neutralises the vertical component of the Earth's field.

With about ½ A flowing in the main coil and compensating coil, and without any specimen, the deflection magnetometer is adjusted until it shows no deflection. Thus any subsequent deflection is due to the intensity of magnetisation produced in a specimen.

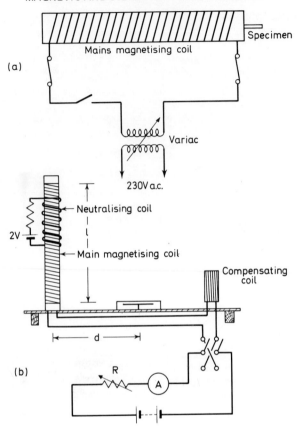

Fig. 14.3. Apparatus for plotting hysteresis loop

With the main magnetising current switched off, the demagnetised specimen is placed in the solenoid, the rheostat R set to the position of maximum resistance, and the current switched on. The current measured by the ammeter and the deflection of the magnetometer is noted. The current is then increased to maximum in suitable steps and the deflection in each case noted. The mean of the readings at each end of the pointer is found. The current must not be decreased at all during this stage.

The current is then reduced to zero in suitable steps and the magnetometer deflection noted in each case. The current is then reversed and increased in suitable steps to maximum in the reverse direction, the magnetometer deflections being noted. The procedure is then continued, reducing the current to zero, reversing, then increasing the current to maximum in the forward direction. The results are tabulated and the graph of current I plotted against $\tan \theta$ plotted as shown in Fig. 14.4.

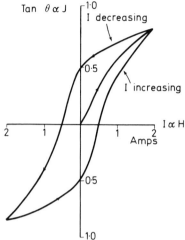

Fig. 14.4. Hysteresis loop

Now $H = \dfrac{NI}{1}$ and $J = \dfrac{H_0}{a\left\{\dfrac{1}{d^2} - \dfrac{1}{(d^2 + l^2)^{\frac{3}{2}}}\right\}} \tan \theta$

where N = number of turns on main magnetising coil, a = area of cross-section of specimen and d and 1 are as shown in Fig. 14.3.

Thus H is directly proportional to I, and J is directly proportional to $\tan \theta$, therefore a graph of H (abcissa) plotted against J (ordinate) will be the same as that shown in Fig. 14.4 but to a different scale. The graph is then called an 'hysteresis loop'. The above expression for J shows that the calculations are rather tedious and this is a laborious method in general for plotting the hysteresis loop. Chapter 7 shows how the hysteresis loop can be directly shown on the screen of a cathode-ray oscilloscope, and if the c.r.o. constants are known, the area of the loop can be easily calculated.

14.3. FLUX MEASUREMENT

14.3.1. Use of Ballistic Galvanometer

The ballistic galvanometer, described in Chapter 2, can be used as an indicator of flux density as follows (see Fig. 14.5).

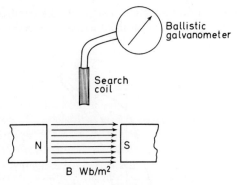

Fig. 14.5. Ballistic galvanometer as fluxmeter

The search coil of area A m^2 and N turns is *suddenly* placed perpendicular to a field of B tesla in δt seconds.

Change in flux $\delta\phi = BA$ webers.

Change in flux linkage $= N . \delta\phi = BAN$ webers.

Induced e.m.f. $e = N\dfrac{\delta\phi}{\delta t}$ in magnitude $= \dfrac{BAN}{\delta t}$

Induced current $i = \dfrac{e}{R} = \dfrac{BAN}{R . \delta t}$ where R = resistance of whole galvano-

meter circuit.

Therefore $i\,\delta t = \dfrac{BAN}{R} = Q$, the change which passes through the

galvanometer and gives a throw θ.

Thus $\qquad Q = \dfrac{\text{change in flux linkage}}{\text{resistance of circuit}} = \dfrac{BAN}{R} = K\theta,$

where K is a constant for a given galvanometer.

Ballistic galvanometers can be used to compare fluxes or fields but it cannot be calibrated once and for all like a proper fluxmeter, since if the resistance R of the circuit is altered, the throw for a given flux change is also altered.

14.3.2. The Grassot Fluxmeter

This is essentially a modified moving-coil galvanometer. The coil is suspended by a single silk thread so that the controlling torque due to the suspension is negligible. The pointer movement is made almost dead-beat by making the electromagnetic damping large.

Under these conditions the coil does not oscillate but gives a deflection proportional to the change in flux and can be calibrated directly. The operation of this instrument is dealt with in the Appendix to this Chapter.

14.3.3. Hall Effect Probe

The appearance of an e.m.f. across the breadth of a conductor when a current flows along its length and a magnetic field exists at right angles to both these directions is known as the Hall Effect. As shown in Fig. 14.6(a), if a current I amps is passed through a conducting plate t metres thick, placed in a magnetic field of B tesla perpendicular to the plane of the plate, a potential difference V_H is set up between points (a) and (b). The value of V_H is given by

$$V_H = R_H \cdot \frac{B.I}{t} \text{ volts,}$$

where R_H is the Hall coefficient of the conductor in m^3/coulomb.

Thus if R_H is known and t, V_H and I are measured, B can be determined, or for a fixed V_H or I an ammeter or voltmeter respectively can be directly calibrated in terms of B.

In semiconductors the value of R_H is much greater than in metals and the Hall voltage large enough to be useful in engineering applications. In the field probe shown in Fig. 14.6(b) the semiconductor plate is encap-

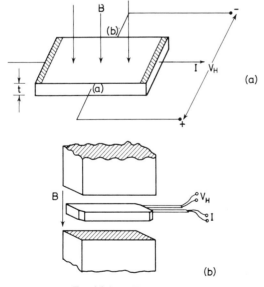

Fig. 14.6. Hall effect device

sulated between insulating non-magnetic plates, sleeved leads being brought out from the edge of the probe as shown. These leads are internally arranged to minimise inductive coupling between magnetic field and output circuits.

14.4. MAGNETIC SUSCEPTIBILITY MEASUREMENTS

For an isotropic material of relative permeability μ_r placed in a magnetic field, then

$$B = \mu_0 H + J$$

or

$$\mu_r \mu_0 H = \mu_0 H + J$$

∴

$$\mu_r \mu_0 \quad = \mu_0 \quad + J/H$$

or

$$\mu_r \mu_0 \quad = \mu_0 \quad + \chi$$

i.e.

$$\mu \quad = \mu_0 \quad + \chi$$

where H = Field in amp/m,
μ_0 = Permeability of free space = $4\pi \times 10^{-7}$
B = Flux density in tesla
J = Intensity of magnetisation in tesla,
$\chi = J/H$ = magnetic susceptibility per unit volume,
$\mu = \mu_r \mu_0$ = absolute permeability of material.

For *diamagnetic* materials, χ is small and negative, so μ_r is slightly less than 1. It is also independent of temperature and field strength.

For *paramagnetic* materials, χ is small and positive, so μ_r is slightly greater than 1. It is also independent of the field strength H, but does vary with the temperature according to the *Curie Law* $\chi = C/T$, where T is the absolute temperature and C is the Curie constant.

For *ferromagnetic* materials, χ is large, in fact often very large, and positive so μ_r is also very large. It also depends on the temperature and the strength of the magnetic field, H. Above a critical temperature θ_f, known as the *ferromagnetic Curie temperature*, the material becomes paramagnetic and χ becomes very small. Well above the temperature θ_f, the susceptibility follows the Curie–Weiss Law, and $\chi = C/(T - \theta)$, where C is the Curie constant and θ is the paramagnetic Curie temperature. (θ may be 20 or more degrees higher than θ_f).

14.4.1. Force Acting on a Body in a Magnetic Field

If a body of absolute permeability $\mu_1 = \mu_r \mu_0$ and volume v is placed in a magnetic field of H amp/m then its energy is,

$$\tfrac{1}{2}BHv = \tfrac{1}{2}\mu H^2 v \text{ joules.}$$

Now if a body of volume v and absolute permeability μ_2 is introduced into a region of permeability μ_1 where the magnetic field is H, then the *change* in energy of the system is

$$dW = \tfrac{1}{2}(\mu_1 - \mu_2)H^2 v.$$

The force F_x on the body, acting in the direction of x in Fig. 14.7, is given by

$$F_x = -\frac{dW}{dx}.$$

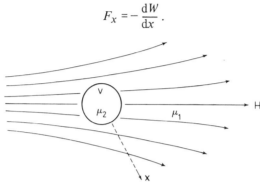

Fig. 14.7. Force on body in magnetic field

By partial differentiation,

$$F_x = \tfrac{1}{2}(\mu_2 - \mu_1)\left(\frac{\partial H^2}{\partial x}\right)v = (\mu_2 - \mu_1)H\left(\frac{\partial H}{\partial x}\right)v.$$

Now, $\mu_2 = \mu_0 + \chi_2$ and $\mu_1 = \mu_0 + \chi_1$,

So that $F_x = \tfrac{1}{2}(\chi_2 - \chi_1)\dfrac{dH^2}{dx}v = (\chi_2 - \chi_1)H\dfrac{dH}{dx}v.$ newtons.

Note that if $(\chi_2 - \chi_1)$ is positive then the body will tend to move in the direction of increasing H, i.e. it will behave as a paramagnetic body and move to the place where the field is strongest.

If $(\chi_2 - \chi_1)$ is negative, the body moves in the direction of decreasing H, i.e. it will behave like a diamagnetic body and move to the place where the field is weakest.

The equations are only correct if the field H is not appreciably distorted by the introduction of the body, i.e. they will not apply to ferromagnetic bodies whose introduction would obviously distort the field. The equations can thus only be used with paramagnetic or diamagnetic bodies.

14.4.2. The Gouy Method

This method is recommended for all cases where a large sample of the material (10^4 mm^3 or more) is available.

Referring to Fig. 14.8, the specimen of magnetic susceptibility χ_2, in the form of a cylindrical rod about 150 mm long and of uniform cross-

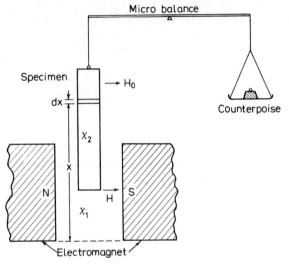

Fig. 14.8. Gouy method

sectional area 'a' m^2, is suspended with its lower end in a *very strong and uniform* field H, between the pole pieces of an electromagnet while the upper end is in a very weak magnetic field H_0.

The specimen is then counterpoised using some form of microbalance.

The force dF_x acting on an *element* of the rod of length 'dx' and hence volume 'a dx' is given by

$$dF_x = \tfrac{1}{2}(\chi_2 - \chi_1)\frac{dH^2}{dx}\,a\,dx = \tfrac{1}{2}(\chi_2 - \chi_1)\,a\,d(H^2) \text{ newtons.}$$

Note that this force will be downwards if χ_2 is greater than χ_1, the susceptibility of the air, and vice versa.

The *total* force F_x on the rod in the vertical direction is given by,

$$F_x = \tfrac{1}{2}(\chi_2 - \chi_1)a\int_{H_0}^{H} d(H^2) = \tfrac{1}{2}(\chi_2 - \chi_1)a(H^2 - H_0^2) \text{ newtons.}$$

If m kilogrammes is the *change* in counterpoise weight required for balance when the field H is switched on, then

$$\tfrac{1}{2}(\chi_2 - \chi_1)a(H^2 - H_0^2) = mg.$$

Note that H_0 is usually negligible compared with H, and χ_1, the susceptibility of air, is usually negligible compared with χ_2, so that

$$\tfrac{1}{2}\chi_2 a H^2 = mg.$$

To measure χ_2 for powders or liquids, the containing vessel is a glass tube, and the *change* in counterpoise weight is found, first with the tube empty and then with the tube full of liquid or power. The *difference* of these two *changes* in the weight is then the appropriate value of m to use in the above equations. This eliminates the effect of the containing tube.

The method can also be used to measure the susceptibility of gases but is more difficult in this case.

14.4.3. The Quincke Method

This is a quick and simple method for liquids. Referring to Fig. 14.9, the surface of the liquid in the narrow limb is arranged to be near the centre of the uniform field H between the pole pieces of the large electro-magnet

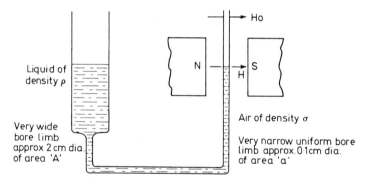

Fig. 14.9. Quinke method

and the meniscus is viewed with a microscope. If the liquid is, as usual, paramagnetic, it will rise a distance h metres in the narrow limb. (If it is a diamagnetic liquid it will fall.) Owing to the disparity in the cross-sectional area of the two limbs, there will be no *appreciable* change in the level of the liquid in the wider limb.

The theory is similar to that for Gouy's method but the upward force on the liquid due to the field is in this case automatically balanced by the force due to the hydrostatic pressure.

Upward force due to field $= \frac{1}{2}(\chi_2 - \chi_1)a(H^2 - H_0^2) = (\rho - \sigma)gha$.

Usually H_0 is negligible compared with H, and the susceptibility of air and density of air are very small, so, approx.,

$\frac{1}{2}\chi_2 H^2 = \rho gh = \rho gh(1 + a/A)$ if fall of liquid in wide limb cannot be ignored.

14.4.4. The Curie Method

This method is very suitable for very small specimens, and when measurements at different temperatures are required, since it is easier to keep small volumes at a constant high or low temperature.

In the Gouy and Quinke methods one end of the *large* specimen is in a *uniform* magnetic field. In the Curie method the *small* specimen is placed in a *non-uniform* magnetic field and the actual force acting on it is measured with a torsion balance.

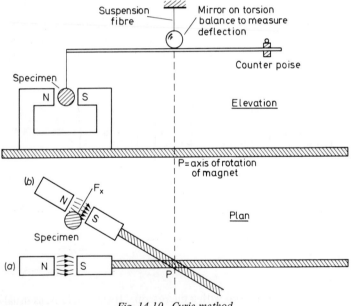

Fig. 14.10. Curie method

The apparatus is arranged as shown in Fig. 14.10, the small specimen being suspended from a torsion balance between the poles of a strong permanent magnet. The force on the specimen is directly proportional to the *angular* deflection of the torsion balance and is measured with a lamp and scale.

In the initial position (a), the specimen is in a *uniform* field so the force on it is *zero*. Now the *magnet* is rotated about the axis P, and the specimen is now in a *non-uniform* magnetic field, and if paramagnetic, is subject to a force F_x in the direction shown in position (b). This force and hence the torsion balance deflection reaches a maximum value when $H(dH/dx)$ is a maximum.

Suppose the maximum torsion balance deflection is θ_2, then

$$(\chi_2 - \chi_1)\left(H\frac{dH}{dx}_{max}\right)v = c\theta_2, \text{ where } c \text{ is a constant.}$$

The experiment is now repeated with a specimen of the same shape and volume v but of *known* susceptibility χ_3 giving a maximum deflection of θ_3, say, then

$$(\chi_3 - \chi_4)\left(H\frac{dH}{dx}_{max}\right)v = c\theta_3$$

By division,

$$\frac{(\chi_2 - \chi_1)}{(\chi_3 - \chi_1)} = \frac{\theta_2}{\theta_3}$$

whence χ_2 can be found if χ_3 is known.

Note that as the magnet is rotated clockwise about the vertical axis in the direction shown, the specimen is pulled round with it and the torsion balance deflection reaches a maximum value when the specimen is in a region where $H(dH/dx)$ is a maximum. On further rotation of the magnet the specimen will be left behind and θ will decrease. In an actual experiment it is wiser to rotate the magnet clockwise till the deflection is a maximum, then rotate it anticlockwise until the deflection is a maximum in the opposite direction, and thus we can measure $2 \times \theta_{max}$ and have no difficulty about the position of zero deflection.

The absolute measurement of susceptibility is not possible by this method, but it is quick, uses very small specimens, and is very useful when measuring susceptibility at different temperatures since the specimen can easily be hung in suitable furnaces or cryostats.

Note: $\chi = M/H$ = *volume susceptibility*, where M = magnetic moment per unit volume.

$k = \chi/\rho$ = *mass susceptibility*, where ρ is the density of the material.

$k_A = k(A)$ = *atomic susceptibility*, where A is the atomic (or molecular) weight.

14.4.5. Forces on Materials in an Electric Field

This problem is so similar to that of the magnetic field that it is worth studying at the same time.

The energy W joules stored in a volume v cubic metres of an electric field is given by

$$W = \tfrac{1}{2}DEv = \tfrac{1}{2}\epsilon E^2 v \text{ joules, since } D = \epsilon_r \epsilon_0 E$$

where D = electric displacement or flux density in coulombs/m^2,

      E = electric field strength in volts/m or newtons/coulomb,

      $\epsilon = \epsilon_r \epsilon_0$ = absolute permittivity of the material.

Now suppose a volume v of a medium of absolute permittivity ϵ_1 is replaced by the same volume of material of absolute permittivity ϵ_2, then change in potential energy of the spaces = $(\tfrac{1}{2}\epsilon_1 E^2 - \tfrac{1}{2}\epsilon_2 E^2)v$ joules = W joules

Now Force = $-$ grad W, so the force F_x on the body in the x direction is given by

$$F_x = \frac{\mathrm{d}W}{\mathrm{d}x} = \tfrac{1}{2}(\epsilon_2 - \epsilon_1)\left(\frac{\mathrm{d}E}{\mathrm{d}x}\right)^2 v = (\epsilon_2 - \epsilon_1)E\left(\frac{\mathrm{d}E}{\mathrm{d}x}\right)v.$$

Note that particles for which ϵ_2 is greater than ϵ_1 tend to move to places where the electric field is strongest, and in uniform fields they do not move at all.

14.4.6. Force between Plates of Parallel Plate Capacitor

Referring to Fig. 14.11, when the field is switched on the energy stored between the capacitor plates of area A m^2 spaced x metre apart is

$$W = \tfrac{1}{2}DEAx = \tfrac{1}{2}\epsilon E^2 Ax \text{ joules.}$$

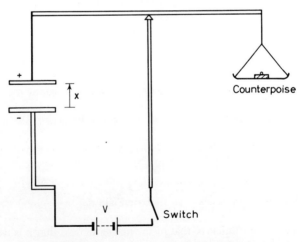

Fig. 14.11. Force between capacitor plates

Thus the force F_x on one of the plates in the upward direction is

$$F_x = -\frac{dW}{dx} = -\tfrac{1}{2}\epsilon E^2 A.$$

Therefore the plates are attracted and an extra mass m kilogrammes is needed to counterpoise the plate and is given by:

$$\tfrac{1}{2}\epsilon\left(\frac{V^2}{x^2}\right)A = mg \text{ newton}$$

and with air dielectric then $\epsilon = \epsilon_0 =$ permittivity of free space
$$= 8\cdot85 \times 10^{-12} \text{ farads/metre}.$$

This is the basic principle of the attracted disc electrometer or voltmeter.

14.4.7. Force on Slab of Dielectric Between Plates of Parallel Plate Capacitor

In Fig. 14.12 the sheet of dielectric of *horizontal* cross-sectional area 'a' m^2 and absolute permittivity ϵ_2 is pulled down into the space of absolute permittivity ϵ_1 when the electric field E is switched on.

The force dF_x on element of slab of length dx is

$$dF_x = \tfrac{1}{2}(\epsilon_2 - \epsilon_1)\left(\frac{dE^2}{dx}\right)a\,dx.$$

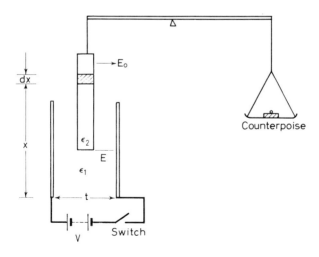

Fig. 14.12. Force on dielectric between capacitor plates

Thus total force F on whole slab in vertical direction is

$$F_x = \tfrac{1}{2}(\epsilon_2 - \epsilon_1)\int_{E_0}^{E} a\,\mathrm{d}(E^2) = \tfrac{1}{2}(\epsilon_2 - \epsilon_1)a(E^2 - E_0^2) = mg \text{ newtons},$$

where mg is the extra counterpoise needed for balance, and $E = V/t$ volts/m. Note that E_0 is almost zero, but ϵ_1 is not negligible compared with ϵ_2.

14.4.8. The Electrostatic Equivalent of Quinke's Method

Referring to Fig. 14.13, the wide limb is a *rectangular* trough with large horizontal cross-sectional area and with the upper part between the

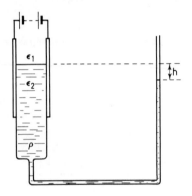

Fig. 14.13. Electrostatic equivalent of Quinke's method

plates of a parallel plate capacitor. On switching on the field E between the plates the liquid rises between the plates and

$$\tfrac{1}{2}(\epsilon_2 - \epsilon_1)E^2 = \rho g h.$$

The theory is similar to that for Quinke's magnetic experiment described earlier.

14.4.9. Dielectric Power Loss

The arrangement shown in Fig. 4.16 of Chapter 4 can be used to measure the power consumed in dielectric materials. It is sometimes known as an 'electrostatic wattmeter' and is based on the theory of the quadrant electrometer. A complete description will be found in (Chapter 9).

14.5. BRIDGE METHODS

As explained in Chapter 8, the Maxwell bridge is used for testing magnetic materials and many commercial magnetic materials test sets are based on this type of bridge. The Schering bridge, described in the same chapter, is often used for measurements on dielectric materials. A summary of bridge methods for measurements on magnetic materials at communication frequencies was given in a Paper by A. C. Lynch at the N.P.L. Symposium on Precision Electrical Instruments.[2]

14.6. MEASUREMENT OF PERMEABILITY

One of the most important properties of a magnetic material is its permeability. Many laboratories use a method of measurement in which toroidal cores have a number of turns of wire wound on them. An impedance bridge (Chapter 8) or Q meter (Chapter 10) is then used to measure the effective inductance and resistance, and the permeability is calculated from these values and the known geometry of the core. When all the losses not contributed by the core are deducted, one can also calculate the dissipation factor.

A simple method used mainly in the powdered-iron range of materials yields the effective permeability and dissipation factor of rods of the material under test. One simply notes the change of inductance or resonating capacitance caused by the insertion of a rod into a standard coil.

A third method used at the U.S. National Bureau of Standards and other laboratories to obtain the highest accuracies involves the use of thin annular discs accurately ground or machined from the core material. These are inserted into a coaxial line whose impedance changes are measured. A complete description was given in a Paper by P. H. Hass.[3]

14.7. TESTING OF PERMANENT MAGNET MATERIALS

Materials used for permanent magnets are among the most important used in electronic devices, and previous chapters have shown their wide use in electrical instruments. Some rather academic methods for testing such materials have already been discussed in this chapter, and we will now outline various practical methods used by industry.

14.7.1. Electromagnet Test

In this method, the specimen is in the form of a short straight bar inserted between the poles of an electromagnet, the diameter of which is much larger than the width of the specimen. The field is measured by means of a flat coil of a few hundred turns of fine wire strapped to one side of the specimen, while the energising coil consists of 20—30 turns of wire wound directly upon the specimen. A Grassot fluxmeter, described earlier, is usually suitable for measurement of both H and B. The full hysteresis loop may be traced out by the use of this apparatus.

14.7.2. B.S. Method

B.S. 406:1931 describes an apparatus in which the specimen is energised by a coil surrounding it and forms part of the magnetic circuit providing the field of a rotating-disc type of dynamo. The voltage output of the dynamo is used to determine the flux density in the magnet under test.

14.7.3. Rotating-coil Magnetometer

A small rotating coil driven by a synchronous motor may be used in conjunction with a potentiometer circuit to measure the field strength in the gap between the poles of a permanent magnet. Such an apparatus can be calibrated directly in field strength.

14.7.4. Search-coil Method

A commonly used method of comparing the strengths of permanent magnets on a production basis is by means of a search coil connected to a Grassot fluxmeter or ballistic galvanometer as previously described in this chapter.

If the field of the permanent magnet in the instrument is uniform the deflection is proportional to the change in flux through the coil.

14.7.5. Current-balance Method

The apparatus used here is essentially a moving-coil ammeter whose permanent magnet can be easily removed and replaced by one made of the material under test. Thus for known currents passed through the meter with the 'standard' and test magnets the scale can be calibrated in terms of field strength. The reason why this is called the current-balance method is because the field from the magnet is balanced against the field from a magnetising coil.

14.7.6. Hall Effect Method

This uses the Hall effect device described earlier in this chapter. In practice, when using such a field probe, an external balancing circuit is connected to the voltage and current leads to correct for misalignment voltage caused by inability to place Hall electrodes on an equipotential.

14.8. MEASUREMENT OF PERMITTIVITY AT HIGH FREQUENCIES

The measurement of the real part of relative permittivity, ϵ', is generally performed by measuring the change in capacitance of a capacitor, brought about by the introduction of the dielectric between its electrodes. The imaginary part, ϵ'', is determined from measurement of $\tan \delta$, the loss factor arising from the introduction of the dielectric.

For frequencies up to 10 MHz, a.c. bridges may be used to measure permittivity as already described. Above 10 MHz inaccuracies occur due to stray capacitances, and resonant circuit methods such as those described in Chapter 10 are used up to 100 MHz. One method is to measure the frequency of a tuned circuit using a two-plate air-spaced capacitor and then note the change in frequency when the dielectric under test is introduced between the capacitor plates. The permittivity can then be calculated.

14.8.1. Transmission-line Measurements

In the V.H.F. range, 100–1000 MHz, the tuned-circuit technique cannot be used due to the impossibility of realising a lumped resonant circuit at these frequencies. Distributed circuits must be used, the common forms of which are transmission-lines and waveguides. The latter are inconveniently bulky in the V.H.F. range, and transmission line methods are generally employed for the measurement of permittivity.

A variety of methods exists, based on travelling-wave and standing-wave measurements. In the one most usually used for solids, the specimen represents a terminating impedance for a coaxial transmission line, causing standing waves to be set up. By measurement of the positions and magnitudes of the maxima and minima, with a probe-type standing-wave detector, the permittivity of the specimen may be determined.

In the arrangement shown in Fig. 14.14 the specimen is in the form of a thin disc of the same diameter as the inner conductor of a coaxial line. The line is terminated a distance of half a wavelength beyond the disc. A probe-type detector can be moved along the length of the line to determine the positions and magnitudes of the maxima and minima of the standing-wave pattern.

With the line initially short-circuited at the receiving end a short circuit is transformed to the plane of the specimen by the $\lambda/2$ length of line. The line may be considered as terminated at this plane in an impedance $Z = R + jX$, due to the specimen. Treating the line as loss-free, with a characteristic impedance Z_0 and propagation constant $\beta = 2\pi/\lambda$, the voltage V_x at a distance x from the specimen is given by

$$V_x = \frac{V_0 e^{-j\beta}}{2} \left(e^{j\beta x} + \rho e^{-j\beta x} \right) \tag{14.4}$$

where V_0 is the input voltage to the line and ρ is the reflection coefficient due to the terminating impedance Z and is given by

$$\rho = \frac{Z - Z_0}{Z + Z_0} \tag{14.5}$$

Equation (14.4) assumes that the generator is perfectly matched to the line so that there are no reflections at the generator end.

Substituting for ρ in equation (14.4) and expanding the exponential terms gives

$$V_x = \frac{V_0 e^{-j\beta}}{Z + Z_0} \left\{ R \cos \beta x + j(X \cos \beta x + Z_0 \sin \beta x) \right\}$$

from which the modulus is

$$|V_x| = \frac{V_0}{Z + Z_0} \left\{ R^2 \cos^2 \beta x + (X \cos \beta x + Z_0 \sin \beta x)^2 \right\}^{\frac{1}{2}}$$

Assuming that a square-law detector is used so that its output voltage is given by $E = A V^2$, where A is a constant, then

$$E_x = \frac{A V_0^2}{|Z + Z_0|^2} \left\{ (R^2 + X^2) \cos^2 \beta x + Z_0^2 \sin^2 \beta x + 2 X Z_0 \sin \beta x \cos \beta x \right\}$$

At a distance of half a wavelength from the specimen the voltage will be a minimum of $Z < Z_0$: then $\beta x = \pi$ and the above equation reduces to

$$E_{x1} = \frac{A V_0^2}{|Z + Z_0|^2} (R + X^2) \tag{14.6}$$

At quarter of a wavelength from the specimen there will be a voltage maximum with $\beta x = \pi/2$ and

$$E_{x2} = \frac{A V_0^2}{|Z + Z_0|^2} Z_0^2 \tag{14.7}$$

Dividing eqn. (14.6) by (14.7),

$$\frac{E_{x1}}{E_{x2}} = \frac{R^2 + X^2}{Z_0^2} \tag{14.8}$$

The positions of minimum and maximum voltage will be interchanged if $Z > Z_0$. If the line is now terminated with its characteristic impedance instead of with a short circuit the above calculation still applies, but the terminating impedance becomes $Z + Z_0$. Then

$$\frac{E'_{x1}}{E'_{x2}} = \frac{(R + Z_0)^2 + X^2}{Z_0^2} \tag{14.9}$$

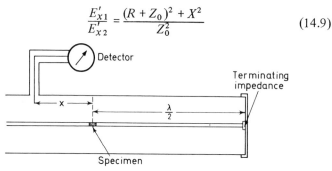

Fig. 14.14. *Measurement of permittivity at v.h.f.*

Subtracting equation (14.8) from (14.9),

$$\frac{E'_{x1}}{E'_{x2}} - \frac{E_{x1}}{E_{x2}} = \frac{2R}{Z_0} + 1 \tag{14.10}$$

Since Z_0 is known and the left-hand side of the equation represents the measured quantities, R is determined, and substitution in equation (14.8) then gives X. Neglecting fringing fields, the capacitance of the specimen will be given by $C = \epsilon' \epsilon_0 a/d$ where a is the area of the disc and d its thickness.

Now $X = -\dfrac{1}{\omega C} = -\dfrac{d}{\omega \epsilon' \epsilon_0 a}$ hence $\epsilon' = -\dfrac{d}{\omega X \epsilon_0 a} = \dfrac{1}{\omega C_0 X}$ (14.11)

Note that in the evaluation of X from equation (14.8) the negative sign should be taken for the square root.

The dielectric conductivity of the material is given by $\sigma = \omega \epsilon'' \epsilon_0$ so it will have a resistance $R_p = d/\sigma a$ effectively in parallel with X. Since the resistance R, evaluated in the experiment, is a series element it is transformed to an equivalent parallel resistance so that $R_p = X^2/R$. Combining these gives

$$\epsilon'' = \frac{\omega \epsilon' \epsilon_0 a R}{d} = \omega \epsilon^2 R C_0 \tag{14.12}$$

For measurements on liquids and gases the transmission line may be filled with the medium being measured. The permittivity may be deduced from measurement of propagation constant of the line.

14.8.2. Microwave Measurements

In the frequency range above 100 MHz it is desirable to use waveguide or cavity resonator techniques. The particular type of measurement used depends upon the nature and quantity of material to be measured.

For solids, if a sufficient quantity of the material is available, the simplest method to deal with theoretically is that in which the whole cross-section of the waveguide is filled with the material. When the specimen is of such length that it corresponds exactly to a number of half wavelengths at the frequency used, in a dielectric medium of permittivity ϵ', the power transmitted through it is a maximum. For a given length of specimen, if the frequency is gradually increased the transmitted power will go through a succession of maxima. If the frequency separation between the maxima is Δf, then

$$\epsilon' = \frac{c}{2d\Delta f} \qquad (14.13)$$

where d is the length of the specimen and c the velocity of light. The fraction, T, of the incident power which is transmitted by the dielectric is given by

$$\frac{1}{T} = 1 + \frac{\epsilon'}{4\left\{1 - \left(\frac{\lambda_0}{\lambda_c}\right)^2\right\}\cos\delta} \cdot \sinh^2\frac{(2d\pi X)}{\lambda_0} + \sin^2\frac{(2d\pi U)}{\lambda_0} +$$

$$+ \frac{1}{2\left\{1 - \left(\frac{\lambda_0}{\lambda_c}\right)^2\right\}^{\frac{1}{2}}} U \sinh\frac{4d\pi X}{\lambda_0} + X\sin\frac{4d\pi U}{\lambda_0} \qquad (14.14)$$

where $U = \dfrac{\{\epsilon'(1 + \cos\delta)^{\frac{1}{2}}\}}{2\cos\delta}$, $X = \dfrac{\{\epsilon'(1 - \cos\delta)^{\frac{1}{2}}\}}{2\cos\delta}$, $\tan\delta = \dfrac{\epsilon''}{\epsilon'}$, λ_0 is the

free space wavelength and λ_c the cut-off wavelength of the waveguide. From this, $\tan\delta$ can be calculated.

Where only a small quantity of the material is available, it is more convenient to use a resonant cavity method of measurement. It can be shown that if a resonant cavity is 'perturbed' by the introduction of a small dielectric specimen its resonant frequency is lowered. The shift in frequency is directly related to the ϵ' of the specimen, whilst the change in the Q factor of the cavity is directly related to ϵ'' for the material.

In a cylindrical cavity, excited in the fundamental mode E_{010}, the E-field is a maximum along the central axis of the cavity. The dielectric specimen is placed in this region, producing a maximum effect. It can be shown for a small specimen that

$$\epsilon' = 1 - 0.539\frac{V_0}{V}\frac{\Delta f}{f_0} \qquad (14.15)$$

where V_0 is the cavity volume, V the specimen volume, and f_0 the original resonant frequency. (Note that Δf will always be negative). Also

$$\epsilon' = 0.269 \, \frac{V_0}{V}\left(\frac{1}{Q} - \frac{1}{Q'}\right) \qquad (14.16)$$

where Q is the magnification factor of the cavity with the specimen present and Q' is the magnification factor of the cavity with the specimen replaced by a supposed loss-free specimen of the same permittivity and dimensions. In practice Q' must be estimated, its theoretical value being given by

$$Q' = \frac{al}{(a + l)t} \qquad (14.17)$$

where l is the axial length of the cavity, t the depth of penetration of current in the cavity walls and 'a' the radius of the cavity. In practice t is greater than that calculated from the skin-effect equations; the method adopted is to measure the Q of the air-filled cavity by measuring the 3 dB width of the resonance curve and to use it as Q' in equation (14.17), calculating a value for t. This value of t is then used, with a suitable correction for the lower frequency, in calculating Q' at the frequency of measurement.

The above theory is based on the assumption of a small perturbation, which means that specimen to cavity radius should be in the region of 1/20 or less. For very low loss materials such a specimen volume means that it becomes very difficult to obtain an accurate value for ϵ''. In such cases the full theory must be used.

The development of the perturbation equation is based on the idea of the field, in the vicinity of the specimen, being the same with and without it present. This is fulfilled for a sufficiently small rod, when the rod stretches from top to bottom of the cavity. When a short rod is used correction must be made for the depolarising field. The corrected value, ϵ', of permittivity will be given by

$$(\epsilon' - 1) = \frac{(\epsilon^* - 1)}{1 - A(\epsilon^* - 1)}$$

where ϵ^* is the measured value of ϵ' and A is the depolarising factor for the specimen. Values for A are given in physical tables.

There are many other methods for measuring permittivity at microwave frequencies. Details of the more important techniques are given in the book 'Microwave Measurements' (Barlow and Cullen)[4]. The reader unfamiliar with the theory of dielectrics is referred to the book by J. C. Anderson[5]. A most readable account of the properties of magnetic materials is given in 'Magnetism' by Prof. E. Lee (Penguin Press).

The testing of semiconductor materials has not been dealt with in this book, but there are many good textbooks available which cover this important subject.

APPENDIX

Theory of the Grassot Fluxmeter

As stated previously, this is a special type of moving coil galvanometer used for measuring magnetic flux density. The coil is large, rectangular, and has a large moment of inertia, and is suspended by a single silk fibre, the current being led in and out by very flexible silver springs (Fig. 14.15) This means that the periodic time $T = \sqrt{P/\tau}$ is very large, of the order of 60 seconds or more, where τ is the controlling torque.

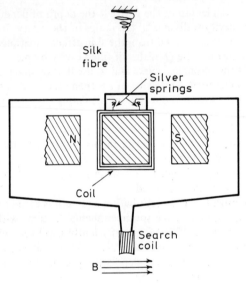

Fig. 14.15. Grassot fluxmeter

The air damping is reduced to a minimum and by using a strong radia field, and keeping the resistance R of the circuit low, the damping of the movement is large but mainly electromagnetic, (i.e. due to currents induced in the galvanometer coil, by Lenz's Law, when it rotates in the radial magnetic field). The damping is proportional to the angular velocity of the coil and $1/R$.

If the flux linked with the search coil is $N\phi$, where N = number of turns on search coil, then if it changes the induced e.m.f. is $e = -N(\mathrm{d}\phi/\mathrm{d}t)$, and a small transient current i flows in the fluxmeter.

There will also be a back e.m.f. of $-L(\mathrm{d}i/\mathrm{d}t)$ due to the self-inductior L of the circuit. Thus due to the change in flux linkage the total applied e.m.f. is $e = -N(\mathrm{d}\phi/\mathrm{d}t) - L(\mathrm{d}i/\mathrm{d}t)$ and the current

$$i = -\frac{1}{R}\left\{N\frac{d\phi}{dt} + L\frac{di}{dt}\right\}.$$

Thus neglecting air damping and control torque due to the suspension fibre, the equation of motion of the coil is

$$P\left(\frac{d^2\theta}{dt^2}\right) + \frac{g^2}{R}\left(\frac{d\theta}{dt}\right) = gi = -\frac{g}{R}\left\{N\left(\frac{d\theta}{dt}\right) + L\left(\frac{di}{dt}\right)\right\}$$

where P is the moment of inertia of the coil and g is the deflecting torque per unit current.

Now if we integrate over the whole time of the deflection from θ_1 to θ_2 while the flux changes from ϕ_1 to ϕ_2 and note that the angular velocity $(d\theta/dt)$ and the current i is zero, both initially and finally, then

$$P\left[\frac{d\theta}{dt}\right]_0^0 + \frac{g^2}{R}\left[\theta\right]_{\theta_1}^{\theta_2} = -\frac{g}{R}\left\{N\left[\phi\right]_{\phi_1}^{\phi_2} + I.\left[i\right]_0^0\right\}$$

whence
$$\frac{g^2}{R}(\theta_2 - \theta_1) = -\frac{g}{R}(\phi_2 - \phi_1)N$$

Thus (change in flux linkage) = kx (change in fluxmeter deflection) where k is constant for a given fluxmeter.

Note that providing the resistance R of the circuit is small enough to make the electromagnetic damping very large the result is independent of R.

In use the search coil, designed to have a small resistance, is put into the field B tesla to be measured. The search coil is pulled out, and the *change* in deflection θ is noted. Then $BAN = k\theta$, where k is constant for a given fluxmeter and A is the area of the search coil in m^2.

With a ballistic galvanometer, the damping is small and the pointer oscillates; the flux change must be made very quickly since the periodic time of the galvanometer is only a few seconds; and the calibration cannot be made once and for all since it depends on the resistance of the circuit.

In the case of the Grassot fluxmeter the damping is very large, the pointer does not oscillate but moves out to the deflected position and stays there due to the heavy damping and small control torque, and the periodic time is 60 seconds or more so that the change in flux need not be made very quickly. The ballistic galvanometer is of course more accurate.

WORKED EXAMPLE

Question. Determine the hysteresis loss in watts for an iron core which is subjected to a sinusoidal flux alternating at 50 Hz. The hysteresis loop for the core has an area of 5×10^3 mm^2 when plotted to scales of 10 mm = 0·008 Wb, and 10 mm = 20 AT.   (L.U., modified).

Answer. The hysteresis loss is given by

$$W = Al \int H \, dB \quad \text{J/cycle}$$

where Al is the volume of iron.

The above equation can be expressed in the form

$$W = \int (Hl) \, d(BA) \quad \text{AT-Wb (J)}$$

where Hl is the magnetising force in ampere-turns, and $d(BA)$ is the differential flux in webers.

The scales given are

$$10 \text{ mm} = 8 \times 10^{-3} \text{ Wb, and } 10 \text{ mm} = 20 \text{ AT}$$

Therefore
$$100 \text{ mm}^2 = 8 \times 10^{-3} \times 20 = 0·16 \text{ AT-Wb.}$$

The total area = 15×10^3 mm^2

$$\therefore \text{ Energy loss} = \frac{15 \times 10^3 \times 0·16}{100} = 24 \text{ J/cycle.}$$

The energy loss per second at 50 Hz = 24×50 J/sec = <u>1200 W</u>   *Answer.*

EXERCISES

1. The primary winding of a long solenoid has 10^3 turns per metre. A secondary winding of 500 turns, which has an effective area of 500 mm^2 is placed at the centre and connected to the fluxmeter. When a current of 3·82 A is reversed in the primary winding a deflection of 20° is obtained on the fluxmeter. Calculate the fluxmeter constant.   (L.U.)

Answer. $1·197 \times 10^{-4}$ weber turns per degree.

2. The circuit shown in Fig. 14.16 consists of a very high gain amplifier μ, a loss-free capacitance C and a resistance R. A change of flux $\Delta\phi$ is produced in the coil L and the reading of a suitable voltmeter V observed.

If $R = 0·1$ MΩ, $C = 0·1$ μF, the coil L has 50 turns and negligible impedance, and during the change of flux the reading of the voltmeter reaches 5 V whilst the current into and out of the amplifier is negligible, find the value of $\Delta\phi$.

Prove all equations and compare the accuracy of this method with that of a conventional moving-coil fluxmeter.   (I.E.E. Part III, June 1966).

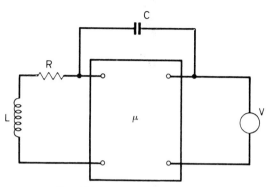

Fig. 14.16. Diagram for Excercise 2

(Hint: Refer, if necessary, to the theory of the integrating operational amplifier given in Chapter 18.)

Answer. 4×10^{-5} Wb.

3. Describe and explain methods for measuring the magnetic susceptibilities of liquids.

4. Give an account of methods of measuring magnetic flux density giving the theory of the methods as far as possible.

5. Give the theory and the important constructional details of a Grassot fluxmeter and briefly discuss typical applications of this instrument.

Describe another method for the measurement of non-uniform fields.

6. Explain how the permittivity of dielectrics is measured at V.H.F. and at microwave frequencies.

7. Derive an expression for the force acting on a weakly magnetic body in a non-uniform magnetic field.

Give an account of the measurement of the magnetic susceptibility of liquids and solids if their susceptibilities are weak.

REFERENCES

1. PERKINS, W. T. and CHARLESBY, A., *A practical course in magnetism, electricity and radio.* George Newnes (1948).
2. LYNCH, A. C., *Bridge methods for measurements on magnetic materials at communication frequencies.* Paper No. 11, Symposium on Precision Electrical Measurements, N.P.L. (1954).
3. HASS, P. H., *A radio-frequency permeameter.* Paper No. 10, Symposium on Precision Electrical Measurements, N.P.L. (1954).
4. BARLOW, H. M., and CULLEN, A. L., *Microwave measurements.* Constable (1950).
5. ANDERSON, J. C., *Dielectrics.* Chapman and Hall (1964).

CHAPTER 15

Measurements on A.F. Amplifiers

The measurements required to be made on amplifiers are gain and amount of distortion introduced. The conditions are somewhat different in the two cases of pure voltage amplification and what is generally called power amplification but the general principles of measurement are the same. The input voltage required to produce a specified output is measured; this is more satisfactory than measuring the output for a known input for several reasons. The main reason is that by fixing the output to a low level the risk of overloading the amplifier is avoided. Another advantage of this method is that comparatively simple means can be employed to 'indicate' the value of the output whereas to measure it accurately would require expensive apparatus. The input can be very accurately determined by using an attenuator (see Chapter 13). It will at once be noticed that the aim is, as with null methods, to use the setting of resistances for the actual measurement and to use deflectional meters to indicate only a variation from a fixed value.

15.1. GAIN MEASUREMENTS

In measuring the overall gain of an amplifier the voltage input required to produce a given *power* output is found. The power output is measured by a thermocouple or rectifier milliammeter, the resistance of the load being known and being, of course, that for which the amplifier was designed. The thermal milliammeter gives an indication of the actual power dissipated in the load, irrespective of waveform, whereas the rectifier meter reads the average value of the current and so only gives a correct power indication for sinusoidal waveform.

For most purposes the gain of an amplifier is measured under 'distortionless' conditions with a pure sine-wave input. Consequently it is not important from a theoretical point of view which method of indication is employed. The thermal meter is more accurate but the rectifier type is much more robust and is therefore that most used.

The input voltage to the amplifier is obtained by using an attenuator to provide known fractions of a voltage produced by a signal generator or l.f. oscillator. The total voltage applied to the attenuator is measured by a thermocouple voltmeter. Fig. 15.1 shows the schematic arrangement of these tests.

The above measurement gives the input voltage required to produce a certain power output and is expressed by the ratio, watts per volt. Every amplifier has a finite input impedance and hence, for the best results, some sort of matching system is necessary. For example, a microphone

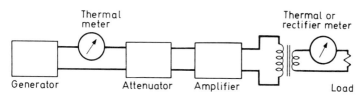

Fig. 15.1. A.F. amplifier test set-up

may be coupled to an amplifier by means of a transformer as in the case of a transmission line. In the latter case it is desirable that the line itself shall be correctly loaded, so the transformer turns ratio is so chosen that the amplifier, in effect, provides this critical loading. It is then a comparatively simple matter to match an amplifier to a given oscillator and attenuator and then to provide an output transformer of such a ratio that the load resistance is of the same value as the attenuator circuit.

Fig. 15.2 shows the arrangement. With an amplifier so matched to work between equal impedances, the power amplification is obviously equal to the square of the ratio of the input and input currents, or of the output and input voltages. This ratio can of course be obtained from the

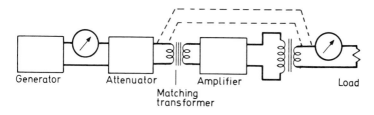

Fig. 15.2. Test set-up with matching system

readings of the two thermocouple milliammeters or from the readings taken by means of an electronic voltmeter. A better way, however, is to connect the attenuator directly to the output-load circuit (shown dotted), set the attenuator so as to obtain a mid-scale reading on the output milliammeter, then introduce the amplifier and note the new setting of the attenuator required to produce the same reading on the output meter.

The ratio of the two attenuator settings is obviously a voltage ratio but since it has been arranged that the output and input circuits are of equal impedance, this ratio can be converted to a power ratio and expressed in decibels. Methods of this type are known as substitution methods.

This subject has been dealt with at some length because it is important to understand what is meant by the statement that 'the gain of an amplifier is so many decibels'.

15.2. VOLTAGE AMPLIFICATION

The voltage amplification of one or more stages in an amplifier can be obtained by a similar method. Fig. 15.3 shows one stage of a resistance-capacitance coupled amplifier, with its input and output circuits. The

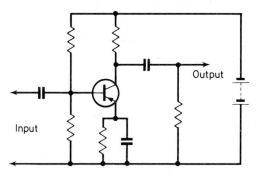

Fig. 15.3. Single stage transistor amplifier

gain of this stage can be found by measuring the voltage across the input and output of the stage while the whole amplifier is working. An electronic voltmeter would, of course, be used.

A more usual method, however, is first to apply the source of power across the output of the stage and adjust the input voltage so that a convenient reading on a meter connected to the output circuit (of the complete amplifier) is obtained. The source of input voltage is then transferred to the input of the stage and the input voltage readjusted so that the same output power is obtained. The ratio of the two input voltages is evidently the required gain of the stage.

It is important in performing this test that all the stages of the amplifier are connected because the gain of the stage considered may be affected by feed-back from other stages, so that misleading readings would be obtained by isolating one stage.

The frequency response of an amplifier is best determined by connecting a signal generator through an attenuator to the input circuit, and using an output meter to indicate merely an output power 'reference level'. The oscillator is set to 400 Hz, the attenuator set to a mid position and the input signal amplitude set to obtain a convenient reading on the output meter. The input frequency is then changed and the attenuator reset to obtain the same reading on the output meter. The attenuator readings can then be plotted against frequency.

This is a type of result that can and *should* be expressed in decibels. The setting for 400 Hz is taken as 'zero dB' and other values obtained above and below this arbitrary zero. This measurement is concerned solely with the ratio of power delivered by the amplifier at any frequency to that at the arbitrary standard. Moreover, as discussed in Chapter 1, the human ear responds according to a logarithmic law,

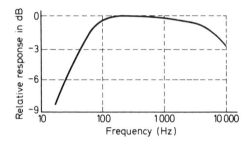

Fig. 15.4. Typical amplifier response curve

hence a decibel scale gives a true picture of the variations in 'loudness'. Fig. 15.4 shows a typical amplifier response curve. A logarithmic scale is used for frequency because the *apparent* change of frequency is proportional to the logarithm of the ratio of two frequencies.

The reason for using an attenuator is that the range available on the scale of any ordinary output meter is necessarily restricted to few dB, so that it would in any case be necessary to change the ratio of the shunt for the extreme readings. This necessitates some form of attenuator since changing an ordinary shunt would upset the matching. It is therefore more convenient and more accurate actually to make the measurements in terms of attenuator settings.

The attenuator can be used on the input side since the circuit impedances are sensibly independent of frequency. The readings then refer to input power and will be inversely proportional to the gain, i.e. a high input resistance represents a drop in gain at a particular frequency. This method is more convenient for simple gain measurements as described earlier, but for response curves the output attenuator is better since under actual working conditions the amplifier will have a more or less constant input.

Thus the response curve is seen as nearly as possible under working conditions, arranging for zero dB to be the output normally required to operate the loudspeaker (or other device). For simple gain tests this method may result in overloading, since one does not wish to spend time ensuring that the output is normal. This test is therefore more quickly and reliably made by a method that ensures definite under-loading.

A much quicker way of running response curves is by means of a cathode-ray oscilloscope. The pair of Y plates is connected across the amplifier load resistance and the X plates supplied with a voltage which varies with the applied frequency. There are several ways of accomplishing this last requirement.

One method of obtaining a frequency base was described in Chapter 7. There, a 'wobbly oscillator' or 'wobbulator' was used, its variable capacitor being driven by a motor on the shaft of which was also a pair of contacts which triggered the linear time base. This method is applicable here by arranging for the wobbulator to form one of the r.f. oscillators in a beat-frequency combination. The varying capacitance is arranged to give the required range of beat, say 0 to 10 000 Hz.

A variation of this method is to arrange a variable resistance to be operated by the motor and to use the varying p.d. across this to produce the horizontal deflection. This method dispenses with the time-base generator but for accurate results the variable resistance must be so designed that it produces a p.d. directly proportional to change in frequency.

Yet another variation is to make use of the fact that the input capacitance of a valve is a function of its gain, if the load is a pure resistance. A variable-μ valve is used and its bias controlled by the a.c. mains, which also provides the p.d. for horizontal deflection. In this way the input capacitance, and hence the oscillator frequency, is made to vary

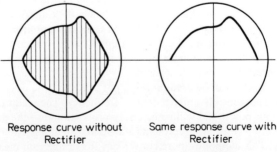

Response curve without   Same response curve with
Rectifier   Rectifier

Fig. 15.5 Action of rectifier on c.r.t. display

proportionally with the voltage applied to the c.r.t. plates. (The variable-frequency oscillator forms one oscillator of a b.f.o.). This method avoids the need for rotating machinery and is thus useful where the amount of work being done is small. Care must be taken to ensure that the variation is only over that part of the valve characteristic where μ varies linearly with grid bias.

An improvement on the scheme described in Chapter 7 is to insert a rectifier in the supply of the Y plates. If this rectifier is of the square-law type the vertical plate voltage will be proportional to the r.m.s. value of the amplifier output. Thus a single trace is obtained instead of the envelope and enclosed oscillations obtained when the deflecting voltage is proportional to the instantaneous value (Fig. 15.5).

15.3. NON-LINEAR DISTORTION

It is more important to test amplifiers for the introduction of spurious tones than for lack of frequency linearity, though the fact is often over-looked. Non-linear distortion introduces harmonics which may be very distressing to the ear.

In Fig. 15.6 the first wave shows even harmonics due to the bottom bend in the I_a/E_g (or I_b/V_{be} for a transistor) characteristic. The second wave shows odd and even harmonics due to bottom bend and grid or

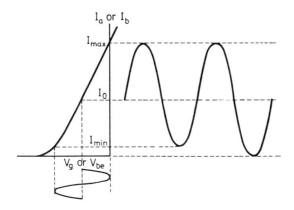

Fig. 15.6. Types of non-linear distortion

excess base current. Thus non-linear distortion occurs chiefly when one or more of the valves in the chain is operating on the bend of its characteristic or is running into grid current. Usually, as the input voltage is gradually increased, both phenomena do not occur simultaneously, since it is unlikely that a valve is biased exactly to the midpoint of its characteristic.

Consider the case where the bottom bend is reached by the excursions of signal voltage. This produces a certain amount of anode-bend rectification thus causing a rise in anode current. This rise in anode current in turn produces an increase in grid bias (assuming automatic cathode biasing) this making matters even worse. When grid current is produced the situation may not be so bad since the main effect is an increase in the load on the previous stage (equivalent to a considerable reduction in anode-load resistance) over part of the cycle. In either case a change in anode current occurs and this can easily be detected by a d.c. milliammeter.

A certain amplifier was being operated 'flat out' but was so placed that the operator could not hear the loudspeaker very well. He had no difficulty, however, in knowing approximately when he was overloading the output stage because a lamp fuse in the h.t. negative lead to earth glowed brighter on loud passages. All the operator had to do was to ensure that these flashes did not become very marked. The brightness was proportional to r.m.s. current and for full load this rose to only $\sqrt{(3/2)}$ of the normal value. This crude but effective method serves as a good illustration of the need for a sense of proportion in measurement; contrast it with the measurement of frequency to a few parts in ten million.

When a milliammeter is used to show this unwanted rectification, its deflection from the no-signal reading is roughly proportional to the amount of distortion present. A more accurate method is desirable for general testing and research work. The r.m.s. value of the output voltage of an amplifier should be directly proportional to the r.m.s. value of the input voltage. If these two are plotted, being read by valve voltmeters, the point where the curve ceases to be straight will be clearly seen and

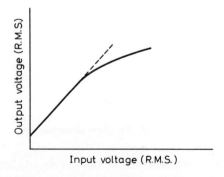

Fig. 15.7. Amplifier overloading

gives the point where overloading commences (Fig. 15.7). This method applies equally whatever stage in the amplifier introduces the distortion.

Class-B and Q.P.P. amplifiers require rather different treatment. The above-mentioned method, of course, still applies but a method is required that will show the nature of any trouble. The introduction of d.c. milliammeters in the anode circuits gives little useful information since each valve is deliberately arranged to act as a rectifier. Such meters could, however, be used to show any difference in the behaviour of each valve of the pair, i.e. any mismatching.

In the case of Class-B amplifiers the peak voltage on the grid and the trough value of anode voltage are both measured with a peak electronic voltmeter. The grid voltage must never exceed the anode voltage or else serious distortion will occur.

The cathode-ray oscilloscope can, of course, be used to great advantage for showing waveform distortion. As mentioned in Chapter 7, all that is necessary is to feed one pair of plates with a voltage proportional to the output. The resulting trace is in general an ellipse, or, if there is no phase shift, a straight line. Any departure from the straight line indicates the presence of distortion. The trace can easily be made straight, i.e. the ellipse closed, by providing a phase-adjustment device in the circuit feeding one of the pairs of plates. The actual waveform is easily found by feeding the Y plates from the output and the X plates

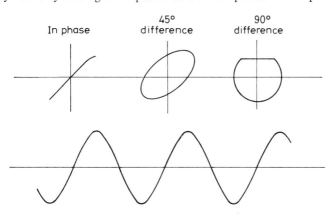

Fig. 15.8. Waveform distortion

from a linear time base. This process will be quite clear from an inspection of Fig. 15.8. It will be seen that the bending down of the line at the top shows a flat-topped wave such as would be produced by grid current.

It may be better to use a saw-tooth time base for this work, for then the actual waveform is directly traced and the harmonics can be analysed by mathematical processes if desired.

Mention has just been made of phase shift. As explained in Chapter 7, the amount of shift is easily found from the dimensions of the ellipse. The input frequency can then be varied throughout the whole range required. This phase shift is of no significance in audio-frequency amplifiers but is very important in television amplifiers and in apparatus required for measuring purposes.

It is sometimes desirable to investigate accurately the nature and amount of the harmonics in a waveform. This is done by employing a tuned circuit between the circuit under test and the measuring device, e.g. electronic voltmeter or thermal meter. The tuned circuit is set to resonate with the harmonics in turn and their value measured directly. If the tuned circuit has a sharp resonance curve very accurate results can be obtained but if a wide range of frequencies are to be examined the equipment becomes elaborate.

For amplifier noise measurement, the input test signal is used only to provide a reference level with which to standardise the sensitivity of a distortion factor meter. Once this has been done the input signal is switched off, so that the residue measured by the distortion factor meter is the amplifier noise. This is likely to be composed of two main components, namely, the mains hum and the white noise generated in the early stages of the amplifier. If the white noise is heard on a loudspeaker, the sensation is that of a predominantly hissing sound, because the human ear is most sensitive to frequencies in the band 3 to 6 kHz. It is thus more realistic to assess the noise after it has been weighted according to the frequency/sensitivity characteristic of the average ear and reproducing device.

15.4. MEASUREMENTS OF OVERALL CHARACTERISTICS

In modern electronic equipments, far more stringent tests are necessary than those applied to earlier and simpler radio equipment. With improved means of reproduction, so that the microphone and loudspeaker may no longer be inherently the weakest links in the chain, as was the case in the earlier days of broadcasting, greater attention to fidelity is necessary to keep pace with improvements.

In communications equipment, where several channels of information are conveyed over a single continuous band of frequencies, it is necessary to make sure that there is no interaction between contiguous channels. In television equipment, new standards of frequency characteristic and limits of distortion are set.

Measurements can be made in relation to any of these problems, either over a whole equipment, or to locate distortion when present, over the various parts of a chain. The remainder of this chapter outlines the various forms of distortion possible, together with its importance in various connections, and considers the means available for appropriate measurements.

15.5. FORMS OF DISTORTION

There is a certain amount of variation in the use of terminology with regard to distortion. For instance, some people try to lay down three distinct forms of distortion known as non-linear, harmonic, and amplitude, as if no form of distortion could ever come under two or more of these headings. It is always better to see just why names are applied to various phenomena, rather than to try and accept or justify blind definitions. In this instance quoted non-linear distortion is named after the effect to which the distortion is due. The term is applicable to any device of which linearity might be expected.

If we are considering a valve characteristic in an amplifying change used for a sound channel, then spurious harmonics might well result from non-linear distortion, in which case non-linear distortion gives rise to harmonic distortion. In all probability both the distortion and the degree of effective amplification would vary with input amplitude, so we should also have amplitude distortion. But if the non-linear distortion occurs in a carefully balanced push-pull stage, and is resolvable into even harmonics only, then harmonic distortion may not be present at the output, although amplitude distortion may still show up.

If non-linear distortion occurs in a timebase amplifier, then obviously it has no connection with harmonic distortion in the normal sense, and may not introduce amplitude distortion from the viewpoint of the cathode-ray tube, although it certainly will be evident in the form of a non-linear distortion of the trace. The best plan is to try and use the words functionally, so that no ambiguity as to real meaning occurs.

15.5.1. Frequency Response

In analysing the effect of a chain upon inputs composed of various frequencies of sinusoidal waveform and steady amplitude, the variation of output with frequency for constant input amplitude is probably best termed the frequency response.

If the output over a range of frequencies is uniform, the response is said to be straight. Variation from straight is designated as up or down, according to whether the output at the frequency in question is more or less than that at the reference frequency, which is usually on the straight portion of the response. In order to line up lack of uniformity in frequency response with other forms of distortion, the term frequency distortion is sometimes used. The objection raised to this is that it is not the frequency which suffers distortion. The idea of frequency distortion implies that when 1000 Hz is applied to the input, the output delivers 990 or 1010 Hz instead of 1000, which is obviously not what is meant.

The term amplitude distortion is inadequate and confusing, as also are most other expressions in this connection, and it is suggested that the term frequency response, together with a statement of reference terms, most directly conveys the required meaning.

Frequency response is a characteristic of equipment essentially related to the reproduction of sound, because the frequency of the electrical signal corresponds to the pitch of the reproduced sound. It is also applicable to ranges of frequencies in radio, responsible for conveying sound information.

In television, the idea of frequency response has no direct connection with the reproduced picture, but as an indication of the behaviour of the equipment in transmitting the composite signals of which the picture information is composed, it provides useful information upon which the quality of the picture does depend particularly as to the frequency range necessary in the radio spectrum for accommodation of the information content.

15.5.2. Transient Distortion

The word transient means 'passing quickly', or 'of short duration'. In electronics it is applied to any form of signal that is not periodic or continuously repetitive. Generally it takes the form of a pulse of some kind. In music, the percussion instruments have transient components in the waveforms produced. A television signal is practically all composed of transients.

Theoretically, transients can be analysed by the Fourier method into an equivalent band of frequencies, up to infinite in width. A single step from one steady value to another can be represented as a sum of all the frequencies from zero to infinity. Obviously, whether such a pulse represents sound or vision, the initial displacement must be restored sometime in practice. A single displacement lasting indefinitely would have, in theory, to permanently displace our eardrums, while a permanent step in a television picture would represent a change in brilliance which would never return. This fact means that practical composite transients do not start from zero frequency, but in theory, for perfect shaping, they require a range of frequencies extending up to infinity.

In the case of sound, our ears cannot detect frequencies above a certain limit. This means that our ears could not hear a perfect transient truly, even supposing it could reach the ear undistorted; this is impossible, due to the absorption characteristic of the air. In the case of a video signal, a satisfactory approximation to the ideal transient can be made with an equipment having a certain frequency range and the correct shaped cut-off characteristic at the high frequency end.

It appears that the ear behaves somewhat after the fashion of a Fourier analyser, breaking all sounds up into their component frequencies. This being the case, any distortion of waveform is not in itself detectable, provided that it does not represent a serious departure from a straight frequency response over the audio range, and provided that there is no serious time difference in the arrival of the different components of the composite wave. Thus, to be satisfactory for reproduction of audio frequencies, a chain must have a sensibly flat frequency response, both to steady tones and to the various frequency components of a transient, and it must have sensibly the same phase delay in time to all the components of the signal.

It might appear that if a chain is sensibly flat over a certain range to steady tones within that range, then it must also be flat to short duration pulses within the range, but this is not necessarily true. To illustrate this, take the case of the circuit shown at Fig. 15.9. This might be the equiva-

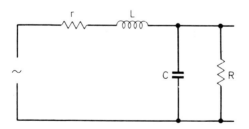

Fig. 15.9. Equivalent circuit of coupling transformer at h.f.

lent circuit of an interstage coupling transformer at high frequencies, where r is the equivalent impedance of the output circuit of the preceding stage, L is the leakage inductance between primary and secondary referred to the primary, and C and R are the total secondary shunt impedance referred to the primary.

It can be shown that the condition for a flat frequency response, that is one in which there are no peaks, when steady tones are applied, is

$$\frac{1}{LC} < \frac{r^2}{2L^2} + \frac{1}{2R^2C^2} \qquad (15.1)$$

At the boundary condition, when

$$\frac{1}{LC} = \frac{r^2}{2L^2} + \frac{1}{2R^2C^2}$$

the response to steady tone signals goes from level to one going down at a 12 dB per octave slope, through a transition point 3 dB from the reference level at a frequency given by

$$f = \frac{1}{2\pi} \sqrt{\frac{R}{R+r} \cdot \frac{1}{LC}} \qquad (15.2)$$

On the other hand, the condition that the circuit shall be critically damped, that is that it shall not produce damped oscillations when excited by some transient, is

$$\frac{1}{LC} < \frac{r^2}{4L^2} + \frac{1}{4R^2C^2} \qquad (15.3)$$

Obviously, if the circuit falls between condition (15.1) and (15.3), then although it will manifest no peak in its response to steady tones, it will produce damped trains of oscillations when excited by transients, at a frequency given by

$$f = \frac{1}{2\pi} \sqrt{\frac{1}{LC} - \frac{r^2}{4L^2} + \frac{1}{4R^2C^2}} \qquad (15.4)$$

For example, if the boundary condition above is excited, it will generate damped oscillations of frequency

$$f = \frac{1}{2\pi} \sqrt{\frac{1}{LC} - \frac{1}{2LC}} = \frac{1}{2\pi} \cdot \frac{1}{\sqrt{2LC}} \qquad (15.5)$$

which will be lower than that given by (15.2) except for the one possible case when

$$r = R = \sqrt{L/C}.$$

For circuits of this type falling within condition (15.1) the response takes the form from a level going gradually through 6 dB per octave slope to an ultimate 12 dB per octave. It is thus evident that, in this case, freedom from 'ring' on transients means that the cut-off must not start by falling off at greater than 6 dB per octave. Extending the consideration to more complex circuits, involving more than one or two couplings, it can be shown that with no arrangement must the cut-off be of greater slope than 12 dB per octave at its commencement, if a tendency to 'ring' is to be avoided on transients.

It may be wondered how a succession of circuits, having no effective L, but only C and R components, could produce an effective 'ring' when excited by transients. One way of viewing the matter is as follows. A transient may be considered as made up of a number of frequencies, each a steady tone, but which, by virtue of their number and variety, cancel one another leaving no resultant signal, except at just the one point in time at which the transient appears, where the cancellation fails owing to some peculiar phase relation between all the component frequencies at just this point in time. If, at some point in the frequency spectrum, a sudden change of phase occurs, such as happens before any appreciable reduction in relative amplitude takes place, when a number of identical circuits are connected in cascade, then cancellation will also fail in the region of the frequency where the phase change takes place. This means that a short transient, additional to the original, and taking the form of a 'ring' at a frequency where the rate of change of phase is greatest, will appear in the output.

Another source of transient distortion, of much more noticeable magnitude than that already referred to, is a length of incorrectly loaded transmission line. This results in a comparatively unattenuated transmission in which the higher frequencies present may be delayed longer by quite a noticeable time than the lower frequencies. On steady tones this is unimportant, but for transients, it means that the low-frequency components of the transient will arrive a noticeable period – an appreciable fraction of a second – before the high-frequency components. The reader may have noticed this effect on a high-quality receiver, when listening to transmissions that have been relayed by land line from the studio to the transmitter at audio frequency.

The above forms of transient distortion can each be computed from a complete story of the frequency and phase characteristic of the chain. But But there is another form of transient distortion which is not necessarily related in this way. If, in an amplifier, variation in amplitude of signal produces a change of operating potentials on some electrodes, which in turn modifies the gain, and due to circuit time constants this change of gain takes time to take effect, then the envelope of the transient waveform will suffer modification due to what may be regarded as delayed amplitude distortion.

Since close adherence to actual video signal wave shape and not mere frequency composition is essential to faithful picture reproduction, careful attention to all possible sources of transient distortion is essential to a far greater degree than in audio frequency signal chains.

15.5.3. Phase Distortion

Phase distortion means the changing of the relative phase of different component frequencies in a composite signal. The fact that a signal suffers a *time* delay does not of itself constitute *phase* distortion, if all components of the signal suffer the *same time* delay. In reference to phase, if all the various frequency components undergo a phase delay which is directly proportional to their frequency, then no phase distortion will result, because the delay applied to each component corresponds to the same *time* interval.

If electron transit time can be ignored, then valves or transistors do not themselves introduce any time delay. The phase reversal is not in this case a time factor, but merely a reversal of direction. Reactance components in circuits (including interelectrode capacitances) introduce phase advance and delay at various frequencies, which phase changes must represent time differences. Low-frequency discriminative circuits (cut-offs) which, in general, produce phase advance obviously cannot cause an output signal to be delivered before the input is applied, although, on a steady signal of low frequency, a given phase position reaches the output before the corresponding phase position is applied at the input. It is seen that such a phase advance must produce some distortion at the growth and decay of a low-frequency component, which will fall under the heading of transient distortion, when transients contain such frequencies as components.

High-frequency limiting circuits introduce a phase delay in the vicinity of cut-off. A single $R-C$ or $L-R$ network will produce a constant time delay within the pass range until cut-off is reached. When the response is falling at 6 dB per octave the circuit introduces a constant phase delay of $90°$, which means that time delay has now become inversely proportional to frequency. Thus frequencies in the vicinity of cut-off and beyond will suffer a time advance (although it is a phase delay), which gives rise to phase distortion, if their amplitude is sufficient to be of any consequence. If a number of coupling networks have identical cut-off characteristics, these effects will become additive, thus exaggerating the phase distortion and, as explained previously, consequent transient distortion. By arranging the different coupling networks to have differing cut-off characteristics, a closer approximation to constant time delay can be reached, extending further into the cut-off region, so that when a frequency is reached having effective time advance in relation to others, its amplitude is small enough to render it of little consequence.

15.5.4. Non-linear Distortions

The foregoing forms of distortion are all produced by resistance and reactance components having linear characteristics. That is, their values are not subject to alteration during a waveform. Other forms of distortion are introduced if components whose electrical properties change during the waveform are incorporated in the circuit. Such non-linear devices are thermionic valves, transistors, metal rectifiers, and inductances with iron cores. The effect of such components is to change the shape of the original waveform, not by modifying the amplitude or phase relation of existing component frequencies, but by effectively introducing spurious components. As these spurious components will always be multiples of any periodic waveform applied in frequency, this type of distortion becomes known as harmonic distortion, especially when applied to audio frequencies.

It steps are taken to introduce cancellation of the spurious frequencies at the output, their presence may still have some effect upon the operating conditions of the amplifier, in such a way that the gain, or the effective values of certain components, will vary with the amplitude of the applied signal. In this case, although harmonic distortion may be considerably reduced and even (theoretically at least) eliminated, the non-linear effects may give rise to amplitude distortion. That is to say change of input amplitude by a certain ratio will not produce a change in output amplitude by the same ratio.

Amplitude distortion is introduced here for the sake of completeness but more properly belongs in Chapter 13. In the reproduction of sound, the ideal distortion-free reproduction will produce the same sound field, in both intensity and waveform, at the ear as that which would be experienced if the listener were situated at some appropriate point in the original sound field. If the frequency content and relative amplitudes of the component frequencies are preserved, and there is no phase distortion or harmonic distortion, but the whole sound is of greater or lesser intensity at the ear than there would be in the original sound field, then the apparent balance of frequency content will be disturbed, due to the curious response characteristics of the ear. This subjective distortion due to the ear's characteristics is termed 'scale distortion'. Efforts are sometimes made to correct for this distortion in a reproduction chain.

15.6. METHODS OF MEASURING DISTORTION

There are several methods available for checking or measuring the characteristics of equipment, but there is, so far, no single method capable of telling the 'whole story'. Frequency response can best be measured by equipment of the type outlined in Chapter 13. Phase distortion can be computed from results obtained with a cathode-ray tube ellipse, provided that both input and output waveform at the measurement frequencies is free from harmonics. There are several ways of detecting or measuring harmonic distortion, each of which is useful in its particular sphere.

For checking the total quantity of spurious signal introduced, a pure sinusoidal waveform should be injected at the input. If the output from a signal generator is not sufficiently pure, it may be purified by means of a suitable low or band-pass filter. The output from the equipment under test is then passed to a type of harmonic meter that

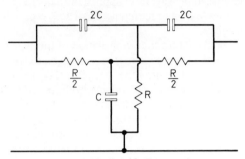

Fig. 15.10. Double-T network

eliminates the fundamental, usually with a double-T type network (Fig. 15.10), and compares the amplitude of the residual signal with the r.m.s. value of the fundamental.

As the fundamental is sinusoidal, a rectifier instrument can readily be calibrated in r.m.s. values, but the value of the residual components indicated will be proportional to the mean value (rectified), even if it is calibrated on a sinusoidal signal to read r.m.s. values. However, the error so introduced is usually small, and as the indication is really highly informative, since it does not discriminate between components, it is usually sufficiently accurate to use a rectifier instrument. Some equipments provide for the use of a thermal type and these are usually known as distortion factor meters.

Harmonic meters are useful for routine testing, but for more serious research work it is desirable to know more about the harmonics. A useful instrument for this purpose is the wave analyser and a block diagram of a negative feedback type is shown in Fig. 15.11. An amplifier having a flat characteristic is used with a negative feedback network having a response which is zero at the pass frequency, rising sharply towards unity on either side. In this way the amplifier has its full gain at the pass frequency, with a falling characteristic on either side, similar to that of a tuned circuit. It has the advantage that the effective circuit Q is not dependent upon frequency, so that the bandwidth is of constant shape when plotted on a logarithmic frequency base. The feedback network is an adaptation of the Wien bridge, suitable for asymmetrical circuits, known by its configuration as the double-T network, and has already been introduced in Fig. 15.10.

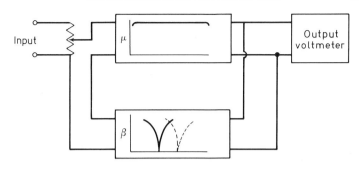

Fig. 15.11. Negative-feedback type wave analyser

While the foregoing undoubtedly gives the most accurate quantitative information about harmonics, it is sometimes better, in order to locate the source of distortion and correct it, to be able to see in just what way the actual wave shape itself is distorted. The foregoing types of equipment give no information as to phase relation of the harmonics present, and even if they did, the actual waveform would need to be synthesised to see how the distortion originates. This is where methods of observing a comparison of waveforms with the aid of a cathode-ray tube are of great assistance.

For large degrees of distortion the waveform may simply be inspected as displayed against a linear timebase, but for smaller degrees of distortion, confined particularly to the lower order harmonics, a waveform may appear sensibly sinusoidal when displayed against a linear timebase and more precise methods are required. The best method is to use a voltage taken from the input source for the X deflection, whilst applying the output to the Y deflection. A phase shift may be incorporated in the X deflection circuit to offset the effects of phase shift in the equipment under test, so that the ideal display would take the form of either a straight line or a circle, preferably the former. For closer inspection, a bridge arrangement may be used for obtaining the Y deflection so that the fundamental component in the output voltage is removed, having found its phase relation to the input, when the harmonic components may be expanded to greater amplitude.

By providing calibration arrangements, precise measurements may be taken that will be as informative as either of the previous methods of measurement, and will give much better information as to the way the output waveform departs from the ideal, thereby greatly assisting in locating the probable source(s) of distortion.

15.6.1. Square Wave Generator and its Uses

So far, the tests described all operate on steady tone signals, so that no test has been given for detecting or measuring transient distortion. It would be possible to devise methods whereby steady tones could be applied to the input intermittently, and the effects at commencement and termination of the pulses observed or measured. A far simpler type of test, that gives results which are far more easily interpreted, uses an input of square waveform, instead of the usual sine wave. This subject has been dealt with by W. Schultz.[1]

A square-wave generator may consist of a multivibrator, possibly fed through some extra stages where grid current and anode bend 'chopping' serves to steepen the sides and level the top and bottom of the waves, so as to give a nearer approach to a perfect square. With a multivibrator, the circuit can be adjusted so that top and bottom half of the waves occupies either equal or unequal time.

A more popular method consists in passing an existing oscillator signal through a square-wave generator which merely consists of a series of greatly overloaded stages, each fitted with grid current-limiting resistors to increase the squareness. While this type can only produce symmetrical square waves, it has the advantage that the frequency of the square wave can be adjusted over a wide range simply by varying the input oscillator frequency. Usually, however, the necessary information obtainable from the use of a square-wave generator does not require the use of a continuously variable frequency, a few spot frequencies yielding just as much information.

The output from an equipment, when a square wave is applied at the input, is observed by displaying it on a cathode-ray tube against a standard linear timebase. Departure from squareness in various ways gives indication of transient distortion, and according to the way in which the waveform departs from the square, the way in which the overall characteristic departs from that necessary to avoid transient distortion can be deduced.

The method in which various defects modify a square waveform is illustrated in Fig. 15.12. It will be seen from this that by injecting about three different frequency square waves in turn into an equipment, a great deal of information can be obtained concerning its frequency response and phase distortion characteristics; at least as much as could be obtained from a continuous frequency characteristic of the amplifier using a sinusoidal input. It should be noted that the use of a sinusoidal input cannot be dispensed with altogether for a complete test. As accentuation or reduction of any of the various frequency components of the square wave produce distortion of its shape, and as, for a symmetrical square wave, it can be resolved into a series of component frequencies bearing

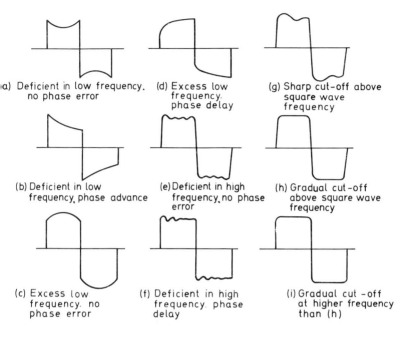

(a) Deficient in low frequency. no phase error

(d) Excess low frequency. phase delay

(g) Sharp cut-off above square wave frequency

(b) Deficient in low frequency, phase advance

(e) Deficient in high frequency, no phase error

(h) Gradual cut-off above square wave frequency

(c) Excess low frequency. no phase error

(f) Deficient in high frequency. phase delay

(i) Gradual cut-off at higher frequency than (h)

Fig. 15.12. Testing with square wave

simple harmonic relations to the fundamental (as can be shown by Fourier analysis).

It might be thought that harmonic distortion, by accentuating or reducing some of these components, would also result in modification of the waveform, but this is not necessarily true. Suppose that none of the usual causes for distortion of a square wave exist in an equipment, but that some of the valves in the chain have non-linear characteristics, then the signal applied at the valve grids will be a true square wave and the straight top and bottom of the waves will maintain the valve at constant grid potentials, giving rise to constant anode potentials to correspond. The immediate transition from one to the other will be to all intents and purposes instantaneous, so although a progressive change in grid potential will not be accompanied by a proportionate progressive change in anode potential this will not be given time to show up and the non-linearity will have no sensible effect upon the wave.

Theoretically, if the input wave is a perfect square, then any amount of non-linear distortion would have absolutely no effect upon the output waveform. In practice, the transition can never be made from

top to bottom or bottom to top in zero time, so a perfect square wave
is a practical impossibility, but it will be realised that any non-linear distortion of the vertical stroke of the wave will be very difficult to
observe, due to the small amount of time it occupies compared with the
rest of the wave. The only possibility would be to arrange that the
horizontal sections of the wave at the output are just off the screen, and
then to speed up the timebase so that the 'vertical' sections appear at a
slope. The very high spot velocity would render necessary increased
brilliance to make the trace visible. It is simpler in practice to use a sinusoidal input to detect non-linear distortion separately.

15.6.2. Distortion Measurements Using Sine Wave

Both amplitude and phase distortion in a working circuit can be detected
by applying to the X plates a deflection derived from the source generator

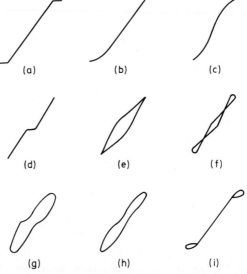

Fig. 15.13. Distortion measurements using sine wave

which should be sinusoidal and of variable frequency. The output signal
from the circuit is applied to the Y plates. Fig. 15.13 shows some
defects and their resultant appearance on the tube screen. These represent

(a) Grid current distortion in a full-wave push-pull stage.
(b) Anode bend distortion.
(c) Tetrode or pentode curvature distortion.

(d) Change-over distortion in a Class B output stage.

(e) Magnetising current distortion.

(f) As (e) with phase distortion later in the chain.

(g) As (d) with phase distortion earlier in the chain.

(h) As (c) with phase distortion earlier in the chain.

(i) As (a) with phase distortion later in the chain.

Application of a typical musical programme, or speech, to an audio amplifier will assist in detecting transient distortion.

Suppose that negligible non-linear distortion is observed on sinusoidal inputs, and that phase shift is quite small over the frequency band. When a complex input signal is applied, spurious loops may appear from time to time at the side of the trace, due to the tendency of the circuit to 'ring' when excited by a transient.

WORKED EXAMPLE

Question. Explain what is meant by the term non-linear distortion when applied to an amplifier.

The dynamic I_b/V_{be} characteristic of a transistor with a resistive load may be represented by $I_b = a + bV_{be} + cV_{be}^2$. Deduce the ratio of the second-harmonic component in the output to the fundamental.

If the transistor has a steady no-signal base current of 60 μA, and the application of a sinusoidal base voltage causes the base current to vary between 105 and 25 μA, calculate the percentage second harmonic in the output current.

(Based on I.E.E. (Advanced Electrical Engineering) 1957).

Answer. Let $V_{be} = V \sin \theta$, then $I_b = a + bV \sin \theta + cV^2 \sin^2 \theta$

$$= a + \frac{cV^2}{2} + bV \sin \theta - \frac{cV^2}{2} \cos 2\theta$$

$$= A_0 = A_1 \sin \theta - A_2 \cos 2\theta$$

where $A_0 = a + \dfrac{cV^2}{2}, A_1 = bV, A_2 = \dfrac{cV^2}{2}$ = amplitudes of d.c., fundamental and second harmonic components respectively.

Now when
$$\theta = 0, \ I_b = I_0$$

$$\theta = \frac{\pi}{2}, \ I_b = I_{max}$$

$$\theta = \frac{3\pi}{2}, \ I_b = I_{min} \quad \text{(See Fig. 15.6)}$$

Substituting these values gives

$$I_0 = A_0 + 0 - A_2$$
$$I_{max} = A_0 + A_1 + A_2$$
$$I_{min} = A_0 - A_1 + A_2$$

Solving these equations for A_1 and A_2,

$$A_1 = \frac{I_{max} - I_{min}}{2} \text{ and } A_2 = \frac{I_{max} + I_{min} - 2I_0}{4}$$

$\therefore$ Percentage second harmonic distortion $= \dfrac{A_2}{A_1} \times 100\% = \dfrac{I_{max} + I_{min} - 2I_0}{2(I_{max} - I_{min})} \times 1$

Substituting given values, percentage second harmonic distortion

$$= \frac{105 + 25 - (2 \times 60)}{2(105 - 25)} \times 100\% = \underline{6.25\%} \qquad \textit{Answer.}$$

EXERCISES

1. Describe, with a diagram of connections, a modern negative-feedback wave analyser, suitable for the lower harmonics of voltages having fundamental frequencies between 4 and 4000 Hz.

In the diagram the amplifier, but not the feedback circuit, may be shown as a four-terminal box.   (I.E.E. Part III, 1966).

2. Comment on the various forms of distortion possible in an electronic amplifier, and describe briefly various types of equipment which could be used to measure each.

REFERENCE

1. SCHULTZ, W., *Measuring and testing with square-wave signals.* Philips Technical Library (1966).

CHAPTER 16

Measurements at Very High Frequencies

16.1. WAVEGUIDES

Previous chapters have shown that, for a certain range and provided certain precautions are observed, the same measurement methods can be applied for high frequencies as for lower ones.

At extremely high frequencies the very nature of the circuits employed changes and new methods of measurement must be devised. Instead of regarding the components in terms of electrical circuits, the transmission of energy must be envisaged in terms of the transmission of electromagnetic waves at these frequencies; the form of the waves being controlled or modified by the geometrical structure of the conductors, dielectrics etc.

The admittance bridge described in Chapter 8 is capable of useful work up to a hundred or so megahertz, i.e. down to metric wavelengths; but for higher frequencies, different methods of measurement must be employed.

While, for the sake of analogy, equivalent circuits, in terms of inductance, capacitance and resistance are drawn, the viewpoint adopted in considering the behaviour of components must be in terms of their effect upon the passage of electromagnetic waves. For lower frequencies, parallel conductors can be used for the transmission of energy, but as frequency increases, the loss by radiation from parallel conductors also increases, so that the use of concentric conductors is rendered essential to eliminate radiation.

With a concentric cable, the characteristic impedance is given by $\sqrt{L/C}$ approximately, where L and C are the inductance and capacitance per unit length. The propagation or attenuation constant is given approximately by $R/2Z + GZ/2$, where Z is the characteristic impedance, R is the total conductor resistance per unit length, and G is the equivalent dielectric conductance per unit length. It will be realised that R increases due to skin effect as frequency increases, and G, which at alternating potentials is chiefly the dielectric loss expressed as a shunt conductance, also increases with frequency. This means that any given type of concentric line will have a cut-off frequency, beyond which attenuation becomes serious.

In addition to these effects, consider the field in the space between the conductors. At low frequencies, the current in both conductors at any point along the length being in opposition, both the magnetic field and electric field due to the potential will be confined to the space between the conductors. At higher frequencies, the field due to current in the centre conductor will reach the outer conductor when the current in the latter is a little later in phase. The space between the conductors, instead of being occupied by a progressive electromagnetic wave, will begin to show a component of this wave in radial directions. The inner conductor by itself would radiate all the energy, but the outer conductor by itself becomes more efficient as a guide to the waves as the frequency increases.

The inner surface of the conductor should be as good a conductor as possible, because a perfect conductor will behave as a perfect reflector of electromagnetic waves, so confining all of the wave to the inside of the tube, maintaining a plane wave, and resulting in loss-free transmission. Practical tubes are not perfect conductors, so that the theoretical wave shape is not produced exactly and loss is introduced into the line.

Obviously it is impractical to attempt to measure voltage or current by any absolute method at these wavelengths, or the actual components of a field, electric and magnetic as separate entities. Measurements are made from which the results are computed. Satisfactory computation of results must depend upon a satisfactory conception of what happens in the transmission of electromagnetic waves along waveguides.

16.1.1. Mode Designation

First the designation applied to various modes of propagation must be defined. Any complex mode can be broken down into a series of components of the fundamental types. In any wave travelling along a tube whose length lies in the x direction and whose cross-section can be designated in terms of dimensions in y and z directions, both electric and magnetic fields may have components in all three directions. In free space, a wave has only components of electric and magnetic field in the y and z directions, but in a waveguide, due to the effect of the guide, there will be components of at least one form of field along the x direction. The basic modes of propagation, of which more complex modes are built up, are those in which there is only one form of field along the x direction. Those having only a magnetic component longitudinally (in the x direction) are designated H waves or TE (transverse electric) waves. Those having only an electric component along the x direction

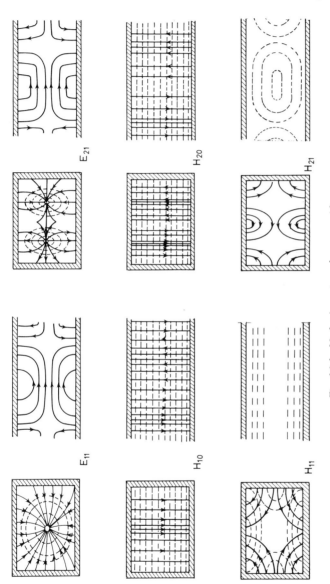

Fig. 16.1. Modes in rectangular waveguide

are similarly designated E waves or TM (transverse magnetic) waves. The generally preferred terms are H and E, but the other forms are sometimes met, so the reader should be prepared to recognise them by either designation.

Following the letter, there are usually two subscript numerals, to indicate the pattern of field in a transverse cross-section. In the case of rectangular waveguides the numerals indicate the number of complete half cycles of either field found at any instant along two axes of the tube taken at right angles (y and z direction). In the case of cylindrical waveguides, the first numeral represents the number of complete half cycles between the centre and periphery (except at nodal diameters), whilst the second numeral designates the number of complete cycles encountered by a rotating vector in passing through the complete circle. Alternatively, the first subscript gives the number of concentric nodal lines, while the second gives the number of nodal diameters. The reader should carefully examine each figure in Fig. 16.1 and 16.2 showing transverse and longitudinal sections of representative types of propagation for rectangular and cylindrical waveguides. In all the diagrams, full lines represent the electric field while dotted lines represent the magnetic field.

Each of these modes will have its own cut-off frequency (low) for any given tube dimensions. The circular guides are now not greatly used, as complex modes are much more likely to appear in them, introducing difficulties, than in the rectangular guides of carefully chosen dimensions. The calculation of cut-off frequency for any given mode in a circular guide involves the use of Bessel functions. As rectangular guides are of more practical application, we will see how the cut-off frequencies arise in these.

16.1.2. Waveguides

It has already been shown that the waves are confined to the guide due to the reflection effects from the walls. Any of the foregoing simple waves can be regarded as made up two complementary waves (for each axis considered) which are reflected back and forth across the guide at a fixed angle dependent upon the relation between wavelength and guide cross-section. At cut-off for a particular mode, the phase when the wave travels from one side of the tube to the other at its propagation velocity in the medium with which the guide is filled is such that the wave travels back and forth across the guide without progressing along the guide. In practice, if this mode is the simplest, then the currents will flow along the guide in such a way as to produce radiation of the energy outside the waveguide. If the mode considered is not the simplest, then it wi

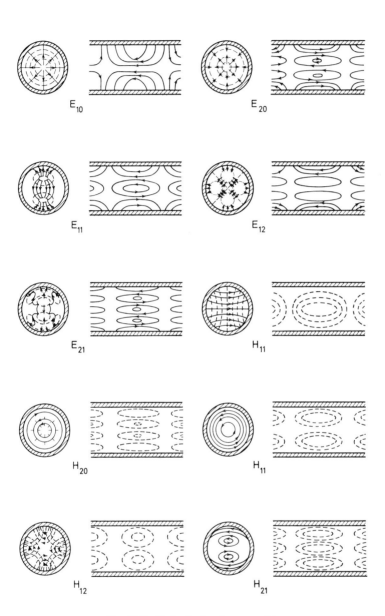

E_{10}

E_{20}

E_{11}

E_{12}

E_{21}

H_{11}

H_{20}

H_{11}

H_{12}

H_{21}

Fig. 16.2. Modes in circular waveguide

merely mean that this mode is precluded, and only simpler modes can be propagated along the guide.

For the simplest modes, the distance across the guide for cut-off will obviously be half a wavelength at the wave's free velocity in the medium with which the guide is filled (usually air or vacuum). At a slightly higher frequency the direction of propagation of the two component waves will be as shown in Fig. 16.3, where the direction of propagation is shown

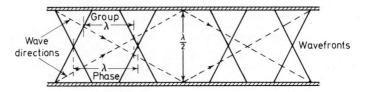

Fig. 16.3. Group and phase velocity

dotted, and the wavefront is shown in full line. Careful consideration will show that, while the component waves will travel along the guide at a velocity less than their free space velocity, due to the fact that only a component of their velocity is along the guide, the effective rate at which the combined wave will travel, during a steady state propagation, as shown by the rate at which either a reflection point at the wall surface, or a point of intersection of the two component wavefronts progresses along the guide, will progress along the guide at a velocity greater than the free space velocity. For any given complex wave, the former velocity is defined as the group velocity, while the latter is defined as the phase velocity. Students of optics will be familiar with these terms.

As the frequency is raised further above cut-off, these two frequencies will come closer together, but the cut-off of other modes will also be passed, so that they may be excited as well, and, with their differing group and phase velocities, produce interaction resulting in loss. It is thus evident that the best modes to use for practical applications are the simplest ones, using guide dimensions that just preclude the possibility of the next higher possible modes.

The critical wavelength in the case where there are components of field in both y and z directions will depend upon the interaction of two pairs of waves travelling diagonally across the guide in two directions (combinations of x and y and of x and z respectively), which could be viewed as two single components travelling to and fro across the guide in complex directions made up of components in x, y and z directions. At cut-off this would mean that the wave is considered as reflected to and fro along a complex direction made up of components in the y and z directions only. Thus it may be shown that the cut-off wavelength for a guide of dimensions a and b, where the type of wave has subscripts m and n for these directions respectively, is given by:

$$\lambda_0 = \frac{2}{\sqrt{\left(\frac{m}{a}\right)^2 + \left(\frac{n}{b}\right)^2}} \qquad (16.1)$$

From which the cut-off frequency may be seen to be:

$$f_0 = \frac{1}{2c} \sqrt{\left(\frac{m}{a}\right)^2 + \left(\frac{n}{b}\right)^2} \qquad (16.2)$$

where c is the propagation velocity in the medium with which the guide is filled.

Having seen how these waves are propagated, attention may now be paid to methods of measurement in connection with them, and to various 'circuits' that are employed for handling them. For aerials, transmitting and receiving, the waves are simply delivered direct to the air, via some form of directional arrangement, and using various matching networks to prevent reflections in the waveguide system.

Every waveguide has its own characteristic impedance, which can be represented by simulation to the electrical network that would exhibit the same properties. Impedances are usually measured relative to the characteristic impedance of the waveguide to the particular mode of propagation. This is because they can easily be calculated in terms of the standing-wave ratio they produce when used to terminate the waveguide. For measurement purposes, it will be necessary to ensure that there is no reflection at the input end of the guide, although for practical application this may not be important, as mismatch at the input end will not cause reflections in the guide, unless there is a return wave to reflect. (If the mismatch causes reflections in the concentric line used to introduce the signal, then steps must be taken to eliminate this effect, but it will not matter if there is a residual mismatch from the point of view of the waveguide, if there are to be no return waves.)

16.2. WAVEGUIDE MEASUREMENTS

There are three principal measurements which are required in relation to waveguides:
(i) frequency or wavelength;
(ii) power;
(iii) intensity of field at various points along the guide.

16.2.1. Frequency Measurements

An instrument capable of measuring frequency correct to the order of 1 part in 10^4 is the cavity resonator type wavemeter. Various shapes could be employed, but a coaxial cylinder gives most definite frequency determination, because of its complete symmetry in the mode of oscillation. Fig. 16.4 shows the basic cross-section. For any particular

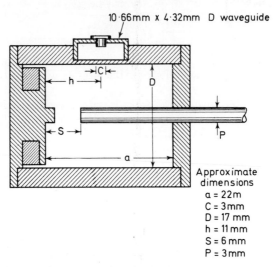

Fig. 16.4. *Cavity resonator for 24 GHz*

frequency setting, the resonance is a hybrid between a cylindrical mode, such as would exist in the absence of the plunger, and the coaxial mode, which would be formed if the plunger made contact with the base. Adjustment of frequency is made by varying the length of the plunger.

With all waveguides, the degree of perfection with which any particular mode is produced is dependent upon the resistance of the wall surfaces being a minimum. In the case of a resonator, introduction of resistance will affect the resonant frequency, in much the same way as it does in an ordinary tuned circuit. A weak point in the design of Fig. 16.4, if it is made adjustable, is the contact between the plunger and the end face of the chamber. The interior is silver-plated and polished to produce absolutely minimum resistance at the surface. A method of overcoming this difficulty, developed by the National Physical Laboratory is illustrated in Fig. 16.5. The plunger has a deliberate precision clearance between the sides of the hole through which it is moved in and out of the chamber, of the order of 0·05 mm, followed by a wider space beyond, and terminating in a fixed end face. It can be shown that, provided neither of the lengths of these channels approach an integral number of half wavelengths (within about 10%), the impedance presented by the arrangement to the cavity will be very small — the equivalent of a short circuit.

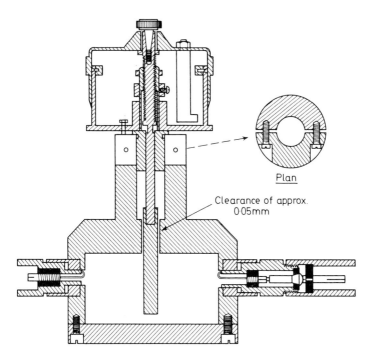

Fig. 16.5. Cavity resonator type wavemeter

The signal must be introduced into the chamber by a means that damps the resonance as little as possible, and also the means of detection must not introduce appreciable damping. For the lower frequencies, the method of coupling is by loops in the walls terminating concentric cables. Critical adjustment of the loop position for each size of resonator produces a minimum damping effect. For the higher frequencies, the resonator is coupled to the side of an appropriate waveguide of adjustable dimensions, to provide a broad-band transmission in the vicinity of the frequency under test, while the resonator introduces an absorption, which, by adjustment to maximum, indicates the frequency. The arrangement is illustrated in Fig. 16.6.

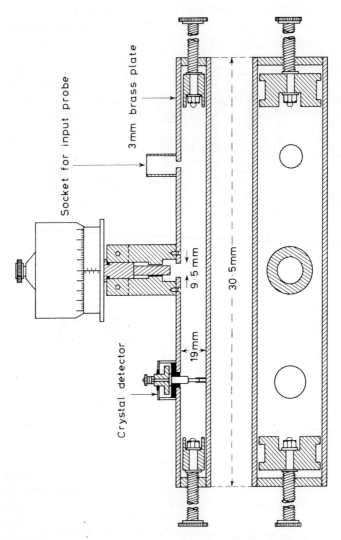

Socket for input probe

3mm brass plate

9·5 mm

30·5 mm

19 mm

Crystal detector

Fig. 16.6. Resonant cavity type wavemeter in waveguide

16.2.2. Power Measurements

For the measurement of power in waveguides, the only absolute method available, since the measurement of current, voltage and phase angle is impractical at these frequencies, is to match the wave impedance along the guide into some form of resistance load, and measure the power dissipated in the load due to the wave by some method. Such a device is called the bolometer (Greek for ray meter). The method employed consists in using a resistor whose resistance changes with dissipation, the value of resistance being determined by including the resistor in one arm

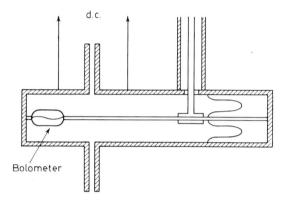

(a) Termination for concentric line

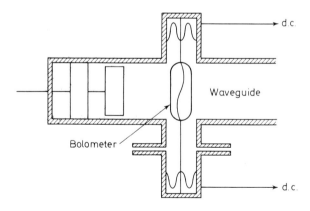

(b) Termination for waveguide

Fig. 16.7. Bolometer arrangements

of a d.c. bridge. It will be appreciated that the power used by the bridge is also producing dissipation in the resistor. In practice this fact is used to adjust the resistance value so as to match the impedance of the guide in which it is placed.

To obtain easily computed results, the bridge is operated by means of a low-frequency signal (about 2 kHz). The power input to the bridge is adjusted, as well as the bridge values until a balance is obtained for the 2 kHz signal with the bolometer resistance at its correct value for matching, or at any specific value required, with the high-frequency signal being passed along the guide. The high-frequency signal is then removed, and d.c. is passed through the bolometer arm of the bridge (the others being blocked, or of such rating that the d.c. will not vary their values) until balance is re-obtained. The dissipation of d.c. in the bolometer, which can be easily calculated, is then equal to the dissipation of radio frequency, by substitution.

The bolometer usually takes the form of a specially-shaped tungsten element enclosed in a low-pressure gas-filled bulb. The waveguide is so constructed as to enable the bridge circuit for d.c. and/or low frequency to be completed without impairing the efficiency of the waveguide to radio-frequency waves. Fig. 16.7 shows a typical arrangement suitable for measurements in the region of 3000 to 20 000 MHz, or 100 mm down to 15 mm.

It will be noted that a non-contact plunger is used to produce the necessary zero impedance termination of the adjustable length stopped limbs, and also a low impedance wall continuity is maintained by a similar method, whilst allowing a discontinuity to d.c. and low frequencies.

16.2.3. Intensity of Field

To measure the intensity of field at a point, a requirement for measuring the standing-wave ratio, it is necessary to obtain a reading which gives a relative indication of field intensity whilst interfering with the field in the guide to the minimum extent. Detectors for H-waves have to detect electric field transversely, so that a straight probe is required in order to produce a signal component.

The dimensions of the aperture through which the probe is introduced and the amount by which the probe protrudes into the guide are determined experimentally to give the minimum interference with the wave configuration, as shown by another probe at a point further along the guide, when the first section containing the probe is exchanged for a piece of plain guide of the same length. Detectors for E-waves have to detect longitudinal field or wall currents along the guide. For this purpose loops such as those shown in Fig. 16.5 can be used, and again, the best dimensions can be determined by experiment.

16.3. WAVEGUIDE TECHNIQUES

Having prescribed methods of measurement, there are many possibilities in the development of waveguide technique, of which it is true to say that only a fraction have as yet been explored. Construction is inherently much simpler than for electrical circuits to achieve the same results at more conventional frequencies. The remainder of this chapter will be devoted to a brief description of some practical 'tricks' that have been successfully employed with waveguides.

The waves found most practical for general application are of the H_{01} type, because the cut-off frequency for this type is separated from all other modes by the greatest possible ratio, and also the fact that the electric and magnetic transverse fields in the guide are planar often proves useful in the design of various types of junction.

For microwaves, the corresponding H_{11} type may be used in a circular waveguide. When rectangular waveguides are used the waves are usually polarised by the actual shape of the guide, its cut-off frequency in the opposite direction precluding propagation in that mode. At these somewhat longer wavelengths the radiators take the form of a rectangular horn and reflector, or with a metallic lens consisting of parallel plates arranged to increase the phase velocity of the wave. These can only operate in one plane. At the higher frequencies sheet metal parabolic reflectors of circular section are used, and can be fed with circular waveguides, polarisation not being necessary. However, it is good practice in this case to use artificially polarised waves, so that outgoing and incoming waves are polarised at right angles to each other and do not interfere with one another. They can use the same radiator and waveguide connection with the equipment without any trouble whatever.

16.3.1. Correction of Mismatch in a Waveguide

It has already been seen that correct matching of a waveguide is of great importance. Failure to obtain correct matching can be corrected at specific wavelengths by the introduction of reactances into the guide at specific points along the standing-wave pattern introduced by the mismatch. An iris across the guide so that the length of the electric field lines is shortened will add shunt capacitance across the guide, whereas an iris the other way, so that some of the electric field lines are short-circuited, behaves as a shunt inductance. An iris restricting the aperture in both directions will behave as a shunt tuned circuit, which if inserted at a point where the standing-wave amplitude introduced by mismatch is a maximum, can correct the impedance of the guide at that point so that standing waves terminate at the iris.

In any form of waveguide junction there is a change of cross-section which introduces mismatch. The nature of mismatch will depend upon the plane in which the junction is present, i.e. whether the wave is divided along or across the electric field. Irises placed at appropriate distances from the junction can correct this mismatch, so that no standing waves appear beyond the irises in each limb. The disadvantage with this method is that correction will only be achieved over a narrow band of frequencies, because the correct position for the irises varies with frequency. A better method is to modify the section at the junction, so that mismatch is corrected where it arises.

The same remarks apply to corners. By bevelling the corners, so that the section is reduced at some points, the mismatch is corrected. This method of correction is applicable over the whole range of frequencies for which the waveguide itself is useful.

In the circular-type waveguide, an iris can be used to polarise the wave. In this case the aperture in the iris takes the form of a slot across the direction of the electric field in the desired polarisation plane. This behaves as a capacitance across the line, the effect of which is neutralised by the inductive effect due to the metal at the ends of the slot (which does not extend for the whole diameter of the guide) thus allowing waves in this direction to pass freely. To waves polarised in the opposite direction the iris behaves as a short circuit across the guide, and reflects the wave. Appropriate positioning of the iris enables this reflection to be used to transfer the energy in a wave polarised in this direction to its correct destination along another limb of the system, where it will be received.

This system behaves in much the same way as a hybrid coil, except that with this method no dummy load is required, and so transmission of both waves is basically loss-free. The conventional hybrid coil loses 6 dB on both channels because half the energy in each case is delivered to the dummy load.

There are various hybrid arrangements possible with waveguides. These have certain advantages over their low-frequency counterparts. Constructionally they are simpler, and also, due to the small wavelengths being handled, phase reversal can be achieved in small distances, so that various arrangements employing two hybrid junctions with differently placed reflector arms enable the energy in both arms to be used.

In principle the phase in one arm is reversed, so that energy again becomes additive and the necessary control of waves travelling in different directions is achieved without the inherent 6 dB loss. A full discussion of these methods is beyond the scope of this book.

16.3.2. Waveguide Attenuators

Assume a rectangular waveguide operating in the TE_{01} mode. In this mode the electric lines of force are perpendicular to the broad sides of the guide and have maximum strength in the centre of the guide. If, therefore, any slab of resistive material is placed in the guide parallel to the narrow walls, then the electric lines of force will cause currents to flow in the slab. Thus energy will be dissipated as heat and since this energy must come from the electromagnetic wave being propagated, this wave will suffer attenuation.

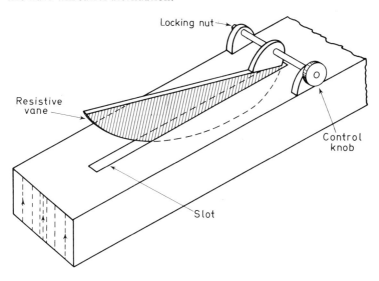

Fig. 16.8. Waveguide attenuator

Fig. 16.8 shows a commonly used variable attenuator based on this principle. A narrow slot in the centre of the broad side of the guide allows a resistive vane to be moved into the guide in the region of maximum electric field intensity. The more the vane is inserted, the more will be the current flowing in it, and hence the greater will be the losses and the attenuation. Such a vane must introduce a mismatch in the guide since it disturbs the field configuration, and it is usual to reduce this mismatch as much as possible by shaping the vane so that for any setting it only enters and leaves the guide at a small angle to its length.

An alternative arrangement which obviates radiation from the slot is to move a 'lossy' vane on some traversing mechanism out from the side wall where the E field is zero towards the centre of the guide where the field is a maximum. Suitable dials can be incorporated so that the attenuators may be calibrated in terms of decibels of attenuation.

16.3.3. Generation of Microwave Frequencies

Generation of frequencies for test purposes is dealt with in Chapter 9 and 13 and mainly concerns generation of audio and the lower radio frequencies. As the reader will be aware, generation of microwave frequencies requires a different form of technique. A detailed description of the various methods is beyond the scope of this book, but a popular method of producing unmodulated or modulated signals up to 4 GHz is described below. This is the klystron oscillator.

Referring to Fig. 16.9, the electron beam from a normal heater/cathode arrangement first passes the gap of a resonant cavity B, setting

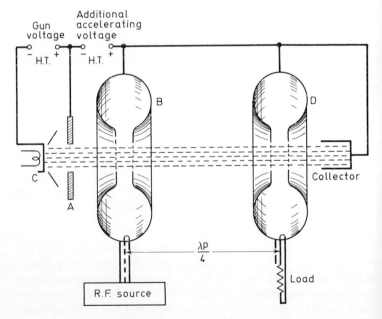

Fig. 16.9. Two-cavity klystron

it into oscillation. The resonant cavity can be considered as a tuned circuit, where the two grids at the cavity gap represent a low-value parallel-plate capacitor and the walls of the cavity represent a low-value inductor. (Remember that the resonant frequency of a tuned circuit is inversely proportional to the square root of L and C.) The reactive effect of the cavity on the electron beam is to convert it into a stream of electron bunches; for this reason the first cavity is often known as the 'buncher'. When this stream arrives at the gap of the second cavity D the energy of the bunches is transferred to this cavity, which for this reason is often known as the 'catcher'. A coaxial line (not shown) couples the two cavities so that energy is fed back from D to B and the oscillation of the system is assured. The output is taken from the small coupling loop in the second cavity. The first cavity is set into initial oscillation by a small signal on the coupling loop into B. Modulation can be effected by varying the potential of the grid A following the cathode.

WORKED EXAMPLE

Question. Explain the meaning of the terms:
(*a*) reflected wave
(*b*) standing-wave ratio
with reference to a transmission line.

A low-loss transmission line of 600 Ω characteristic impedance is connected to a transmitting aerial of impedance $400 + j200$ Ω. Calculate the amplitude of the reflected wave relative to the incident wave and the standing-wave ratio.   (C. & G. Radio IV, 1949).

Answer.
(*a*) *Reflected wave.* A transmission line *abcd* of characteristic impedance Z_0 is shown in Fig. 16.10. It is terminated in an impedance Z_1 and energised from a generator, also of impedance Z_0. The current I at any point is the phasor sum of the current I_i incident on the load Z_1, and a current I_r reflected from the load. The amplitude and phase of the reflected wave is given by

$$\frac{I_r}{I_i} = \frac{Z_0 - Z_1}{Z_0 + Z_1}.$$

Z_0 is generally a pure resistance and when the load Z_1 is also a resistance of equal value to Z_0 it can be seen from the above equation that the reflected wave amplitude is zero; under these conditions the transmission line is said to be correctly terminated. For other values of Z_1 a reflected wave exists, its amplitude being equal to that of the incident wave when

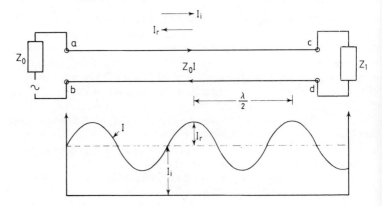

Fig. 16.10. Standing waves on transmission line

Z_1 is zero (short-circuit termination) or when Z_1 is infinite (open-circuit termination).

(*b*) *Standing-wave ratio.* The phase difference between the incident and reflected current waves is different at various points along the transmission line, the phase varying through 2π radians in a distance equal to one half-wavelength for a line in which the phase velocity is equal to that of light.

Thus the resultant current I, which is the phasor sum of the incident current I_i and the reflected current I_r, varies from a maximum to a minimum and back to a maximum again in a distance equal to one half-wavelength as shown in the lower part of Fig. 16.10. When I_r is much less than I_i, the variation of the amplitude of the resultant with distance is approximately sinusoidal. When $I_i = I_r$ the maximum value of I is $2I_i = 2I_r$ and the minimum value is zero. The standing wave ratio is defined as

$$\frac{|I_{\min}|}{|I_{\max}|} = \frac{|I_i| - |I_r|}{|I_i| + |I_r|} = \frac{1 - \dfrac{|I_r|}{|I_i|}}{1 + \dfrac{|I_r|}{|I_i|}}$$

The standing-wave ratio may also be defined in terms of the voltage, when it is known as the V.S.W.R., and this is the most common practice. The reciprocal of the ratio defined by the above equation is also often used, but the original definition is preferable since the ratio is then always less than unity, and since the S.W.R. can also be regarded as a reflection coefficient, this appears to be the most logical practice.

Since $Z_0 = 600 + j0 \ \Omega$ and $Z_i = 400 + j200 \ \Omega$,

$$\frac{\text{reflected wave}}{\text{incident wave}} = \frac{Z_0 - Z_1}{Z_0 + Z_1} = \frac{600 - 400 - j200}{600 + 400 + j200} = \frac{1 - j1}{5 + j1}$$

$$= \frac{1 \cdot 414 / -45°}{5 \cdot 09 \ / +11 \cdot 3°} = 0 \cdot 277 \ / -56 \cdot 3°$$

Thus the amplitude of the reflected wave is 0·277 times that of the incident wave.

The standing-wave ratio is given by

$$\text{S.W.R.} = \frac{1 - 0 \cdot 277}{1 + 0 \cdot 277} = 0 \cdot 565$$

Alternatively, the S.W.R. can be expressed as

$$\frac{1}{0 \cdot 565} = 1 \cdot 77$$

EXERCISES

1. Explain why concentric conductors act as a low-pass filter, while a waveguide acts as a high-pass filter. What happens in each case outside the pass range?

2. Explain the significance of phase and group velocity with reference to (a) concentric line conductors, and (b) waveguides. Show how phase velocity can exceed propagation velocity.

3. Upon what factors does the cut-off frequency for a waveguide depend? Show why it is desirable to propagate only one mode along a guide, and give reasons for the mode usually chosen.

4. What types of instrument are used for measuring power at very high frequencies? Explain how correct matching is achieved.

5. Of what use is information concerning standing-wave ratio in waveguide techniques? State briefly how standing-wave ratio can be measured.

6. If a certain waveguide is being used as a common channel for a wide band of frequencies, describe how you would couple a branch to it so that only a frequency at the bottom of the band would be accepted by the branch.

CHAPTER 17

Standards for Comparison Purposes

17.1. INTRODUCTION

By far the greatest factor involved in the construction of standards for comparison purposes is the question of the many and varied temperature coefficients. Most materials have a nearly linear coefficient of expansion; in addition practically all the electrical properties such as resistance, permittivity, dielectric loss and permeability have coefficients with temperature in different materials. The methods of solving this problem fall into two groups;

    (1) designing the component so that the different temperature effects compensate for one another, so that the resultant variation with temperature of the standard quantity (e.g. inductance) is zero,

    (2) taking steps to ensure that the temperature does not vary.

It might appear that either of these methods could be adopted in any particular case, according to whichever presented the least difficulty; but the general position is that each method is only partially effective, so that both have to be employed. On the one hand, combination of various temperature coefficients can usually only be arranged to produce an effective zero temperature coefficient in some quantity over a limited range (usually a transition from positive to negative coefficient) so that temperature control is necessary to keep the operating temperature within that range. On the other hand it is not possible to obtain absolute control of temperature, so that it does not vary at all, and it is therefore necessary to pay attention to the resultant temperature coefficient within the range of variation, so that the standard quantity may have the absolute minimum of variation.

17.2. TEMPERATURE COMPENSATION

Inductance and capacitance may vary due to variation of permeability or permittivity with temperature, but usually the variation of these quantities is to a greater degree dependent upon changes of dimension due to temperature. Some changes of dimension increase the resultant value, while others decrease it, and the design problem consists in choosing dimensions in which the combination of all the thermal coefficients results in almost zero temperature coefficient over a certain range.

17.3. INDUCTANCE

For a coil of fixed proportions, i.e., constant ratio of length to diameter, it can easily be shown from first principles that the inductance is proportional to the square of the diameter, and inversely proportional to the length. Thus, if such a coil expands so that its proportions are unchanged, its inductance will increase directly in proportion to its linear expansion. The method of compensating for this rests in producing a coil former having a greater linear coefficient of expansion lengthwise than in diameter. If the above law related to coils of any shape, then the coefficient of expansion lengthwise would need to be just twice that for diametric expansion. In practice, of course, such expansion means that the coil is changing shape, so that this relation is not exactly true.

A constructional problem arises in the fact that the coil former will have a different coefficient of expansion from that of the wire of which the inductor itself is wound. If the coil former expands more than the wire, then expansion will stretch the wire, changing its diameter, and at the same time allowing it to become loose when contraction takes place.

A method of construction that overcomes these difficulties and enables standards to be built having a temperature coefficient of the order of 5 parts in one million (0·0005%) is used by A. W. Sullivan Ltd. The former is constructed of two materials which differ in linear temperature coefficient. The side cheeks have a lower temperature coefficient than the bars on which the coil is wound. These bars are fixed to the side cheeks at points on a larger radius than that of the actual coil.

The temperature coefficient of both materials is greater than that for the copper wire of which the coil is wound, and the dimensions are such that the resultant diametric expansion matches that of the wire. At the same time the expansion in length is greater than the diametric expansion, and is arranged so that over a fairly wide range of temperatures the increase of inductance due to increase in diameter is equal to the decrease in inductance due to increase in length. Individual turns are accurately located in grooves in the coil former so that the relative spacing of turns lengthwise is maintained.

This particular inductor is manufactured by Sullivan in values from 1 to 100 μH, in a single layer solenoid. Its actual accuracy of value can be produced to well within 1% and it can be certified (by the N.P.L.)

to well within 0·1%. The temperature coefficient of inductance per
degree centigrade is 0·00025%, and is cyclic to within 0·00005%, that
is to say, in successive variations of temperature its variation as it
passes through a given temperature will always be within 0·00005% of
the same absolute value. This means that the variation of 0·00025%,
which may be either positive or negative in individual components
(and will, of course, in general be less than this limit), can be offset
by the use of other components having an equal and opposite temperature coefficient. This fact is useful when the inductances are to be used
in the construction of frequency standards.

Higher values of inductance are obtained by the use of multilayer coils
of similar construction. Self-capacitance is kept to a minimum by spacing
of the turns and layers, and by the fact that the bulk of the spacing has
air dielectric, but capacitance will introduce inaccuracies in inductance
values at higher frequencies. However, since most of this capacitance has
air dielectric, and will only have very small variations with temperature in
comparison with the effect of the capacitance upon the inductance value,
the variation of inductance can be specified to a high degree of accuracy
by means of correction curves, which will maintain the value to which the
inductance is known at that frequency within a very close tolerance.

The Q of the coils (see Chapter 10) reaches its maximum at various
frequencies, according to the inductance value. For a 1 H, multilayer
inductor, the optimum Q is about 140 at a frequency of about 5 kHz.
For a 1 μH inductance, the Q reaches about 200 at a frequency of
15 MHz. The highest Q is obtainable in inductances of the order of
100 μH, being 530 at about 1 MHz. It maintains this high value from
about 350 kHz to about 2 MHz.

Another type of inductance standard for use in the laboratory is the
variable type, known as a variometer or inductometer; many firms
manufacture this type. For example, H. W. Sullivan make a series which
is wound on thermally-compensated formers similar to those already
described for fixed inductances. For this to be of advantage, precision
mechanical construction and calibration is necessary, if a scale reading of
comparable accuracy can be utilised. Actually the scale readings enable
an accuracy of 1 part in 1800 to be read, related to the whole angular
rotation of the instrument. This means that the precision of construction
is well inside the readable accuracy.

For the lower frequencies it is not possible to obtain adequate Q with
air-cored inductors, so that, in practice, the high degree of accuracy
obtainable is masked by losses. It is possible to produce a range of inductances of greater utility, if not such high accuracy, at lower frequencies
by the introduction of various forms of core material.

One commercial type employs toroidal coils with molybdenum per-
malloy dust cores which have a high constancy of permeability owing to

the discreet nature of their structure. Four coils are used having relative values of 1, 2, 2, 5, and can be switched in combination to produce a decade of inductance values. Due to the toroidal construction, inter-action between adjacent coils is negligible. The accuracy of each coil is controlled largely by the number of turns necessary to obtain the inductance value.

An inductance requiring a large number of turns can be adjusted to a higher accuracy than the lower inductance values. The optimum Q occurs at a frequency varying between 2 and 5 kHz, according to inductance value, and varies in value from 200 to about 300.

An alternative method which has been used for the construction of decade inductances for use at audio frequencies with a Q of about 60 in the range from 400 to 1000 Hz, is to use a conventional silicon iron core with an air gap arranged to equalise the copper and iron losses at about 600 Hz. The turns are arranged to give inductance steps at decade intervals, and the wire gauge is adjusted so that the d.c. resistance is pro-portional to the inductance steps. This means that the first step, repre-senting unit inductance, occupies about 62% of the total winding space, while the remaining turns to build up to ten times the inductance, occupy the remaining 38%. The Q available in this way is over 80% of the optimum Q available by winding for a single fixed value on the same core. The air gap controls the inductance value to well within 1% at any specific frequency, provided the core is not saturated. A set of these inductors is very useful in audio frequency laboratories.

17.4. CAPACITANCE

Capacitors for use as standards may be grouped as fixed or variable. Fixed capacitors may have either air or mica for dielectric. Attention must be paid in the design to the question of residual inductance. It is inevitable that a capacitor will possess some inductance, since the terminals cannot be coincident, and even a straight piece of wire has inductance. In the ideal case, however, the inductance of a capacitor should exceed the inductance of a straight wire joining its terminals by as small an amount as possible. This is achieved by arranging the plates so that the magnetic fields due to displacement currents neutralise each other to the greatest possible degree.

In the case of a capacitor with air dielectric, change in capacitance with temperature is due solely to the linear expansion coefficient of the plates and their mounting. The area of the plates will be determined by their own expansion, while the space between them will be determined by the spacing material. Choice of material that gives the spacing between plates a thermal coefficient twice that of the linear coefficient of expansion of the plates themselves results in a capacitance with sensibly zero temperature coefficient. The linear coefficient of expansion of aluminium is 0·0023% per °C, so that a capacitor having air dielectric and using a completely aluminium assembly for both sets of plates has an inherent temperature coefficient of 0·0023%. By employing a spacing arrangement that gives a thermal coefficient to the plate spacing of the order of 0·0046%, a capacitor with practically zero temperature coefficient is obtained.

With mica dielectric capacitors the range over which the thermal coefficient of capacitance approaches zero is limited, owing to the change in the dielectric constant with temperature, which does not follow a linear law. However, this is reasonably linear below about 50°C, so provided that higher operating temperatures can be avoided, a good degree of constancy can be obtained. According to individual assembly details, such as the quantity of air trapped between the mica and the plates, and the quality of the mica, mica capacitors have a resultant temperature coefficient varying between −0·002% and +0·001%. Selection of values having known temperature coefficients of opposite signs can be made so that a composite capacitor has a value with sensibly zero temperature coefficient.

In using a standard capacitor, it is very important that stray capacitances should be accurately known or reduced. For this reason, the standard is usually specified as having its calibrated value when one terminal is either earthed or at earth potential, and no other conductors are in the vicinity, or the whole capacitor is mounted in a screened case in which it was calibrated.

What has been said regarding fixed capacitors applies also to variable (air dielectric) capacitors. The bearings must be of precision construction, so that the plate clearance is accurately maintained, in addition to giving accurate determination of plate position.

17.5. RESISTANCE

Most composition resistors have a negative temperature coefficient. Although high stability composition type resistors with practically zero temperature coefficient are made, it must be remembered that the instability in the value of normal type composition resistors often only appears after a considerable time of operation. Therefore accelerated life tests should be applied to any resistor of this type if it is being considered for measurement work.

The accepted form for standard resistors uses metal alloy resistance material. All the resistance alloys have a positive temperature coefficient, but those chosen for resistance have a very small temperature coefficient at room temperatures. The resistance-temperature characteristics for Manganin are shown in Fig. 17.1.

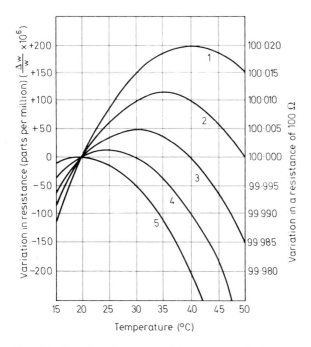

Fig. 17.1. Variation of resistance with temperature for Manganin

Since complex alloys are used for resistance standards there is the possibility, if different parts of the circuit are at different temperatures, that thermo-electric effects will interfere with measurements by introducing thermo-electric e.m.f.'s in the circuit. Provided precautions are taken to maintain the whole of the apparatus at constant temperature, this effect can be avoided.

Both inductance and capacitance can be troublesome in nominally resistance elements. For fixed elements, various methods are adopted to minimise these effects. Resistors of value less than 1Ω may be simply loops. Between 1 and 100Ω, the Ayrton Perry method of winding is usually adopted. Two parallel and equal lengths of resistance wire are wound in opposite directions on the same card, and have their ends joined. Above 100Ω, bifilar winding is sometimes adopted, in which the wire is doubled before being wound, and if a high resistance is being wound, separate sections are set in slots on a bobbin, to reduce self-capacitance. Alternatively, unifilar sections are wound in consecutive slots on a bobbin, having their direction of winding reversed in adjacent slots.

For variable resistance units, either of the decade or continuously-variable type, variation of inductance or capacitance with setting must be avoided. A simple method to overcome this difficulty is to use two windings, one of resistance wire and the other of copper wire, both identical in form, and so arranged that copper wire sections are removed from circuit exactly corresponding to the resistance wire sections inserted. In this way both inductance and capacitance can be maintained constant. In some circuits it is more important that the ratio of inductance to resistance (i.e. the phase angle at any given frequency) remains constant. For this purpose very careful attention to the design will be necessary. It can generally be arranged that a residual resistance, such as that due to the copper wire sections when they are all in and the resistance wire sections are all out, and a residual but constant inductance, can be compensated for in the main circuit so that they need not enter into the calculations.

17.6. FREQUENCY STANDARDS

Frequency standards in general are dealt with in Chapter 9. The highest degree of accuracy normally required can be maintained at high frequencies by means of crystals. While the tuning fork, temperature controlled, is generally used as a reference standard for the audio range, a variable standard is sometimes desirable.

Resistance-capacitance oscillators are popular for this purpose, but a very useful precision instrument is the beat-frequency oscillator. It employs one fixed frequency and a variable frequency which is used to beat with it to provide the calibrated audio-frequency output. The essential feature is the frequency stability of the high-frequency oscillators, which is produced by the use of temperature-compensated inductors and capacitors in the oscillator circuits. Crystal and resistance-capacitance oscillators are described in Chapter 9.

17.6.1. Atomic Frequency Standard or Caesium Clock

The most accurate, and probably the ultimate, standard of frequency is the atomic frequency standard, which is based on atomic transitions (changes from one atomic state to another) in elements such as ammonia, rubidium and caesium. Taking caesium as an example, this is one of the 'alkali metals' which have a single valency electron per atom. This electron can spin either in the same direction as the nucleus or in the opposite direction. The energy of the atom as a whole depends to a small extent on which spin direction, so if it changes from one state to the other there is an energy change, which happens to correspond to a precisely known frequency of 9 192 631 830 Hz.

Atomic transitions can be stimulated by a signal of the right frequency. For frequency-standard purposes one must be able to tell when the frequency is right. This necessitates detecting when the transitions are being caused at the maximum rate, and to do this the frequency of a local signal generator, variable around 9192 MHz, is adjusted until the rate is a maximum.

The problem, then, is to detect transitions. The amount of radiation caused is too small to be measured, so transitions are detected by making use of the fact that a spinning electron, being a spinning electric charge, is equivalent to a small current around a small turn, and there-fore to a tiny magnet, so it reacts on an applied magnetic field. If the atoms are shot between the poles of a powerful magnet they are deflected in opposite directions according to the direction of spin. If this is done twice, atoms having the same spin throughout are deflected twice in the same direction. But if they change state en route between the magnets, the second deflection cancels out the first.

In a typical arrangement, caesium atoms released by heating the metal, are made to stream into a vacuum. The two opposite types of atoms are deflected in opposite directions by a magnet. Two cavity resonators, energised by an oscillator, are next encountered, and if the atoms are changed thereby, a second magnet deflects them on to the detector; if not, they are deflected away from the detector.

The target for the changed atoms is a heated tungsten wire, from which the atoms boil off minus an electron. Being now positively charged, they can be collected by a negative electrode and amplified to work an indicator.

Since a frequency standard is also a time standard, the device just described is sometimes referred to as a caesium clock. The accuracy of such a clock is such that it is correct to the order of one second in 1000 years.

17.7. STANDARD CELLS

For measurement purposes it is highly desirable to have a standard of e.m.f. Owing to the comparative ease with which certain chemicals can be obtained in a pure condition, it has been found that certain cells con-structed in a certain way will always produce the same e.m.f. Thus *standard cells* are possible; the two chief types being the Clark cell and the Weston cadmium cell. For many reasons the latter has become the standard, although it was in terms of the e.m.f. of the Clark cell that the volt was once defined.

The use of standard cells has already been mentioned in this book in connection with potentiometers, and they are often used as reference voltage sources in electronic instruments, particularly digital voltmeters.

17.7.1. The Clark Cell

The construction of a Clark cell is shown in Fig. 17.2(a). The e.m.f. of this cell is 1·434 V at 15°C. This varies with temperature, and the e.m.f. at any temperature can be calculated from the formula:

$$E = 1·433[1 - 0·00077(t - 15)] \text{ volts}$$

where t is the temperature at which the e.m.f. is required.

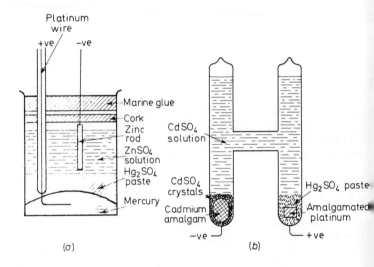

Fig. 17.2. Standard cells (a) Clark cell; (b) Weston cadmium cell

The Clark cell is unsatisfactory in several ways. The change of e.m.f. with temperature is comparatively large, and it suffers from a temperature 'lag', i.e. the change of e.m.f. with temperature is slow. Also, owing to the slow interaction between zinc and water, the cell tends to become polarised.

17.7.2. The Weston Cadmium Cell

The essential details of this cell are shown in Fig. 17.2(*b*). The e.m.f. of his cell is 1·0183 V at 20°C. Its temperature coefficient is about 1/30th hat of the Clark cell. The e.m.f. at any temperature *t*°C is given by:

$$E = 1·0183 - 0·0000406(t - 20) \text{ volt.}$$

In using standard cells it is imperative that no current should be taken rom them, and hence they are often protected by the permanent attach-ment of a high resistance. For this reason, when electronic equipment containing standard cells is being serviced one must be careful not to shunt the cell with a low resistance test meter. A concise summary of standard cells and their use in digital voltmeters has been prepared by :. W. Tucker![1]

WORKED EXAMPLE

Question. Describe briefly the means commonly employed to minimise he reactance (either positive or negative) of resistors for use in measur-ng apparatus at power or audio-frequencies.

Give the theory of the method of compensating for capacitance by he addition of series inductance obtained by winding a small portion of he resistor inductively.

How much series inductance would be required to render a 1000-Ω esistor with a shunt capacitance of 10 $\mu\mu$F practically non-reactive over reasonable range of frequency?   (B.Sc. II (Internal), 1943).

Answer. Although an old question, this is very relevant to the subject matter of the present chapter. The required compensation method is not discussed in the text but should be clear from the qualitative treatment which follows. Referring to Fig. 17.3, we must first establish the condi-

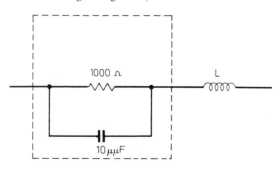

Fig. 17.3. Compensation for self-capacitance of resistor

tion for the reactive part of the impedance Z to be zero. Then, since the circuit is not to resonate at any particular frequency, the resonant angular frequency ω_r must be set to zero.

$$Z = j\omega L + \frac{R/j\omega C}{R + 1/j\omega C} = j\omega L + \frac{R(1 - j\omega CR)}{1 + \omega^2 C^2 R^2}$$

For the circuit to be non-reactive, the complex part of Z must be zero, i.e.

$$j\omega L - \frac{j\omega_r CR^2}{1 + \omega_r^2 C^2 R^2} = 0, \text{ so that } L + \omega_r^2 C^2 R^2 L - CR^2 = 0.$$

Then $L = \dfrac{CR^2}{1 + \omega^2 C^2 R^2}$, and when $\omega_r = 0$ as required, $L = CR^2$.

Thus $L = 10 \times 10^{-12} \times 10^6 = 10\ \mu H$ *Answer*

EXERCISES

1. Why is the tolerance within which a value can be maintained often of greater importance than the accuracy with which the value can be ascertained in absolute measure?

2. Describe briefly the problems in the construction of standards of inductance, capacitance, and resistance, with particular reference to the variation with (*a*) frequency, and (*b*) temperature.

3. What is the voltage of a Weston cadmium cell at 30°C?

Answer. 1·017894 V.

REFERENCE

1. TUCKER, E. W., *Standard Cells*. Muirhead Technique **21**, 3, (July 1967).

CHAPTER 18

Measurement of
Non-Electrical Quantities

18.1. MEASUREMENT OF pH

The measurement of the degree of acidity or alkalinity of a solution is a matter of some importance to a wide variety of industries, typical of which are agriculture, ceramic manufacture, cosmetics, dyestuffs, electroplating, food preservatives, gas by-products, industrial chemistry, am manufacture, leather dressing, milk processing, paper manufacture, plastics, sewage disposal, textile production, and water purification. In general, the effective acidity or alkalinity of a solution is not directly dependent upon the total quantity of acid or base present, although sometimes this relation may be important, in which case it can be measured by chemical titration. The effective acidity or alkalinity of a solution does, however, bear a direct relationship to the concentration of hydrogen ions in the solution.

For pure water alone, a small quantity is always dissociated into hydrogen $+(H)$ and hydroxyl $-(OH)$ ions. The product of the concentrations of each of these ions is a constant for water, and for aqueous solutions, termed the dissociation constant. At normal temperatures, for pure water, with neither acid nor alkaline properties present, there are concentrations of 10^{-7} gram ions of each of these ions per litre of water, so that the dissociation constant of water is $10^{-7} \times 10^{-7} = 10^{-14}$. If a small amount of acid, with surplus hydrogen ions, is added to water, the concentration of hydroxyl ions decreases in order to maintain the value of the dissociation constant. On the other hand, addition of alkali increases the concentration of hydroxyl ions and decreases the concentration of hydrogen ions. From this it is evident that an indication of the concentration of hydrogen ions alone will provide an index as to the acidity or alkalinity of a solution. In this connection, the pH scale provides a useful system of units. The pH unit is the logarith to the base 10 of the hydrogen ion concentration. As all the logarithms are negative, the negative sign is omitted. From the above, it is seen that pure water, and neutral solutions, will have a pH of 7. A lower value represents an acid, and a higher value an alkali.

The oldest method of indicating pH is the use of litmus paper, which has the property of changing colour according to the pH value of the solution in which it is placed. While this method enables small degrees of acidity or alkalinity to be detected, it cannot give accurate readings where the solutions are appreciably acid or alkaline. Also, it is obviously not suitable where the solution has colouring matter of its own, such as in the production of dyestuffs.

The electrical method commonly used for both industrial and laboratory measurement of pH of solutions employs two half cells of constant e.m.f., one being a silver/silver chloride, and the other a mercury/calomel. The e.m.f. of the whole arrangement is modified by the pH value of the solution placed between these half cells, which serve as electrodes to the solution, according to a definite lay by which the instrument can be calibrated using standard pH value buffer solutions. The standard half cells communicate with the solution under test through special glass electrode containers, having a low conductivity (fc glass). The internal resistance of the whole arrangement is of the order of 50 MΩ, so that a high-impedance input millivoltmeter is required to giv the pH reading. Alternatively, a high-sensitivity potentiometer arrangement could be used.

The electrometer used in this instrument may consist of a pentode arranged to operate as a d.c. amplifier, taking a low and constant grid current, and having a linear grid-potential/anode-current characteristic. The small constant current taken from the electrode system modifies the measured e.m.f. value, but this modification has a constant value, since the grid current is constant. Hence the effect can be compensated in the initial adjustment of the instrument, which takes account of the half cell e.m.f.'s anyway. Most commercial instruments of this type are portable and consist of a box with hinged lid containing the bottles of standard solutions and the stand and electrode assembly. Some electro assemblies have special arrangements for substituting different solution in the test vessel quickly, as well as for flushing the vessel between tests with distilled water.

This whole arrangement is typical of ideal arrangements from the industrial point of view. While bridge and potentiometer methods may be well suited to the academic viewpoint of the laboratory worker, the industrial employee has to do things in a hurry. He wants something that gives a direct reading on a scale — 'at the end of a pointer' — as R. H. Thorpe, of the Wellcome Physiological Research Laboratories aptly put it. At most, the reading should require a calibration adjustme to a red line on the meter scale, or to zero, followed by a direct indication of the required result. Compare the ease of reading a ohmmeter with that of a Wheatstone bridge for the measurement of resistance (se Chapter 3). For a reading to within 1%, the ohmmeter will be quite

adequate, providing it has been accurately calibrated, but for results to
3 significant figures, the Wheatstone bridge is necessary. For most practical work, the facility of being able to just connect the resistance and
read the result without making any adjustments is a greater advantage
than knowing the value to 3 figures.

18.2. STROBOSCOPIC TECHNIQUES

Investigation of the exact nature of high-speed movements is often
important, and for this purpose investigation under the illumination
from a flashing source of light, so controlled that the repetition rate is
very nearly equal to the speed of rotation or the rate at which some
particular part of the operation repeats, enables a high-speed
phenomenon to be examined as though it were moving quite slowly.

The usual method employed is similar in principle to the linear
timebase of a cathode-ray tube, but instead of using the discharge of
the capacitor to produce the flyback, its energy is used to flash a discharge lamp. Synchronising can be achieved by similar methods.

18.3. SINGLE ACTION TIME METERING

It is sometimes necessary to measure exactly the operating time of a
relay, the time constant of an instrument movement, or some other
action that is not essentially periodic. For this purpose an instrument
is required that can accurately measure known intervals of time. A
simple method of achieving this is by means of a pulse generator that
produces accurately spaced pulses one millisecond, or some other known
interval, apart. Multivibrator counter mechanisms act as divider circuits
to produce pulses at successively longer intervals, such as 10 milliseconds
and 100 milliseconds. Presetting of the instrument controls can then be
arranged to select, by further counter mechanisms, any combination of
pulses in succession so that any length period, correct to the nearest
short pulse period — usually one millisecond — can be measured off
accurately. Further electronic mechanisms can arrange that pulses are
delivered at the start and finish of the period, or that contacts are made
and broken, or any desired functions performed accurately to time.

Such an instrument can usefully be employed with a stroboscopic
lamp, arranged so that the lamp is flashed just once at the end of the
desired period. In this way relay contact bounce, etc., can be carefully
investigated on single operation sequences.

18.4. THE DRIMETER

This is a development originally produced by the British textile industry, and manufactured by Fielden Electronics Ltd. of Manchester, its purpose being to measure and control the moisture content of fabrics in the course of manufacture, particularly in drying. Although it is no longer made, it illustrates the type of problem put before electronic engineers in industry and is a simple form of 'automation'. The whole principle of action will be described, in order to show how the use of the instrument safeguards all the various contingencies likely to be met

The Drimeter itself consists of a bridge system, operated at a frequency of 500 kHz, modulated by 500 Hz. One arm of the bridge takes the form of two electrodes so placed that the fabric runs between them without making physical contact. It is evident that the properties of the cloth will effectively vary the capacitance of the plates, by modifying the dielectric constant. The output from the bridge is demodulated and amplified. The bridge is adjusted so that, with no fabric present, the bridge is balanced and there is no output. Thoroughly dried cloth will produce a small out-of-balance, which will be increased according to the moisture content. The gain of the amplifier is adjusted for any given sample of dry cloth to a fixed 'zero moisture' position on the scale of a rectifier voltmeter at the amplifier output. Above this position the scale is calibrated in numerical reference terms representing different degrees of moisture. The electrodes test the cloth at the output from the drying machine, so that the speed of transit can be operated so as to produce the required degree of moisture at the output. As the cloth takes considerable time in transit it will be realised that considerable skill will be required in controlling the machine if the results are not to be patchy, since the dryness of any particular patch depends upon the time taken by the patch to traverse the machine. Suppose that the cloth now emerging from the machine is too dry; then the machine will be speeded up; but the more moist cloth will not begin to show until the part which has already been in the machine has come through, so that the machine may be speeded up too much, while the output still shows too dry; then later, cloth will be coming through that will not be dry enough. This 'hunting' process may result in the spoilage of a considerable quantity of cloth, so electronic measurement gear has been devised, in addition to the actual Drimeter, for the purpose of making the entire control automatic with the minimum of wastage. Fig. 18.1 shows the schematic arrangement of the whole equipment.

A fractional horse-power motor is used to vary the setting of the speed control of the drying machine. To control the setting, the fractional H.P. motor is controlled by a contactor unit, while controls both the direction

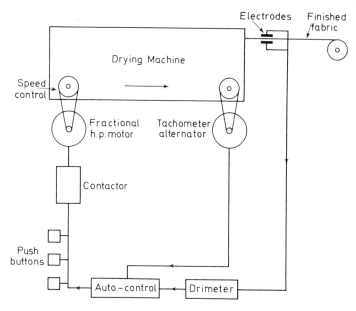

Fig. 18.1. Drying equipment

of rotation, and, by the time for which the contacts are made for either way, the amount of variation applied. These contactors may be controlled either by the push buttons shown (which are usually used for setting up an approximately correct position of the control when starting up with new cloth) or by the auto-control unit. The auto-control unit operates on information supplied by means of the Drimeter, but also in conjunction with information supplied from an alternator speed indicator, so that due to the delay in adjustments taking effect, the machine does not overdo it and set up 'hunting'.

Fig. 18.2 shows a simplified schematic arrangement of the auto-control system. The output from the Drimeter is amplified and fed (*a*) to a bolometer bridge (this output is of the modulation frequency 500 Hz), and (*b*) to the phase gate.

The bridge is adjusted to suit the moisture content required, so that balance is obtained for the output of the amplifier corresponding to that moisture content. The input to the second amplifier will then be zero for correct moisture content, and will change in phase as well as magnitude according to the error from this value. The output from this amplifier is fed to the phase gate and to the flip-flop generator. The phase gate is a simple arrangement consisting of two pentodes biased normally to cut-off, and arranged so that the combination of signals fed from amplifier 1 and

2 differentially to their control and suppressor grids causes one or other of two relays, connected one in each anode circuit, to operate according to the phase of the signal from amplifier 2 compared with that from 1. In

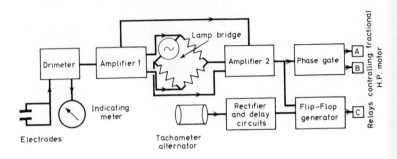

Fig. 18.2. Complete auto-control system

the absence of a signal from amplifier 2 neither operate. The contacts of these relays determine the direction of rotation of the control motor, when the contactor C makes the necessary final contact, operate signal lamps on the main control panel, and complete the circuit of contactor C so that the flip-flop generator signal will operate it.

The flip-flop generator is of special design. It is essentially a multivibrator, but the charge time constants in each direction are controlled by different factors. The time during which contactor C is in the made position is determined by the output delivered to the generator from amplifier 2, so that the degree of speed correction applied is proportional to the error registered at the time. The time during which contactor C is in the off position is controlled by the output from the speed indicating alternator, so that the slower the dryer is running, the longer will be the interval before another correcting flip can be made. This prevents hunting and at the same time, by appropriate care in circuit design, gives a maximum precision in control resulting in very low wastage.

Two other possibilities have to be considered, having seen that the machine adequately takes care of continuous operation. Suppose the machine has been stopped and is later restarted; the cloth in the machine during this period will inevitably be overdried, but it will be desirable for the material entering the dryer as soon as it starts again to be correctly dried. To achieve this, the speed should be kept at about its normal figure, so that the machine should ignore Drimeter readings until the cloth starts to arrive; this is achieved by the delay circuits in the alternator rectifier. Whenever the alternator stops the signal fed to the flop part of the flip-flop generator becomes zero, and the flop stays on indefinitely.

The delay circuits include a time constant which does not normally affect operation to any extent, but when starting from zero voltage imposes an additional time constant before the necessary potential to release the flop period reaches the flip-flop generator. During all this the speed setting of the dryer will be unaffected.

The second possibility is that the dryer may run out of cloth, so that for a brief period none will be coming through. Under these conditions the Drimeter bridge will be balanced so that no signal will be applied to the input of the lamp bridge, and therefore there can be no output until some cloth again comes through.

To set the machine up for any given material, the following adjustments are necessary:

(a) Set up the Drimeter gain control for the thickness, quality, etc., of the cloth, by running a completely dry sample between the electrodes, and zero setting.

(b) Set the lamp bridge so that it gives zero output for the required degree of moisture content for the particular material.

To set the gain control with a new cloth, it will be necessary to over-dry a small sample. But for later reference a calibrating arrangement is substituted, consisting of a pair of substitution electrodes with an adjustable calibrated capacitance. At the first setting for the cloth a corresponding setting of this calibrated capacitance is noted, and this value can be used on subsequent occasions when the machine is set up for the same cloth.

18.5. SERVOMECHANISMS USING ELECTRONIC LINKS

The auto-control unit used in conjunction with the Drimeter is quite a good example of the application of electronic equipment to servomechanisms. In this case the velocity of the drying machine is the primary object of control. But due to the nature of the control there is a large time delay, which is similar in effect to the presence of a large reactance in a negative feedback network applied to a straightforward amplifier. In this case the effect of this delay, if continuous control were applied, would be either (a) hunting, due to the feedback becoming virtually positive at some frequency in effect, or (b) if the rate of control by the motor were reduced so as to prevent this, the time taken to find the correct setting would be very long, and hence wasteful of material. The method employed is virtually that of only allowing a narrow band of frequencies to be fed back (corresponding to the reciprocal of the time constant of the machine), and then adjusting feedback for the maximum degree of control with stability at that frequency.

The possible range of applications for servomechanisms of various types is very wide, but the general principles applying to them all are similar. In every case there is the problem of producing stability, whilst giving an adequate degree of control. The mechanism may be designed to cause one rotatable mechanism to follow accurately, as to position, another mechanism at some other point. The method of comparing the positions of the two mechanisms may be basically mechanical, using a mechanical differential mechanism to produce an electrical signal of some sort indicative of the difference in relative position; or it may be basically electrical, by using some form of generator applied to each mechanism which will give indication of the mechanical position in the form of an electrical signal, the two signals being compared to produce the necessary error signal. In either case, the error signal will be used to control driving power supplied to the controlled mechanism, so that the degree with which the controlled mechanism follows the controlling mechanism is as high as possible. This means a high gain, producing the necessary power to operate the drive mechanism. The whole equipment is analogous to a negative feedback chain, although some parts of the chain are mechanical.

Due to the mechanical mass of various moving parts, there will be a delay in following. This delay may or may not matter. In the case of the Drimeter control, an even greater delay was desirable. But sometimes the delay must be reduced to a minimum. As a certain power must be supplied by the control mechanism in order to move the control mass — although for set stationary positions the two mechanisms may be adequately linked — the controlled mechanism must inevitably lag when it is rotating, in order to obtain the necessary power to drive it. A method of overcoming this difficulty is the provision of velocity feedback. Added to the controlling signal is a second signal proportional to the velocity of movement, so that the original error signal has only to correct relative angles of difference at any instant, while the velocity derived signal provides the necessary driving power to obtain the steady velocity component at any instant. Even so there will be a lag, due to the mechanical force required to change the velocity, at such time as the velocity does change. It is possible to reduce this by increasing the degree of feedback in each case, so that a greater correction energy is applied whenever error occurs. An alternative method would be to differentiate the velocity signal so that an acceleration feedback is obtained. The combination would then follow accurately for either set positions, steady velocity, or steady acceleration. But there remains the necessity for transition from one to the other, and hence there will be a lag, *however small*.

With each feedback arrangement there is an associated time constant. Because of this, there is the equivalent of at least one reactive element —

usually many more – in the analogous network. With each type of feedback the delay may be such that at some frequency the correction applied will be in phase, instead of out of phase, with the error producing the error signal. At this frequency hunting will build up.

There are two methods of approach to the problem:

(a) If continuous control is applied, then the gain characteristic round the loop must obey the stability criteria already shown to be necessary in feedback amplifiers. The frequency band under consideration will in general be lower in frequency than that usually encountered in amplifiers for other purposes, in fact it will often be required to start from d.c., if actual position following is required. This requirement can be obviated from the amplifier design point of view by using a modulated r.f. link (or modulated a.f. under certain circumstances.) But the band-pass characteristics of the modulated signal amplifier will have to be considered in relation to the overall low-frequency loop characteristic. In general, one or two reactance elements producing phase shift of the same kind in the same frequency range can be tolerated, provided that any other reactances of the same effect do not produce their effect until a frequency is reached at which the loop gain becomes negligible due to the main reactance or reactances considered. There will almost invariably be more than two networks producing the same kind of phase change, but it is possible to insert inverse networks, either mechanical or electrical, somewhere in the chain so that some of the phase shifts produced are neutralised; but, in general, this process results in a loss of gain. So the best plan is to arrange that the loss of gain occurs at some frequency beyond the desired range of the equipment in one direction or the other.

(b) The alternative is to provide some element in the chain so as to produce a sharp cut-off at a certain frequency by means of some discontinuity, so that the cut-off does not introduce a reactance element. This is, in effect, the method employed in the auto-control used with the Drimeter, since the flip-flop has this effect.

Various types of mathematical analysis similar to those normally applied to the consideration of stability criteria for feedback amplifiers may be applied to method (a) above. If the reader is conversant with them, he may find them helpful to use. It is believed, however, that these problems can be better understood by having in mind a picture of the various possibilities, and methods of obviating difficulties.

18.6. COMPUTERS

Computers are rapidly coming into use for use in measurements, either for the control of electronic measuring apparatus or for analysis of the data obtained in the measurements themselves. An example of such use has been given in Chapter 7 in discussing automatic network analysers. The construction, operation and application of computers in general is of course beyond the scope of this book, and the reader requiring further information on this fascinating topic is recommended to read the book by Jacobowitz,[1] which contains a wealth of useful information on digital and analogue computers. However, because of its wide application in control systems, the integrating operational amplifier will now be described.

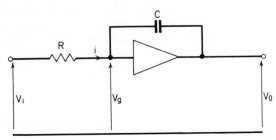

Fig. 18.3. Integrating operational amplifier

Referring to Fig. 18.3, the triangle represents a d.c. amplifier of very high gain so that V_g is so much smaller than V_0 that it can be considered as being at earth potential.

Then $i \propto V_i$ and due to the charging of capacitor C, $\dfrac{dV_0}{dt} \propto i \propto V_i$.

Now
$$i = \frac{V_i}{R} = -C\frac{dV_0}{dt}.$$

Thus
$$V_0 = -\frac{1}{RC}\int V_i \, dt = \frac{1}{T}\int V_i \, dt \text{ where } T = RC.$$

It is thus seen that V_0 is directly proportional to the integral of V_i.

WORKED EXAMPLE

Question. It is required to develop an instrument for the measurement of moisture in either timber or grain. Suggest what factors must need consideration, and what measurements would be made in determining the best arrangement.

Answer. The answer to this question rests upon the effect moisture would have upon the electrical properties of timber, or grain. The chief effects would be:

(*a*) Variation of conductivity, and

(*b*) Variation of dielectric constant.

Measurements would need to be made to determine how both these qualities varied with the particular material for which the instrument is to be designed, and over the range of moisture contents of particular interest to the problem in hand. From the information obtained, the factors determining the best arrangement are:

(*a*) Choice of operating frequency, to give the greatest sensitivity, by taking advantage of both properties.

(*b*) Choice of bridge circuit, so that the way in which the combined properties vary give the greatest sensitivity on unbalance.

It is, of course, important that the test should not produce any destructive effect upon the material tested, due to the development of heat, electrolysis or any other cause.

EXERCISES

1. Describe the pH meter and its applications.

2. A limit resistance bridge, which uses a Wheatstone bridge to measure the 'plus and minus' tolerance of resistors, is mains operated. Does this mean that the Wheatstone bridge is a.c. operated? Give reasons for your conclusion. How could the technique be modified so as to be applicable to the measurement of capacitances in the same way?

3. Explain the principle of operation of the Drimeter used for the measurement of moisture content in the drying of textiles. State what precautions are taken (*a*) to prevent hunting, whilst giving a minimum of wastage, and (*b*) to give the best operation in the event of a stoppage and restarting.

4. On production testing of assemblies, it is found that the biggest single cause of rejects in a certain factory is due to the occasional occurrence of incorrectly coded resistors, which are purchased in quantity from manufacturer who offers the lowest price for these components. These components are stored according to nominal value, but are not tested before use in assembly. Discuss the economic considerations which would influence a decision (*a*) to do nothing about it; (*b*) to change to another supplier of resistors, at a higher price; or (*c*) to institute testing of all resistors at goods-in for value.

5. What is the importance of the measure of acidity to agriculture?

REFERENCE

1. JACOBOWITZ, H., *Electronic Computers Made Simple*. W. H. Allen Ltd. (1967).

INDEX

Abraham voltmeter, 72
Absolute measurements, 3
Absorption wavemeter, 181
Accuracy of reading, 35
Acorn valve, 91
Admittance bridge, 161–162, 164,
    323
Alternating current,
    absolute voltage standards, 60
    average value, 60
    maximum value, 60
    measurement of, 60–79
    r.m.s. value, 60
    unit, 60
Ammeters, 71
    a.c. test of, 160
    swamping resistance used with, 35
    three-ammeter method, 235, 238
Ampere, 2
Amplification measurement, 14
Amplifier gain, 14–15, 89, 252,
    300–302
Amplifier noise measurement, 308
Amplifiers,
    a.c., 80
    a.f., 252
      frequency response, 303
      measurements on, 300–322
      overall characteristics,
        308–309
      test set-up, 301
    buffer, 176, 181
    Class B, 84, 307
    Class C, 86
    Class C power, 241
    d.c., 80, 81, 83, 88, 95, 362
    input voltage, 300
    integrating operational, 362
    negative feedback, 96
    overloading, 306–307
    performance comparison, 14

Amplifiers, *continued*
    power, 15
      Class C, 241
    Q.P.P., 307
    resistance-capacitance coupled,
      302
    response curve, 303–304
    r.f., 252
    transistor, single stage, 302
    voltage, 15
Amplitude control, automatic,
    173–175, 182
Amplitude distortion, 309, 310, 315,
    320
    delayed, 313
Analogue integrator, 95
Analogue-to-digital converter, 93
Anderson's bridge, 156
Angle measurement, accuracy of, 8
Anode-bend meters, 83, 87
Anode-bend rectification, 306
Anode current, equation, 84
Atomic clocks, 167
Atomic frequency standard, 167, 348
Attenuation, 262–263, 268, 269, 324
    of filter, 266
    voltage, 265
Attenuation constant, 323
Attenuators, 251, 254–255, 261–269,
    300, 301, 303
    applications, 266–267
    balanced symmetrical, 268
    balanced T- or H-section, 264
    capacitance, 267
    continuously variable ladder, 265
    decimal, 266
    H-section, 268
    L-section, 265, 267
    ladder, 247, 266–269
    miscellaneous types, 267
    symmetric T-section, 262

365